THE NEW MICROBIOLOGY

THE NEW MICROBIOLOGY

Papers Selected and Edited by

JOHN E. FLYNN

Office of Naval Research

New York, N.Y.

McGRAW HILL BOOK COMPANY

New York St. Louis San Francisco Toronto London Sydney

109678

THE NEW MICROBIOLOGY

Library of Congress Catalog Card Number: 66–26829

21404

1234567890WH721069876

FOREWORD

It would have been difficult to find a person better qualified than John Flynn to select and analyze a collection of scientific reports that point up the outstanding progress and trends in modern microbiology.

During his professional lifetime Dr. Flynn saw biology develop from a group of parochial disciplines into a unified field of science in which each branch relies heavily on all the others for basic information. He saw the biologist change from the "naturalist observer" to a scientist who uses the physical and other "exact" disciplines to attain an understanding of life processes. As long-time Editor of *Biological Abstracts*, he also observed the changing fashions in biological research and had the remarkable ability to remember everything he had read; but, more important, he could put newly acquired information into proper perspective with what was previously known.

It is this talent that made him a happy choice to select, collect, assemble, and evaluate the papers which comprise this *symposium in absentia. The New Microbiology* is not a history of the subject, although it does record some of the outstanding contributions in the several areas of microbiology over a decade. It is more accurate to consider this collection as a report on the state of the art and as a means of stimulating further contributions to science.

We are most fortunate that Dr. Flynn had finished editing the manuscript for this book before his untimely death. It will thus stand as a memorial to a widely known and highly respected scientist whose ambition was always to serve his colleagues.

ROGER D. REID

INTRODUCTION

This volume presents abridgments of a number of original and review papers delineating the transition from classical bacteriology to the modern biological science of microbiology. Choice of articles has been to a large extent arbitrary and reflects an attempt to select from the voluminous journal literature of microbiology some papers that best reflect this scientific transition and, at the same time, illustrate methods of doing and interpreting research. Some of the articles will describe the experimental methods by which scientists have sought, through carefully controlled experiments, to find the solution of important, previously unsolved problems.

"The New Microbiology" is intended primarily as supplementary reading for the college undergraduate taking his first, and possibly his only, course in microbiology or bacteriology. Editing has been done rather freely to improve the readability of the papers and to fit them to the requirements of an undergraduate course, but care has been taken to preserve the author's language and style to the greatest practicable extent. Some of the articles have been reproduced with only minor changes.

The reader should bear in mind that most of the articles are presented in abridged form, and should consult the original sources for experimental methods and other information present in the articles as originally published but omitted here.

Warm thanks are extended to the journals and to the authors who have so kindly permitted their publications to be included in this volume, and to the many kind friends who have been so patient and generous with their advice and critical comments.

TABLE OF CONTENTS

MICROBIAL GENETICS

Most of our modern knowledge of microbial heredity is the result of a long and carefully planned series of experiments that were suggested by a single discovery: that some unknown substance in a digest of killed bacterial cells could change the genetic characteristics of living bacteria of quite a different type and cause the living bacteria to produce off-spring with some of the characteristics of the dead ones. In the following paper, Professor Avery and his colleagues confirmed earlier, rather vague reports of the transformation of one type of pneumococcus into another. They identified the "transforming factor" as deoxyribonucleic acid (DNA), a substance known to be present in the chromatin of plant and animal chromosomes and already suspected of being the physical basis of the genetic transmission of hereditary traits.

For both the geneticist and the microbiologist, the paper is a classic: for the geneticist because it afforded experimental proof of the role of DNA as the carrier of genetic traits; for the microbiologist because it furnished biochemical evidence that the genetic mechanism in the bacteria is basically similar to that in animals and plants.

In the 20 years that have elapsed since this paper appeared, a great deal has been added to our knowledge of microbial genetics. The fact of bacterial transformation has been repeatedly confirmed and has become an accepted basic principle of microbiology. Efforts have been made to find transformation in other microorganisms, in cell suspension cultures of plant and animal cells, and even in vertebrates. Claims have been made of discovery of genetic transformation in birds, but these so far lack confirmation. Actually, only a few species of bacteria, and apparently a flagellate, *Trichomonas,* have as yet been transformed. Cultures of pneumococcus, normally capable of being transformed (competent), may lose this capacity. There are indications that the capacity of a "competent" bacterium to be transformed is related to specific receptor sites on the bacterial wall: if these are present and functional, the bacterium can be transformed; otherwise it cannot.

The work reported in the paper reprinted below was done in the Rockefeller Institute of Medical Research. Dr. Maclyn McCarty is still at the Rockefeller Institute. Dr. MacLeod is deputy director of the White House Office of Science and Technology. Dr. Avery died in 1955.

From *J. Exp. Med.,*
79:137–158, 1944.

STUDIES ON THE CHEMICAL NATURE OF THE SUBSTANCE INDUCING TRANSFORMATION OF PNEUMOCOCCAL TYPES

Induction of Transformation by a Desoxyribonucleic Acid Fraction Isolated from Pneumococcus Type III

BY OSWALD T. AVERY, COLIN M. MacLEOD, AND MACLYN McCARTY

Biologists have long attempted by chemical means to induce in higher organisms predictable and specific changes which thereafter could be transmitted in series as hereditary characters. Among microörganisms the most striking example of inheritable and specific alterations in cell structure and function that can be experimentally induced and are reproducible under well defined and adequately controlled conditions is the transformation of specific types of Pneumococcus. This phenomenon was first described by Griffith [1928] who succeeded in transforming an attenuated and non-encapsulated (R) variant derived from one specific type into fully encapsulated and virulent (S) cells of a heterologous specific type. . . .

The present paper is concerned with a more detailed analysis of the phenomenon of transformation of specific types of Pneumococcus. The major interest has centered in attempts to isolate the active principle from crude bacterial extracts and to identify if possible its chemical nature or at least to characterize it sufficiently to place it in a general group of known chemical substances. For purposes of study, the typical example of transformation chosen as a working model was the one with which we have had most experience and which consequently seemed best suited for analysis. This particular example represents the transformation of a non-encapsulated R variant of Pneumococcus Type II to Pneumococcus Type III.

EXPERIMENTAL

Transformation of pneumococcal types *in vitro* requires that certain cultural conditions be fulfilled before it is possible to demonstrate the reaction even in

4

the presence of a potent extract. Not only must the broth medium be optimal for growth but it must be supplemented by the addition of serum or serous fluid known to possess certain special properties. Moreover, the R variant, as will be shown later, must be in the reactive phase in which it has the capacity to respond to the transforming stimulus. For purposes of convenience these several components as combined in the transforming test will be referred to as the *reaction system*. Each constituent of this system presented problems which required clarification before it was possible to obtain consistent and reproducible results. The various components of the system will be described in the following order: (1) nutrient broth, (2) serum or serous fluid, (3) strain of R Pneumococcus, and (4) extraction, purification, and chemical nature of the transforming principle.

1. Nutrient Broth.—Beef heart infusion broth containing 1 per cent neopeptone with no added dextrose and adjusted to an initial pH of 7.6–7.8 is used as the basic medium. Individual lots of broth show marked and unpredictable variations in the property of supporting transformation. It has been found, however, that charcoal adsorption, according to the method described by MacLeod and Mirick [1942] for removal of sulfonamide inhibitors, eliminates to a large extent these variations; consequently this procedure is used as routine in the preparation of consistently effective broth for titrating the transforming activity of extracts.

2. Serum or Serous Fluid.—In the first successful experiments on the induction of transformation *in vitro*, Dawson and Sia [1931] found that it was essential to add serum to the medium. Anti-R pneumococcal rabbit serum was used because of the observation that reversion of an R pneumococcus to the homologous S form can be induced by growth in a medium containing anti-R serum. Alloway [1932] later found that ascitic or chest fluid and normal swine serum, all of which contain R antibodies, are capable of replacing antipneumococcal rabbit serum in the reaction system. Some form of serum is essential, and to our knowledge transformation *in vitro* has never been effected in the absence of serum or serous fluid.

In the present study human pleural or ascitic fluid has been used almost exclusively. It became apparent, however, that the effectiveness of different lots of serum varied and that the differences observed were not necessarily dependent upon the content of R antibodies, since many sera of high titer were found to be incapable of supporting transformation. This fact suggested that factors other than R antibodies are involved.

It has been found that sera from various animal species, irrespective of their immune properties, contain an enzyme capable of destroying the transforming principle in potent extracts. The nature of this enzyme and the specific substrate on which it acts will be referred to later in this paper. This enzyme is inactivated by heating the serum at 60°–65°C., and sera heated at temperatures known to destroy the enzyme are often rendered effective in the transforming system. Further analysis has shown that certain sera in which R antibodies are present and in which the enzyme has been inactivated may nevertheless fail to support transformation. This fact suggests that still another factor in the serum is essential. The content of this factor varies in different sera, and at present its identity is unknown.

There are at present no criteria which can be used as a guide in the selection of suitable sera or serous fluids except that of actually testing their capacity to support transformation. Fortunately, the requisite properties are stable and remain unimpaired over long periods of time; and sera that have been stored in the refrigerator for many months have been found on retesting to have lost little or none of their original effectiveness in supporting transformation.

The recognition of these various factors in serum and their rôle in the reaction system has greatly facilitated the standardization of the cultural conditions required for obtaining consistent and reproducible results.

3. *The R Strain* (*R36A*).—The unencapsulated R strain used in the present study was derived from a virulent "S" culture of Pneumococcus Type II. It will be recalled that irrespective of type derivation all "R" variants of Pneumococcus are characterized by the lack of capsule formation and the consequent loss of both type specificity and the capacity to produce infection in the animal body. The designation of these variants as R forms has been used to refer merely to the fact that on artificial media the colony surface is "rough" in contrast to the smooth, glistening surface of colonies of encapsulated S cells.

The R strain referred to above as R36A was derived by growing the parent S culture of Pneumococcus Type II in broth containing Type II antipneumococcus rabbit serum for 36 serial passages and isolating the variant thus induced. The strain R36A has lost all the specific and distinguishing characteristics of the parent S organisms and consists only of attenuated and non-encapsulated R variants. The change S → R is often a reversible one provided the R cells are not too far "degraded." The reversion of the R form to its original specific type can frequently be accomplished by successive animal passages or by repeated serial subculture in anti-R serum. When reversion occurs under these conditions, however, the R culture invariably reverts to the encapsulated form of the same specific type as that from which it was derived. Strain R36A has become relatively fixed in the R phase and has never spontaneously reverted to the Type II S form. Moreover, repeated attempts to cause it to revert under the conditions just mentioned have in all instances been unsuccessful.

The reversible conversion of S ⇌ R within the limits of a single type is quite different from the transformation of one specific type of Pneumococcus into another specific type through the R form. Transformation of types has never been observed to occur spontaneously and has been induced experimentally only by the special techniques outlined earlier in this paper. Under these conditions, the enzymatic synthesis of a chemically and immunologically different capsular polysaccharide is specifically oriented and selectively determined by the specific type of S cells used as source of the transforming agent.

In the course of the present study it was noted that the stock culture of R36 on serial transfers in blood broth undergoes spontaneous dissociation giving rise to a number of other R variants which can be distinguished one from another by colony form. The significance of this in the present instance lies in the fact that of four different variants isolated from the parent R culture only one (R36A) is susceptible to the transforming action of potent extracts, while the others fail to respond and are wholly inactive in this regard. The fact that differences exist in the responsiveness of different R variants to the same specific stimulus emphasizes the care that must be exercised in the selection of a suitable R variant for use in experiments on transformation. The capacity of this R strain (R36A) to respond to a variety of different transforming agents is shown by the readiness with which it can be transformed to Types I, III, VI, or XIV, as well as to its original type (Type II), to which, as pointed out, it has never spontaneously reverted.

Although the significance of the following fact will become apparent later on, it must be mentioned here that pneumococcal cells possess an enzyme capable of destroying the activity of the transforming principle. Indeed, this enzyme has been found to be present and highly active in the autolysates of a number of different strains. The fact that this intracellular enzyme is released during autolysis may explain, in part at least, the observation of Dawson and Sia [1931] that it is essential in bringing about transformation in the test tube to use a small inoculum of young and actively growing R cells. The irregularity of the results and often the failure to induce transformation when large inocula are used may be attributable to the release from autolyzing cells of an amount of this enzyme sufficient to destroy the transforming principle in the reaction system.

In order to obtain consistent and reproducible results, two facts must be borne in mind: first, that an R culture can undergo spontaneous dissociation and give rise to other variants which have lost the capacity to respond to the transforming stimulus; and secondly, that pneumococcal cells contain an intracellular enzyme which when released destroys the activity of the transforming principle. Consequently, it is important to select a responsive strain and to prevent as far as possible the destructive changes associated with autolysis.

Method of Titration of Transforming Activity.—In the isolation and purification of the active principle from crude extracts of pneumococcal cells it is desirable to have a method for determining quantitatively the transforming activity of various fractions.

The experimental procedure used is as follows: Sterilization of the material to be tested for activity is accomplished by the use of alcohol since it has been found that this reagent has no effect on activity. A measured volume of extract is precipitated in a sterile centrifuge tube by the addition of 4 to 5 volumes of absolute ethyl alcohol, and the mixture is allowed to stand 8 or more hours in the refrigerator in order to effect sterilization. The alcohol precipitated material is centrifuged, the supernatant discarded, and the tube containing the precipitate is allowed to drain for a few minutes in the inverted position to remove excess alcohol. The mouth of the tube is then carefully flamed and a dry, sterile cotton plug is inserted. The precipitate is redissolved in the original volume of saline. Sterilization of active material by this technique has invariably proved effective. This procedure avoids the loss of active substance which may occur when the solution is passed through a Berkefeld filter or is heated at the high temperatures required for sterilization.

To the charcoal-adsorbed broth described above is added 10 per cent of the sterile ascitic or pleural fluid which has previously been heated at 60°C. for 30 minutes, in order to destroy the enzyme known to inactivate the transforming principle. The enriched medium is distributed under aseptic conditions in 2.0 cc. amounts in sterile tubes measuring 15 × 100 mm. The sterilized extract is diluted serially in saline neutralized to pH 7.2–7.6 by addition of 0.1 N NaOH, or it may be similarly diluted in M/40 phosphate buffer, pH 7.4. 0.2 cc. of each dilution is added to at least 3 or 4 tubes of the serum medium. The tubes are then seeded with a 5 to 8 hour blood broth culture of R36A. 0.05 cc. of a 10^{-4} dilution of this culture is added to each tube, and the cultures are incubated at 37°C. for 18 to 24 hours.

The anti-R properties of the serum in the medium cause the R cells to agglutinate during growth, and clumps of the agglutinated cells settle to the bottom of the tube leaving a clear supernatant. When transformation occurs, the encapsulated S cells, not being affected by these antibodies, grow diffusely throughout the medium. On the other hand, in the absence of transformation the supernatant remains clear, and only sedimented growth of R organisms occurs. This difference in the character of growth makes it possible by inspection alone to distinguish tentatively between positive and negative results. As routine all the cultures are plated on blood agar for confirmation and further bacteriological identification. Since the extracts used in the present study were derived from Pneumococcus Type III, the differentiation between the colonies of the original R organism and those of the transformed S cells is especially striking, the latter being large, glistening, mucoid colonies typical of Pneumococcus Type III. . . .

A typical protocol of a titration of the transforming activity of a highly purified preparation is given in Table IV. . . .

ANALYSIS OF PURIFIED TRANSFORMING MATERIAL

General Properties.—Saline solutions containing 0.5 to 1.0 mg. per cc. of the purified substance are colorless and clear in diffuse light. However, in strong transmitted light the solution is not entirely clear and when stirred exhibits a silky sheen. Solutions at these concentrations are highly viscous.

Purified material dissolved in physiological salt solution and stored at 2–4°C. retains its activity in undiminished titer for at least 3 months. However, when dissolved in distilled water, it rapidly decreases in activity and becomes completely inert within a few days. Saline solutions stored in the frozen state in a CO_2 ice box (−70°C.) retain full potency for several months. Similarly, material precipitated from saline solution by alcohol and stored under the supernatant remains active over a long period of time. Partially purified material can be preserved by drying from the frozen state in the lyophile apparatus. However, when the same procedure is used for the preservation of the highly purified substance, it is found that the material undergoes changes resulting in decrease in solubility and loss of activity.

The activity of the transforming principle in crude extracts withstands heating for 30 to 60 minutes at 65°C. Highly purified preparations of active material are less stable, and some loss of activity occurs at this temperature. A quantitative study of the effect of heating purified material at higher temperatures has not as yet been made. Alloway [1932], using crude extracts prepared from Type III pneumococcal cells, found that occasionally activity could still be demonstrated after 10 minutes' exposure in the water bath to temperatures as high as 90°C.

The procedures mentioned above were carried out with solutions adjusted to neutral reaction, since it has been shown that hydrogen ion concentrations in the acid range result in progressive loss of activity. Inactivation occurs rapidly at pH 5 and below.

Qualitative Chemical Tests.—The purified material in concentrated solution gives negative biuret and Millon tests. These tests have been done directly on dry material with negative results. The Dische diphenylamine reaction for desoxyribonucleic acid is strongly positive. The orcinol test (Bial) for ribonucleic acid is weakly positive. However, it has been found that in similar concentrations pure preparations of desoxyribonucleic acid of animal origin prepared by different methods give a Bial reaction of corresponding intensity.

Although no specific tests for the presence of lipid in the purified material have been made, it has been found that crude material can be repeatedly extracted with alcohol and ether at −12°C. without loss of activity. In addition, as will be noted in the preparative procedures, repeated alcohol precipitation and treatment with chloroform result in no decrease in biological activity.

Elementary Chemical Analysis.—Four purified preparations were analyzed for

TABLE I

Elementary Chemical Analysis of Purified Preparations of the Transforming Substance

Preparation No.	Carbon	Hydrogen	Nitrogen	Phosphorus	N/P ratio
	per cent	*per cent*	*per cent*	*per cent*	
37	34.27	3.89	14.21	8.57	1.66
38B	—	—	15.93	9.09	1.75
42	35.50	3.76	15.36	9.04	1.69
44	—	—	13.40	8.45	1.58
Theory for sodium desoxyribonucleate......	34.20	3.21	15.32	9.05	1.69

content of nitrogen, phosphorus, carbon, and hydrogen. The results are presented in Table I. The nitrogen-phosphorus ratios vary from 1.58 to 1.75 with an average value of 1.67 which is in close agreement with that calculated on the basis of the theoretical structure of sodium desoxyribonucleate (tetranucleotide). The analytical figures by themselves do not establish that the substance isolated is a pure chemical entity. However, on the basis of the nitrogen-phosphorus ratio, it would appear that little protein or other substances containing nitrogen or phosphorus are present as impurities since if they were this ratio would be considerably altered.

Enzymatic Analysis.—Various crude and crystalline enzymes have been tested for their capacity to destroy the biological activity of potent bacterial extracts. Extracts buffered at the optimal pH, to which were added crystalline trypsin and chymotrypsin or combinations of both, suffered no loss in activity following treatment with these enzymes. Pepsin could not be tested because extracts are rapidly inactivated at the low pH required for its use. Prolonged treatment with crystalline ribonuclease under optimal conditions caused no demonstrable decrease in transforming activity. The fact that trypsin, chymotrypsin, and ribonuclease had no effect on the transforming principle is further evidence that this substance is not ribonucleic acid or a protein susceptible to the action of tryptic enzymes.

In addition to the crystalline enzymes, sera and preparations of enzymes obtained from the organs of various animals were tested to determine their effect on transforming activity. Certain of these were found to be capable of completely destroying biological activity. The various enzyme preparations tested included highly active phosphatases obtained from rabbit bone by the method of Martland and Robison [1929] and from swine kidney as described by H. and E. Albers [1935]. In addition, a preparation made from the intestinal mucosa of dogs by Levene and Dillon [1933] and containing a polynucleotidase for thymus nucleic acid was used. Pneumococcal autolysates and a commercial preparation of pancreatin were also tested. The alkaline phosphatase activity of these preparations was determined by their action on β-glycerophosphate and phenyl phosphate, and the esterase activity by their capacity to split tributyrin. Since

TABLE II

The Inactivation of Transforming Principle by Crude Enzyme Preparations

Crude enzyme preparations	Enzymatic activity			
	Phosphatase	Tributyrin esterase	Depolymer- ase for desoxyribo- nucleate	Inactivation of trans- forming principle
Dog intestinal mucosa	+	+	+	+
Rabbit bone phosphatase	+	+	—	—
Swine kidney "	+	—	—	—
Pneumococcus autolysates	—	+	+	+
Normal dog and rabbit serum	+	+	+	+

the highly purified transforming material isolated from pneumococcal extracts was found to contain desoxyribonucleic acid, these same enzymes were tested for depolymerase activity on known samples of desoxyribonucleic acid isolated by Mirsky from fish sperm and mammalian tissues. The results are summarized in Table II in which the phosphatase, esterase, and nucleodepolymerase activity of these enzymes is compared with their capacity to destroy the transforming principle. Analysis of these results shows that irrespective of the presence of phosphatase or esterase only those preparations shown to contain an enzyme capable of depolymerizing authentic samples of desoxyribonucleic acid were found to inactivate the transforming principle.

Greenstein and Jenrette [1940] have shown that tissue extracts, as well as the milk and serum of several mammalian species, contain an enzyme system which causes depolymerization of desoxyribonucleic acid. To this enzyme system Green- stein has later given the name desoxyribonucleodepolymerase [1943]. These in- vestigators determined depolymerase activity by following the reduction in viscosity of solutions of sodium desoxyribonucleate. The nucleate and enzyme were mixed in the viscosimeter and viscosity measurements made at intervals during incubation at 30°C. In the present study this method was used in the measurement of depolymerase activity except that incubation was carried out at 37°C. and, in addition to the reduction of viscosity, the action of the enzyme was further tested by the progressive decrease in acid precipitability of the nucleate during enzymatic breakdown.

The effect of fresh normal dog and rabbit serum on the activity of the trans- forming substance is shown in the following experiment.

Sera obtained from a normal dog and normal rabbit were diluted with an equal volume of physiological saline. The diluted serum was divided into three equal portions. One part was heated at 65°C. for 30 minutes, another at 60°C. for 30 minutes, and the third was used unheated as control. A partially purified preparation of transforming material which had previously been dried in the lyophile apparatus was dissolved in saline in a concentration of 3.7 mg. per cc.

1.0 cc. of this solution was mixed with 0.5 cc. of the various samples of heated and unheated diluted sera, and the mixtures at pH 7.4 were incubated at 37°C. for 2 hours. After the serum had been allowed to act on the transforming material for this period, all tubes were heated at 65°C. for 30 minutes to stop enzymatic action. Serial dilutions were then made in saline and tested in triplicate for transforming activity according to the procedure described under Method of titration. The results given in Table III illustrate the differential heat inactivation of the enzymes in dog and rabbit serum which destroy the transforming principle.

From the data presented in Table III it is evident that both dog and rabbit serum in the unheated state are capable of completely destroying transforming activity. On the other hand, when samples of dog serum which have been heated either at 60°C. or at 65°C. for 30 minutes are used, there is no loss of transforming activity. Thus, in this species the serum enzyme responsible for

TABLE III

Differential Heat Inactivation of Enzymes in Dog and Rabbit Serum Which Destroy the Transforming Substance

	Heat treatment of serum	Dilution*	Triplicate tests					
			I		2		3	
			Diffuse growth	Colony form	Diffuse growth	Colony form	Diffuse growth	Colony form
Dog serum	Unheated	Undiluted	−	R only	−	R only	−	R only
		1:5	−	R "	−	R "	−	R "
		1:25	−	R "	−	R "	−	R "
	60°C. for 30 min.	Undiluted	+	SIII	+	SIII	+	SIII
		1:5	+	SIII	+	SIII	+	SIII
		1:25	+	SIII	+	SIII	+	SIII
	65° C. for 30 min.	Undiluted	+	SIII	+	SIII	+	SIII
		1:5	+	SIII	+	SIII	+	SIII
		1:25	+	SIII	+	SIII	+	SIII
Rabbit serum	Unheated	Undiluted	−	R only	−	R only	−	R only
		1:5	−	R "	−	R "	−	R "
		1:25	−	R "	−	R "	−	R "
	60°C. for 30 min.	Undiluted	−	R only	−	R only	−	R only
		1:5	−	R "	−	R "	−	R "
		1:25	−	R "	−	R "	−	R "
	65° C. for 30 min.	Undiluted	+	SIII	+	SIII	+	SIII
		1:5	+	SIII	+	SIII	+	SIII
		1:25	+	SIII	+	SIII	+	SIII
Control (no serum)	None	Undiluted	+	SIII	+	SIII	+	SIII
		1:5	+	SIII	+	SIII	+	SIII
		1:25	+	SIII	+	SIII	+	SIII

* Dilution of the digest mixture of serum and transforming substance.

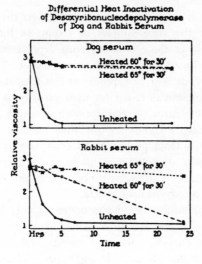

Differential Heat Inactivation
of Desoxyribonucleodepolymerase
of Dog and Rabbit Serum

CHART I

destruction of the transforming principle is completely inactivated at 60°C. In contrast to these results, exposure to 65°C. for 30 minutes was required for complete destruction of the corresponding enzyme in rabbit serum.

The same samples of dog and rabbit serum used in the preceding experiment were also tested for their depolymerase activity on a preparation of sodium desoxyribonucleate isolated by Mirsky from shad sperm.

A highly viscous solution of the nucleate in distilled water in a concentration of 1 mg. per cc. was used. 1.0 cc. amounts of heated and unheated sera diluted in saline as shown in the preceding protocol were mixed in Ostwald viscosimeters with 4.0 cc. of the aqueous solution of the nucleate. Determinations of viscosity were made immediately and at intervals over a period of 24 hours during incubation at 37°C.

The results of this experiment are graphically presented in Chart 1. In the case of unheated serum of both dog and rabbit, the viscosity fell to that of water in 5 to 7 hours. Dog serum heated at 60°C. for 30 minutes brought about no significant reduction in viscosity after 22 hours. On the other hand, heating rabbit serum at 60°C. merely reduced the rate of depolymerase action, and after 24 hours the viscosity was brought to the same level as with the unheated serum. Heating at 65°C., however, completely destroyed the rabbit serum depolymerase.

Thus, in the case of dog and rabbit sera there is a striking parallelism between the temperature of inactivation of the depolymerase and that of the enzyme which destroys the activity of the transforming principle. The fact that this difference in temperature of inactivation is not merely a general property of all enzymes in the sera is evident from experiments on the heat inactivation of tributyrin esterase in the same samples of serum. In the latter instance, the results are the reverse of those observed with depolymerase since the esterase of rabbit serum is almost completely inactivated at 60°C. while that in dog serum is only slightly affected by exposure to this temperature.

Of a number of substances tested for their capacity to inhibit the action of the enzyme known to destroy the transforming principle, only sodium fluoride has been found to have a significant inhibitory effect. Regardless of whether this enzyme is derived from pneumococcal cells, dog intestinal mucosa, pancreatin, or normal sera its activity is inhibited by fluoride. Similarly it has been found that fluoride in the same concentration also inhibits the enzymatic depolymerization of desoxyribonucleic acid.

The fact that transforming activity is destroyed only by those preparations containing depolymerase for desoxyribonucleic acid and the further fact that in both instances the enzymes concerned are inactivated at the same temperature and inhibited by fluoride provide additional evidence for the belief that the active principle is a nucleic acid of the desoxyribose type.

Serological Analysis.—In the course of chemical isolation of the active material it was found that as the crude extracts were purified, their serological activity in Type III antiserum progressively decreased without corresponding loss in biological activity. Solutions of the highly purified substance itself gave only faint trace reactions in precipitin tests with high titer Type III antipneumococcus rabbit serum. It is well known that pneumococcal protein can be detected by serological methods in dilutions as high as 1:50,000 and the capsular as well as the somatic polysaccharide in dilutions of at least 1:5,000,000. In view of these facts, the loss of serological reactivity indicates that these cell constituents have been almost completely removed from the final preparations. The fact that the transforming substance in purified state exhibits little or no serological reactivity is in striking contrast to its biological specificity in inducing pneumococcal transformation.

Physicochemical Studies.—A purified and active preparation of the transforming substance (preparation 44) was examined in the analytical ultracentrifuge. The material gave a single and unusually sharp boundary indicating that the substance was homogeneous and that the molecules were uniform in size and very asymmetric. Biological· activity was found to be sedimented at the same rate as the optically observed boundary, showing that activity could not be due to the presence of an entity much different in size. The molecular weight cannot be accurately determined until measurements of the diffusion constant and partial specific volume have been made. However, Tennent and Vilbrandt [1943] have determined the diffusion constant of several preparations of thymus nucleic acid the sedimentation rate of which is in close agreement with the values observed in the present study. Assuming that the asymmetry of the molecules is the same in both instances, it is estimated that the molecular weight of the pneumococcal preparation is of the order of 500,000.

Examination of the same active preparation was carried out by electrophoresis in the Tiselius apparatus and revealed only a single electrophoretic component of relatively high mobility comparable to that of a nucleic acid. Transforming activity was associated with the fast moving component giving the optically visible boundary. Thus in both the electrical and centrifugal fields, the behavior of the purified substance is consistent with the concept that biological activity is a property of the highly polymerized nucleic acid.

Ultraviolet absorption curves showed maxima in the region of 2600 Å and minima in the region of 2350 Å. These findings are characteristic of nucleic acids.

Quantitative Determination of Biological Activity.—In its highly purified state the material as isolated has been found to be capable of inducing transformation in amounts ranging from 0.02 to 0.003 μg. Preparation 44, the purification of which was carried out at low temperature and which had a nitrogen-phosphorus ratio of 1.58, exhibited high transforming activity. Titration of the activity of this preparation is given in Table IV.

TABLE IV

Titration of Transforming Activity of Preparation 44

Transforming principle Preparation 44*		Quadruplicate tests							
		1		2		3		4	
Dilution	Amount added	Diffuse growth	Colony form	Diffuse growth	Colony form	Diffuse growth	Colony form	Diffuse growth	Colony form
	μg.								
10^{-2}	1.0	+	SIII	+	SIII	+	SIII	+	SIII
$10^{-2.5}$	0.3	+	SIII	+	SIII	+	SIII	+	SIII
10^{-3}	0.1	+	SIII	+	SIII	+	SIII	+	SIII
$10^{-3.5}$	0.03	+	SIII	+	SIII	+	SIII	+	SIII
10^{-4}	0.01	+	SIII	+	SIII	+	SIII	+	SIII
$10^{-4.5}$	0.003	—	R only	+	SIII	—	R only	+	SIII
10^{-5}	0.001	—	R "	—	R only	—	R "	—	R only
Control	None	—	R "	—	R "	—	R "	—	R "

* Solution from which dilutions were made contained 0.5 mg. per cc. of purified material. 0.2 cc. of each dilution added to quadruplicate tubes containing 2.0 cc. of standard serum broth. 0.05 cc. of a 10^{-4} dilution of a blood broth culture of R36A is added to each tube.

The data presented in Table IV show that on the basis of dry weight 0.003 μg. of the active material brought about transformation. Since the reaction system containing the 0.003 μg. has a volume of 2.25 cc., this represents a final concentration of the purified substance of 1 part in 600,000,000.

DISCUSSION

The present study deals with the results of an attempt to determine the chemical nature of the substance inducing specific transformation of pneumococcal types. A desoxyribonucleic acid fraction has been isolated from Type III pneumococci which is capable of transforming unencapsulated R variants derived from Pneumococcus Type II into fully encapsulated Type III cells. Thompson and Dubos [1938] have isolated from pneumococci a nucleic acid of the ribose type. So far as the writers are aware, however, a nucleic acid of the desoxyribose type has not heretofore been recovered from pneumococci nor has specific transformation been experimentally induced *in vitro* by a chemically defined substance.

Although the observations are limited to a single example, they acquire broader significance from the work of earlier investigators who demonstrated the interconvertibility of various pneumococcal types and showed that the specificity of the changes induced is in each instance determined by the particular type of encapsulated cells used to evoke the reaction. From the point of view of the phenomenon in general, therefore, it is of special interest that in the examples studied, highly purified and protein-free material consisting largely, if not exclusively, of desoxyribonucleic acid is capable of stimulating unencapsulated R variants of Pneumococcus Type II to produce a capsular polysaccharide identical in type specificity with that of the cells from which the inducing substance was isolated. Equally striking is the fact that the substance evoking the reaction and the capsular substance produced in response to it are chemically distinct, each belonging to a wholly different class of chemical compounds.

The inducing substance, on the basis of its chemical and physical properties, appears to be a highly polymerized and viscous form of sodium desoxyribonucleate. On the other hand, the Type III capsular substance, the synthesis of which is evoked by this transforming agent, consists chiefly of a non-nitrogenous polysaccharide constituted of glucose-glucuronic acid units linked in glycosidic union. The presence of the newly formed capsule containing this type-specific polysaccharide confers on the transformed cells all the distinguishing characteristics of Pneumococcus Type III. Thus, it is evident that the inducing substance and the substance produced in turn are chemically distinct and biologically specific in their action and that both are requisite in determining the type specificity of the cell of which they form a part.

The experimental data presented in this paper strongly suggest that nucleic acids, at least those of the desoxyribose type, possess different specificities as evidenced by the selective action of the transforming principle. Indeed, the possibility of the existence of specific differences in biological behavior of nucleic acids has previously been suggested but has never been experimentally demonstrated owing in part at least to the lack of suitable biological methods. The techniques used in the study of transformation appear to afford a sensitive means of testing the validity of this hypothesis, and the results thus far obtained add supporting evidence in favor of this point of view.

If it is ultimately proved beyond reasonable doubt that the transforming activity of the material described is actually an inherent property of the nucleic acid, one must still account on a chemical basis for the biological specificity of its action. At first glance, immunological methods would appear to offer the ideal means of determining the differential specificity of this group of biologically important substances. Although the constituent units and general pattern of the nucleic acid molecule have been defined, there is as yet relatively little known of the possible effect that subtle differences in molecular configuration may exert on the biological specificity of these substances. However, since nucleic acids free or combined with histones or protamines are not known to function antigenically, one would not anticipate that such differences would be revealed by immunological techniques. Consequently, it is perhaps not surprising that highly purified and protein-free preparations of desoxyribonucleic acid, although extremely active in inducing transformation, showed only faint trace reactions in precipitin tests with potent Type III antipneumococcus rabbit sera.

From these limited observations it would be unwise to draw any conclusion concerning the immunological significance of the nucleic acids until further knowledge on this phase of the problem is available. Recent observations by Lackman and his collaborators [1941] have shown that nucleic acids of both the yeast and thymus type derived from hemolytic streptococci and from animal and plant sources precipitate with certain antipneumococcal sera. The reactions varied with different lots of immune serum and occurred more frequently in antipneumococcal horse serum than in corresponding sera of immune rabbits. The irregularity and broad cross reactions encountered led these investigators to express some doubt as to the immunological significance of the results. Unless special immunochemical methods can be devised similar to those so successfully used in demonstrating the serological specificity of simple nonantigenic substances, it appears that the techniques employed in the study of transformation are the only ones available at present for testing possible differences in the biological behavior of nucleic acids.

Admittedly there are many phases of the problem of transformation that require further study and many questions that remain unanswered largely because of technical difficulties. For example, it would be of interest to know the relation between rate of reaction and concentration of the transforming substance; the proportion of cells transformed to those that remain unaffected in the reaction system. However, from a bacteriological point of view, numerical estimations based on colony counts might prove more misleading than enlightening because of the aggregation and sedimentation of the R cells agglutinated by the antiserum in the medium. Attempts to induce transformation in suspensions of resting cells held under conditions inhibiting growth and multiplication have thus far proved unsuccessful, and it seems probable that transformation occurs only during active reproduction of the cells. Important in this connection is the fact that the R cells, as well as those that have undergone transformation, presumably also all other variants and types of pneumococci, contain an intracellular enzyme which is released during autolysis and in the free state is capable of rapidly and completely destroying the activity of the transforming agent. It would appear, therefore, that during the logarithmic phase of growth when cell division is most active and autolysis least apparent, the cultural conditions are optimal for the maintenance of the balance between maximal reactivity of the R cell and minimal destruction of the transforming agent through the release of autolytic ferments.

In the present state of knowledge any interpretation of the mechanism involved in transformation must of necessity be purely theoretical. The biochemical events underlying the phenomenon suggest that the transforming principle interacts with the R cell giving rise to a coordinated series of enzymatic reactions that culminate in the synthesis of the Type III capsular antigen. The experimental findings have clearly demonstrated that the induced alterations are not random changes but are predictable, always corresponding in type specificity to that of the encapsulated cells from which the transforming substance was isolated. Once transformation has occurred, the newly acquired characteristics are thereafter transmitted in series through innumerable transfers in artificial media without any further addition of the transforming agent. Moreover, from the transformed cells themselves, a substance of identical activity can again be recovered in amounts far in excess of that originally added to induce the change. It is evident, therefore, that not only is the capsular material reproduced in successive generations but that the primary factor, which controls the occurrence and specificity of capsular development, is also reduplicated in the daughter cells. The induced changes are not temporary modifications but are permanent alterations which persist provided the cultural conditions are favorable for the maintenance of capsule formation. The transformed cells can be readily distinguished from the parent R forms not alone by serological reactions but by the presence of a newly formed and visible capsule which is the immunological unit of type specificity and the accessory structure essential in determining the infective capacity of the microorganism in the animal body.

It is particularly significant in the case of pneumococci that the experimentally induced alterations are definitely correlated with the development of a new morphological structure and the consequent acquisition of new antigenic and invasive properties. Equally if not more significant is the fact that these changes are predictable, type-specific, and heritable.

Various hypotheses have been advanced in explanation of the nature of the changes induced. In his original description of the phenomenon Griffith [1928] suggested that the dead bacteria in the inoculum might furnish some specific protein that serves as a "pabulum" and enables the R form to manufacture a capsular carbohydrate.

More recently the phenomenon has been interpreted from a genetic point of view. The inducing substance has been likened to a gene, and the capsular antigen which is produced in response to it has been regarded as a gene product. In discussing the phenomenon of transformation Dobzhansky [1941] has stated that "If this transformation is described as a genetic mutation—and it is difficult to avoid so describing it—we are dealing with authentic cases of induction of specific mutations by specific treatments. . . ."

Another interpretation of the phenomenon has been suggested by Stanley [1938] who has drawn the analogy between the activity of the transforming agent and that of a virus. On the other hand, Murphy [1935] has compared the causative agents of fowl tumors with the transforming principle of Pneumococcus. He has suggested that both these groups of agents be termed "transmissible mutagens" in order to differentiate them from the virus group. Whatever may prove to be the correct interpretation, these differences in viewpoint indicate the implications of the phenomenon of transformation in relation to similar problems in the fields of genetics, virology, and cancer research.

It is, of course, possible that the biological activity of the substance described is not an inherent property of the nucleic acid but is due to minute amounts of some other substance adsorbed to it or so intimately associated with it as to escape detection. If, however, the biologically active substance isolated in highly purified form as the sodium salt of desoxyribonucleic acid actually proves to be the transforming principle, as the available evidence strongly suggests, then nucleic acids of this type must be regarded not merely as structurally important but as functionally active in determining the biochemical activities and specific characteristics of pneumococcal cells. Assuming that the sodium desoxyribonucleate and the active principle are one and the same substance, then the transformation described represents a change that is chemically induced and specifically directed by a known chemical compound. If the results of the present study on the chemical nature of the transforming principle are confirmed, then nucleic acids must be regarded as possessing biological specificity the chemical basis of which is as yet undetermined. . . .

In the genus *Escherichia* and in a few closely related genera, cells conjugate under certain conditions; part of a chromosome of one cell passes over into the other cell of the conjugating pair in a manner somewhat resembling the fertilization process associated with conjugation of cells in many green algae, and also vaguely resembling the fertilization of egg by sperm in the higher animals and plants. Bacterial conjugation was originally discovered in *Escherichia coli,* and the following discussion will deal exclusively with the phenomenon as observed in this species.

It was originally supposed that any cell in a culture could mate with any other cell, but this has been found not to be the case. In the isolates of *E. coli* in which mating has been observed, two mating types occur: a "male" type, or genetic donor, and a "female" type, or genetic recipient. A donor cell and a recipient cell become attached, usually end-to-end, and a part of one of the two chromosomes of the donor passes through into the recipient cell.

Conjugation in *Escherichia* has one remarkable feature that clearly distinguishes it from fertilization and mating processes among other organisms. Male cells are cells that are infected with a viruslike sex factor, known as the *F agent.* Upon infection with the F agent, uninfected F^- female (recipient) cells, and their progeny, acquire the capacity (*a*) to infect an F^- cell with the F agent upon conjugation and (*b*) in rare cases to endow it with the capacity to transfer a part of one of its chromosomes into an F^- cell with which it has conjugated.

In an ordinary strain of *E. coli,* when cells from an all-male, or F^+, culture are mixed with cells from an F^- culture, the cells conjugate and the progeny are all F^+. In a minute fraction of the conjugating pairs, chromosome transfer from F^+ to F^- takes place; the progeny of such cells will be found to show many of the specific genetic traits, or *genetic markers,* of the F^- culture, along with some of the genetic characteristics of the F^+. Inheritance from the F^+ is incomplete and is limited to genetic traits that are determined by genes in the portion of the F^+ chromosome that succeeds in passing into the F^- cell.

In recent years there have appeared several mutant male strains of *E. coli* in which transfer of a portion of the F^+ cell's chromosome into the F^- occurs frequently rather than in rare instances. Discovery of these mutant *high-frequency recombination,* or *Hfr, strains* has greatly expedited research on bacterial conjugation and bacterial genetics.

The following paper, typical of recent work on bacterial conjugation, reports some ingeniously planned experiments intended to clarify a crucial point. When a portion of one chromosome of the F+ cell enters the F-, it adds to the genetic complement of the fertilized cell, or zygote, a part-chromosome which duplicates, or almost duplicates, a portion of the corresponding chromosome already present. The duplication, of course, may be inexact: some of the genes in the intruding F+ portion may differ from those in the corresponding portion of the F- chromosome. The progeny of this zygote are likely to show some of the genetic characters introduced by the F+ intermingled with some of those contributed by the corresponding part of the F- chromosome. How does this happen? Do the chromosomes intertwine and break, pieces of one chromosome replacing corresponding pieces of the other (breakage and reunion)? Or does some mechanism within the zygote form a single chromosome by copying portions of the F+ and portions of the corresponding part of the F-? The manner in which Wood and Marcovich attempted to decide between these possibilities affords a neat exercise in scientific method.

The authors are distinguished researchers in this field. Dr. Marcovich is a member of an eminent group of researchers on bacterial genetics in the Institut Pasteur, Paris. Dr. Wood is Visiting Science Faculty Fellow of the National Science Foundation, working permanently in the Department of Physics, University of Pennsylvania; a physicist originally, he has applied his knowledge of radiation physics to the elucidation of some of the problems concerned with the entrance of the chromosome of the F+ into the F- cell.

Additional information may be found in the following books:

Edward A. Adelberg (ed.), "Papers on Bacterial Genetics," Little, Brown and Company, Boston, 1960, 400 pp.

F. Jacob and E. L. Wollman, "Sexuality and the Genetics of Bacteria," Academic Press Inc., New York, 1961.

From *Genetics,*
49:779–786, 1964.

EFFECTS ON GENETIC RECOMBINATION OF ESCHERICHIA COLI K-12 PRODUCED BY X-RAY AND ALPHA-PARTICLE IRRADIATION OF THE FEMALE

BY T. H. WOOD AND H. MARCOVICH

The appearance of recombinant cell types in *Escherichia coli* K-12 has been shown to depend on a sequence of consecutive steps: (1) an effective contact between two cells of opposite mating types; (2) a transfer of a portion of the genetic material from the donor cell to the recipient cell; (3) an integration of the genetic information from both parental strains into a recombinant cell with the subsequent production of a clone. (See Clark and Adelberg 1962 and Jacob and Wollman 1961, for reviews.) High frequency recombination strains (Hfr) are able to transfer to the recipient cells with high frequency genetic determinants in a sequential order which depends on the particular strain. The probability of transfer of a given character decreases with its distance from the portion of the chromosome first injected (the origin). Two alternative, but not mutually exclusive, mechanisms have been considered for the integration processes which are involved in the production of recombinants: (1) an interchange of DNA fragments between the two parental chromosomes (Breakage-and-Reunion); and (2) a *de novo* synthesis of a recombinant chromosome by copying alternatively the base sequences from the two parental chromosomes (Copy-Choice).

Perturbations applied to the genetic material of the parental cells might affect selectively the various steps in the recombinational process. Earlier studies (Marcovich 1961 . . .) have shown that X-ray and alpha-particle irradiation of the donor strain results in a decreased probability of effective transfer of the male markers to the zygote, the radiosensitivity for this process being directly proportional to the distance between the origin of the chromosome and the selected marker. An analysis of the unselected markers reveals that no measurable radiation damage at moderate doses is carried on the material transferred to the zygote, the transfer process *per se* effectively eliminating radiation induced lesions by causing them to be expressed operationally as breaks that

23

prevent their transfer. Hence X-ray or alpha-particle irradiation of the donor cells gives no information on those steps in the recombination process subsequent to transfer of genetic information to the female.

However, if the recipient cells are irradiated before mating, the transfer process *per se* is not found to be measurably affected, and any change in the relative frequencies of appearance of the various recombinant types is therefore due to modifications brought about by radiation in those steps subsequent to transfer. In the experiments to be reported, X- or alpha-irradiation of the recipient cells before mating causes drastic changes in the recombinational frequencies for the various markers utilized in the cross as if there were a preferential utilization of the male genetic information.

MATERIALS AND METHODS

Strains: Escherichia coli K-12. *Recipient:* F⁻ PA-309 (*thr, leu, try, his, arg, thi, lac, gal, mtl, xyl, mal, T1ʳ, strʳ*), where the abbreviations symbolize threonine, leucine, tryptophan, histidine, arginine, thiamine (vitamin B_1), lactose, galactose, mannitol, xylose, maltose, coliphage T1, and streptomycin, respectively. The gene symbols as written above indicate that the strain shows dependence for the various amino acids and thiamine or cannot use a particular sugar in lieu of glucose as an energy source; *s* and *r* indicate sensitivity or resistance of the strain to an agent.

Donor: HfrH (*thi, strˢ*). The markers used in this study were: *thr⁺* (8), *leu⁺*(8.5), *gal⁺* (24), *try⁺*(33), and *his⁺*(59), where the numbers in parentheses refer to the minimum time in minutes required for the transfer of the marker from the male (HfrH) to the zygote. Streptomycin sensitivity is transferred with low frequency to the zygote under the conditions used here.

Media: M medium: the minimal synthetic medium previously described (Marcovich 1961) plus 0.4 percent glucose and 4 µg/ml thiamine. Tryptone Broth: nutrient broth (Difco) 0.3 percent, bacto tryptone (Difco) 0.5 percent, NaCl 0.5 percent. For solid media, agar was added at a concentration of 1.5 percent. Selective solid media: M medium plus agar fortified with streptomycin 60 µg/ ml, leucine 30 µg/ml, threonine 30 µg/ml, tryptophan 8 µg/ml, histidine 8 µg/ ml, and arginine 30 µg/ml. For characterization of the markers utilized here, one of the amino acids threonine, leucine, tryptophan, or histidine was omitted or galactose was substituted for glucose at equal concentration.

Mating and assay: Male and female cells were grown in broth to a concentration of 2 to 3 × 10⁸ cells/ml (exponential phase). Aliquots of the female cells were pulled down as single layers on 25 mm millipore filters (type HA), irradiated, and subsequently removed from the filter by agitation in 3 ml of M medium. To facilitate the removal of the cells from the filters, base layers of *E. coli* B (*strˢ*) cells were pulled down on the filter before the female cells. Recovery efficiencies with this technique were 80 ± 10 percent. Hfr cells were washed on millipore filters and resuspended in M medium.

Aliquots of male and female cells totaling 2 ml were mixed together for mating and gently agitated at 37°C for 90 minutes. Since the irradiated female cells are damaged at random, males might conjugate preferentially with the least damaged ones. This bias would be greatest at low mating ratios (the ratio of Hfr to F- cells in the mating mixture). Variations between 1/20 and 20/1 in the mating ratio do not affect any of the results reported here; a mating ratio of 1/20 was used generally in these experiments. All calculations were made with respect to the input number of the minority parent in the mating mixture.

After proper dilution, aliquots were plated on the various assay media and the numbers of colony-forming units were counted after incubation at 37°C for 48 hours. The presence of the unselected markers among recombinants (genetic constitution) was determined by inoculation of colonies from the selective plates onto a master grid plate. After growth, these colonies were replicated on various test plates.

Irradiation: The alpha particle source (30 millicuries of Po^{210}, deposited on a nickel disc 1 cm in diameter and located 20 mm from the millipore filters) gave a corrected dose rate of approximately 20 kilorads/min as determined by calculation. The X-ray source . . . gave a dose rate of 43 kilorads/min at an anode-to-filter distance of 56 mm when operated at 37.5 kv and 40 ma as determined by ferrous sulfate dosimetry. . . .

RESULTS

Effect of irradiation on recombinational frequencies of selected markers: To best illustrate two different points, data for X-ray and alpha-particle irradiation of the female are plotted in different ways in Figures 1a and 1b. In Figure 1a "Marker Presence" (the ratio of the number of recombinant cells of a particular class following X-irradiation of the female (N_R) to the number of cells of the input minority parent (N_I)) is shown as a function of dose. The value of this ratio with no irradiation is proportional to the normal gradient function (e^{-kx}) and will be designated as N_{RO}/N_I. The survival (colony-forming ability) of the F- cells is also shown. In Figure 1b the ordinate, "Marker Survival", is the ratio of Marker Presence following alpha irradiation of the F- population to that with no irradiation, $\dfrac{N_R}{N_I} \bigg/ \dfrac{N_{RO}}{N_I} = N_R/N_{RO}$. Marker Presence and Marker Survival curves for both types of radiation are qualitatively similar.

Figure 1 shows that the Marker Presence and F- survival curves converge with increasing dose delivered to the female while Figure 1b shows a divergence with dose of the Marker Survival curves from one another and from the F- survival curve. Other points concerning the curves of Figures 1a and 1b are also pertinent: (1) the Marker Presence and Marker Survival of all markers decrease with irradiation dose and may be considered to be exponential within the experimental errors; (2) the slopes of these curves increase in absolute value in the inverse order of the distance of the selected markers from the origin; (3) the slope of the F- survival curve is greater than the slope of the

Marker Presence or Marker Survival curve of any marker; and (4) X rays and alpha particles have qualitatively equivalent biological effects although quantitatively a given dose of alpha particles is about 1.7 times as effective as the same dose of X rays.

The recombinational rate for an Hfr marker located at a distance x from the original can be written as Ce^{-kx}, where C is the recombinational rate of a marker located at the origin of the male chromosome and k, the overall gradient, is a constant for the specific mating conditions used. This overall gradient may be considered to be the sum of the gradient of transfer and the gradient of integration and segregation. With unirradiated cells, the gradient of transfer is larger than the gradient of integration and segregation; this latter is often assumed to be negligible. It can be seen from the convergence of the curves in Figure 1a that at higher doses there is a relative enhancement in the appearance of the distal markers compared to the proximal ones, that is, the overall gradient k is decreased. This can be confirmed by plotting the logarithm of marker presence against x, marker position, for various doses. Female irradiation would not be expected to decrease the gradient of transfer. Therefore, the observed decrease in the overall gradient can be associated with radiation effects on those recombinational events that follow transfer, that is, on the integrative and segregational processes. In these experiments, these processes involve an undamaged portion of the male chromosome and the radiation damaged female chromosome. The more distal the selected marker, the larger the segment of the male chromosome that is known to be within the zygote. These results suggest that the presence of a portion of the male chromosome may prevent lethal expression of radiation-induced lesions on the corresponding portion of the female chromosome. Thus the apparent negative gradient of integration and segregation observed after female irradiation can be viewed as due to a selective advantage conferred on those recombinants which receive larger portions of the male chromosome.

The convergence of the marker survival curves at high doses (Figure 1a) can be visualized to result from a preferential utilization of the male genetic information. At high dose levels where the female chromosome may be badly damaged, viable recombinants may receive their genetic information almost entirely from the male chromosome.

Effect of irradiation on inheritance of unselected markers: The graphs in Figure 2 give the fraction of the recombinant population prototrophic for a selected marker and resistant to streptomycin that is also prototrophic for a second marker not originally selected for in the cross (the unselected marker) as a function of radiation dose received by the female. A selected marker operationally divides the male chromosome into two regions: the region between it and the origin (the anterior region) and the other part of the chromosome (the posterior region). Several generalizations can be made from the data: (1) X rays and alpha particles are qualitatively and approximately quanti-

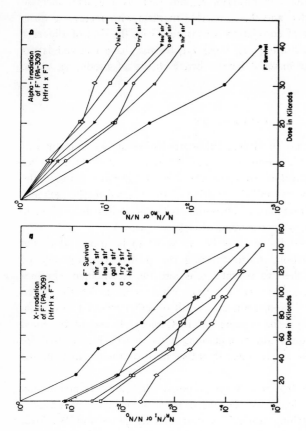

FIGURE 1

Effect of X rays (a) and alpha particles (b) on the recombination frequencies for selected markers in a cross between a nonirradiated male and an irradiated female. *E. coli* HfrH and *E. coli* F- PA-309 are grown in broth to a concentration of 2 to 3 × 10^8 cells/ml. The females are irradiated on millipore filters with different doses of either X rays or alpha particles. After removal from the filters cell survival is assayed by scoring ability to form colonies on minimal medium ("Survival"). Aliquots of the irradiated females for each dose are mated with males (3 × 10^8 F- and 2 × 10^7 Hfr cells/ml) for 90 min at 37°C with gentle agitation. Aliquots for each dose are plated and grown for 48 hr at 37°C on the proper media to determine the various recombinant classes. Counter selection is by streptomycin. In "a" the ordinate is "Marker Presence" (the ratio of the number of recombinant cells of a particular class following X-irradiation of the female (N_R) to the number of cells of the input minority parent (N_I). In "b" the ordinate is "Marker Survival" (the ratio of "Marker Presence" following alpha-irradiation of the F- population (N_R/N_I) to that with no irradiation (N_{RO}/N_I), or N_R/N_{RO}). "Survival" in both graphs refers to the ratio of F- cells surviving irradiation (N) to those initially present (N_0). The abscissae are the radiation doses delivered to the F- cells.

tatively equivalent in their effects on the inheritance of unselected markers. (2) In general, an unselected anterior marker appears with a frequency of 0.5 ± 0.1 in a cross involving an unirradiated F population and its frequency increases with dose to the 0.8 ± 0.1 level. No change is observed for the closely linked markers threonine and leucine (0.5 minute apart) which show a linkage of about 90 percent even at high dose. (3) The frequency of appearance of an unselected posterior marker rises from a value characteristic of the distance between the two markers (e^{-kx}) to a much higher value (between 0.5 and 0.9).

Thus in both the anterior and posterior regions there is a general increase in correlation of the selected and the unselected markers with increasing dose. This high level of increase of correlation is consistent with the data of Figure 1 and leads to the same conclusion, *i.e.*, those zygotes that have received larger pieces of the male genetic material have a better chance of producing viable recombinants.

DISCUSSION

The effects of either X-ray or alpha-particle irradiation of the recipient cell before mating can be briefly summarized: (1) the radiosensitivity for marker appearance or marker survival is inversely related to the distance between the origin of the male chromosome and the position of the selected marker (Figure 1); and (2) there is a preferential utilization with increasing dose of male genetic information in surviving recombinant cells (Figure 2).

Two types of operational lesions may be envisaged to be produced in the female genome by irradiation: those affecting the relative contributions of genetic information from the two parental cells into the recombinant chromosome (switching or breakage lesions); and those which result in lethality when present in the recombinant chromosome as a result of either material incorporation (Breakage-and-Reunion) or copying (Copy-Choice). It should be noted that at the doses used in these studies mutations at the genetic loci utilized are several orders of magnitude less frequent than the effects on the recombinational processes considered here.

The two simple models that have been proposed for genetic recombination predict somewhat different dose-response patterns for these two types of lesions:

(1) Copy-Choice: Switching lesions, as suggested by Jacob and Wollman (1958), could cause the copying to be selectively switched away from the irradiated female template to the male one, leading thereby to a progressive utilization with dose of genetic information from the donor cell. Lethal lesions could also bring about selection for recombinants having primarily the information from the male genome because of linkage between the female characters and the radiation lethals on the recipient chromosome. Thus either type of lesion would result in an apparent increase in linkage between male characters in the recombinants with increasing radiation dose (Figure 2).

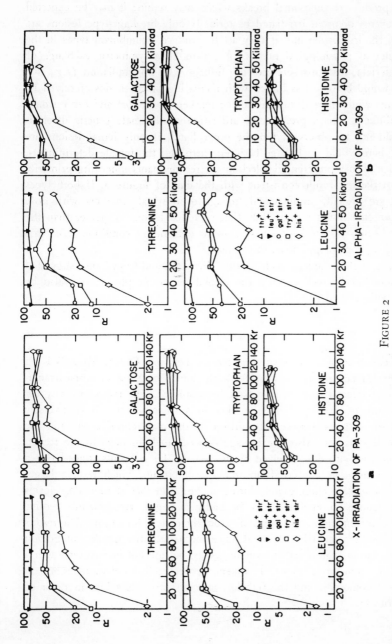

FIGURE 2

Effect of X rays (a) and alpha particles (b) on the presence of unselected markers in a population of recombinants selected for a specific character. The recombinant colonies appearing in the experiment described in Figure I are reisolated and tested for the presence of the other markers not selected for in the cross. The ordinate above is the percent of these colonies which contain also the unselected marker (R). The abscissa is the dose given to the female cell. From 100 to 200 colonies were tested for each point.

(2) Breakage-and-Reunion: It is known in higher organisms that ionizing radiations produce chromosomal breaks which may rejoin; it may be expected that such events occur in irradiated bacteria. If only breakage-type lesions are induced by the irradiation and if they act to produce recombinant types in the same manner as physiological breaks (*i.e.*, through a symmetric exchange of genetic material), male markers showing linkage with no irradiation (*e.g.*, *thr⁺* and *leu⁺*) would become less linked with increasing radiation dose received by the recipients while more distant, unlinked markers (*e.g.*, *thr⁺* and *his⁺*) would remain unlinked; thus a preferential utilization of the male genetic determinants would not be observed. On the other hand, if only lethal lesions are produced, there would be linkage between them and the female determinants. This could lead to a preferential selection for recombinants inheriting primarily the male markers, a result consistent with the data of Figure 2. If both types of lesions are present, an increased linkage of the male markers with dose would occur only if the rate of induction of lethal lesions is greater than the rate of induction of breakage ones, a more demanding condition than that imposed by a simple copy-choice mechanism.

More complicated models, such as the "Breakage-and-Copy" one suggested by Meselson and Weigel (1961) for recombination in phage, may also be consistent with these data. . . .

SUMMARY

In genetic recombination involving crosses between *Escherichia coli* K-12 donors (HfrH) and recipients (PA-309), the effects of X-ray or alpha irradiation of the recipient before mating have been studied. The radiosensitivity for the appearance of a selected male marker in a recombinant cell is inversely related to the distance between the origin of the male chromosome and the position of the marker. Also, the linkage between male markers in the recombinants increases with dose received by the female. These results suggest that a selective advantage is conferred on those recombinants which receive larger portions of the male chromosome during mating and that at high dose levels where the female chromosome may be badly damaged, recombinants receive their genetic information almost entirely from the male chromosome. The results can be easily interpreted by a Copy-Choice mechanism for genetic integration in which radiation lesions act as switching sites, but are not inconsistent with a Break-and-Reunion model in which linkage between lethal radiation lesions on the female chromosome and the female characters provides a bias in favor of male inheritance.

THE GENETIC CODE

The "breaking" of the genetic code in the late fifties and early sixties of our century will undoubtedly rank as one of the supreme scientific achievements of all time. It provides a fitting climax to a sequence of discoveries, spanning more than 60 years, which have led us to a fairly clear understanding, at least in general terms, of the age-old riddle of the process of transmission of inherited traits from generation to generation.

The resemblance between offspring and parent and within sibling groups has been noted over nearly the entire span of recorded literature. In fact, intuitive knowledge of hereditary transmission of parental traits must have antedated by centuries man's first written record: primitive agriculturists improved their domesticated animals and plants by judicious selection of superior individuals as breeding stock. By the middle of the nineteenth century there was considerable literature, mainly anecdotal and speculative, on the transmission of hereditary characteristics—literature that is interesting to the historian but well-nigh valueless to the scientist owing to the absence of carefully planned, controlled experimentation. Gregor Mendel's experiments on the breeding of peas, published in an obscure central-European journal in 1866–1867, demonstrated that what is transmitted in heredity is single unit traits, rather than broader features of general resemblance. Mendel's work was overlooked, or its significance was not appreciated, until the principle of the inheritance of unit traits was rediscovered in 1901, simultaneously and independently, by three distinguished botanists, Hugo de Vries, Carl Correns, and Eric Tschermak.

The rediscovery of Mendel's laws led to a tremendous spurt of research on the breeding of a great variety of wild and domesticated animals and of ornamental and crop plants. The broad principles of the present-day science of genetics were quickly established. It was proved that the cell nucleus, not the cytoplasm, contained the *genes* that carry the inherited characteristics. The carrier of genetic traits was soon further localized in the chromosomes and was eventually identified as one of the chemical constituents of the chromosomes, deoxyribonucleic acid (DNA). It is of interest to the microbiologist that the identification of DNA—one of the outstanding achievements of the present century— was confirmed by experiments on bacterial transformation by Avery, McCarty, and MacLeod (see the first paper in this volume).

All the genetic traits of man and of animals and plants are carried on the helically coiled, stringlike linear polymer DNA. Just before the formation of reproductive cells, the two strands of the DNA helix uncoil and form two new strands by assembling in the correct linear order the four pieces, or components—adenylic, guanylic, thymidilic, and cytidilic acids—out of which DNA strands are made. At other times, a similar replication of strands takes place, in which ribose substitutes for deoxyribose and uridine for thymine; in the plants and animals possessing organized nuclei, the resultant polymer, ribonucleic acid, passes out of the nucleus into the cytoplasm, where it serves to determine the order in which the 23 amino acids present in solution in the cytoplasm are assembled to form proteins.

The genetic traits of microorganisms are similarly encoded in the DNA helix. The order in which the bases adenine, guanine, cytosine, and thymine appear ultimately determines the formation of the proteins—enzymes—which express the organism's morphological, pathogenic, or biochemical characteristics.

Further information may be found in Philip E. Hartman and Sigmund R. Suskind, "Gene Action," Prentice-Hall, Inc., Englewood Cliffs, N.J., 1965, 158 pp.

Dr. Jukes, the author of the following review, is at the Space Sciences Laboratory, University of California at Berkeley.

From *Am. Scientist,*
51:227–245, 1963.

THE GENETIC CODE

BY THOMAS H. JUKES

The most important property of living organisms is their ability to produce off-spring having the general characteristics of their parents. It is this property which has led to the existence and maintenance of life on the earth. Life as we know it occurs in individual units which maintain their existence by utilizing external sources of energy. Each unit typically contains the information that can be translated into the production of a new, living copy of itself, similar to but not identical with its progenitors.

The large array of characteristics of each living species: the complex archi-tecture of animals and plants; the fantastically ingenious modifications of struc-ture and· function that enable species to compete and survive; all these must pass through the eye of an ultramicroscopic needle before they are seen again in the form of a new individual. The thread that passes through the eye of this needle is, in point of fact, a filamentous molecule: the strand of deoxyribo-nucleic acid (DNA). Entrained in this thread is a long, sequential message written as a cryptogram in the language of a four-letter alphabet. The formation of each new cell invoives the transation of the cryptogram into a series of instructions for the synthesis of the enzymes that control the continuous proc-esses of life. The key to this translation is the genetic code. The steps that have led to these conclusions are familiar. Research by geneticists, microbiologists, and biochemists showed that the units of heredity are carried in linear series in the chromosomal strands of the cell. Each of these units, the genes, is responsible for the sequence of amino acids in the production of a specific protein. Most of these proteins are enzymes that synthesize or metabolize other substances.

Many experimental pathways have led to the identification of DNA as the carrier of genetic information. Some of these are as follows: Staining proce-dures showed that the chromosomes were rich in DNA, and that this was true of all species examined. It was found possible to transform nonvirulent pneu-monia bacteria into virulent forms by treating them with a preparation of DNA from a virulent form of the same organism, and the transformation was in-herited by succeeding generations, for the DNA had entered the nonvirulent cells and had transformed their genetic apparatus. Analyses of DNA from many species of animals, plants and bacteria showed that the different samples were identical in all respects except for the relative proportion and sequence of the four basic constituents of the DNA molecule, these are adenine, cytosine, guanine, and thymine (A, C, G, and T).

Experiments with the mold *Neurospora* showed that genetic changes were produced by treatment with X-rays or ultraviolet light and that these changes were accompanied by alterations in the enzymes of the molds. An analysis of the results led to the conclusion that single genes are responsible for making single enzymes. Since enzymes are proteins, a connection was proposed between the DNA of the gene and the amino acids of the protein. This led to the statement of what has been termed the "coding problem," as follows: There must be a relation between the sequence of the four bases in nucleic acid and the sequence of the twenty amino acids, that are the building stones of all the proteins. These are alanine (ala), arginine (arg), asparagine (asN or asp NH_2), aspartic acid (asp), cysteine (cys), glutamic acid (glu), glutamine (glN or glu NH_2), glycine (gly), histidine (his), isoleucine (ilu or ileu), leucine (leu), lysine (lys), methionine (met), phenylalanine (phe), proline (pro), serine (ser), threonine (thr or thre), tryptophan (try), tyrosine (tyr), and valine (val). Some proteins contain other amino acids, such as hydroxyproline, but it is concluded that these are modifications produced subsequently to the formation of these proteins. The fact that twenty amino acids participate in protein synthesis means that the four bases must arrange themselves into at least twenty different permutations, each of which is the code for an amino acid. Only sixteen permutations can be formed by four different bases taken in pairs. Therefore, the protein code must consist of bases arranged at least in triplets rather than in pairs. This principle was first stated by Dounce in 1952, as follows: "We have the following possible immediate surroundings for adenine: A-A-A, G-A-A, C-A-A, U-A-A, C-A-G, G-A-G, U-A-G, U-A-U, C-A-U, and C-A-C (total of 10), assuming that direction does not determine specificity (i.e., C-A-G equivalent to G-A-C for example). (C = cytosine, U = uracil.) There will also be ten possible neighborhoods for guanine, cytosine, and uracil, making a total of forty possible neighborhoods. If direction were to be of importance, the possibilities would be increased. In any case there are more than enough configurations to account for all amino acids known to occur in proteins.

"It can be calculated that assuming a molecular weight of about 100,000, there can exist about 4×10^{87} different nucleic acids, assuming complete freedom of choice in arranging the order of the four nucleotides. Thus a sufficient number of nucleic acids could theoretically exist to account for the large variety of proteins in nature, assuming that protein specificity is dependent upon amino acid arrangement in peptide chains. . . . In addition, nucleic acid acting as an energy-transferring factor would utilize energy obtained from ATP to bring about the synthesis of peptide and phosphate-ester bonds."

In the following year, the structure of DNA was described by Watson and Crick [1953] who showed that the pattern of the double-stranded molecule provided a perfect explanation for the transmission of the genetic message from generation to generation in the form of a long word written in an alphabet of four letters.

In the formation of new strands of DNA or of ribonucleic acid (RNA) the bases are selected on a complementary basis by means of hydrogen bonding. The complementation is such that A pairs with T or uracil (U), and C pairs with G. The complementary pairing procedure is shown in Figure 1. The sequence of the bases is thus preserved during successive replications. C can also pair with hypoxanthine (H) if this base is formed from adenine by deamination.

The translation of this message into proteins is a complex and intricate procedure that took some years to elucidate. It is thought to take place as follows: An enzyme, RNA-DNA polymerase, makes a "complementary" copy of one strand of the DNA molecule. This modified copy is called *messenger ribonucleic acid (messenger RNA)* because it carries information from the DNA to another part of the cell and because it contains ribose rather than deoxyribose. It contains a sequence of bases which complement the bases in one of the two DNA strands: A in the DNA strand is replaced by U in messenger RNA, C is replaced by G, G is replaced by C, and T is replaced by A. The messenger RNA strand separates itself from DNA and migrates into the cytoplasm of the cell where it attaches itself to a special structure termed a *ribosome.* Simultaneously, amino acids in the cytoplasm become attached to adaptor molecules of a second type of RNA, termed *transfer RNA.* Furthermore in a specific region of each transfer RNA molecule there is a coding sequence of three bases which complement a corresponding sequence on the messenger strand; thus

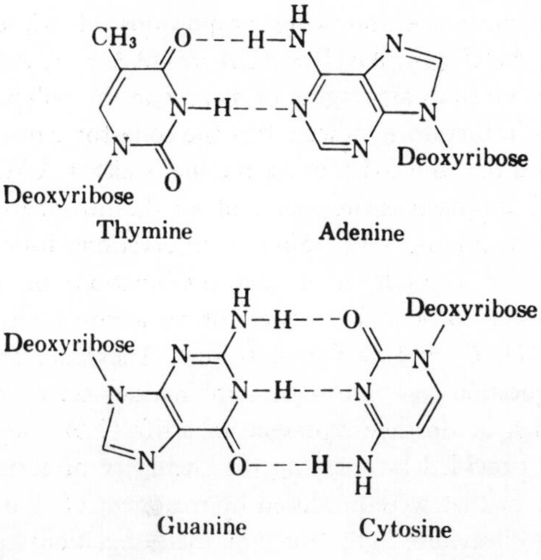

FIGURE 1

AUG on the messenger strand would provide the complementary site for the coding sequence of UAC on a transfer RNA molecule. It is attractive to suppose that there is a different transfer RNA molecule corresponding to each coding triplet on the strand of messenger RNA. Each transfer RNA molecule contains about seventy bases and is specific for an amino acid. This specificity is due to the presence of a "recognition site" on the transfer RNA molecule for the amino acid. The "recognition site" is at a location different from the coding sequence. It may recognize the amino acid, or instead it may recognize the activating enzyme that is specific for the amino acid. It is convenient to assume that there are twenty different types of recognition site, one for each amino acid. The amino acid molecules, guided by the coding sequences on the transfer RNA molecules to which they are attached, arrange themselves in the correct order along the messenger RNA strand and join together to form a protein molecule.

The first clue as to the relationship between the base composition of messenger RNA and a specific amino acid came about as the result of experiments in 1961 by Nirenberg and Matthaei with an artificial messenger, polyuridylic acid, which in terms of the code is a long sequence of Us formed by molecules of uridine phosphate joined in 3′, 5′ linkages between the phosphate and ribose groups. This sequence when used in the cell-free protein-synthesizing system obtained from *E. coli* produced a string of phenylalanine molecules joined together to make a miniature protein. Other discoveries followed rapidly. It was shown in Ochoa's laboratory that, when various combinations of the other RNA units, A, C, and G, were added to the strands of poly U, other amino acids were incorporated into the strands of polyphenylalanine. The ratio of phenylalanine to the other amino acids was approximately proportional to the expected occurrence of various triplet permutations in random sequences formed by mixtures such as 5U:1A, 6U:1C:1G, and so on. For example, 5U:1A should furnish the following proportions of triplets: UUU = 25, UUA = UAU = AUU = 5, AAU = AUA = UAA = 1, AAA = 0.2. A ratio of phenylalanine: tyrosine: asparagine of 25:5:1 in the polypeptide obtained by using 5U:1A should therefore indicate that the code for tyrosine is either UUA, UAU, or AUU and that the code for asparagine is either AAU, AUA, or UAA. This experimental approach is the source of all the information on the composition of the genetic coding units. Similar observations followed from Nirenberg's laboratory. As a result, 22 triplet combinations of A, C, G, and U, all containing U, were proposed as codes for 19 amino acids, together with an inferred code of U, C, and G for glutamine. These are shown in Table 1.

The next big question was: Do these combinations correspond to the genetic code in living cells, or do they represent an artifact? A clue to the answer to this question was provided by studying the chemistry of certain mutations that occurred naturally or that were produced by treatment of living organisms with chemicals or with ultraviolet light. Some of these mutations contained a change in one, and only one, amino acid in one of their proteins. A most dramatic

TABLE I

Relation between Code Triplets and Amino Acids

Triplet	Amino Acids
3U	Phenylalanine
2U, 1A	Isoleucine, leucine, tyrosine
2U, 1C	Leucine, serine
2U, 1G	Valine, cysteine, leucine
1U, 2A	Asparagine, lysine
1U, 2C	Proline
1U, 2G	Tryptophan, glycine
1U, 1A, 1C	Threonine, histidine, asparagine
1U, 1A, 1G	Methionine, glutamic acid, aspartic acid
1U, 1C, 1G	Glutamine,* alanine, arginine

* By inference.

example of this occurred in the hereditary disease, sickle-cell anemia. Patients with this disease are normal in all respects except that they produce an unusual type of hemoglobin that distorts and breaks up the red blood cells. It is possible to study the amino acids in hemoglobin by the following procedure: The hemoglobin is purified and is digested with trypsin, which splits it into smaller fragments or "peptides." The breaks between the fragments always take place at the same locations. These are the locations in the protein chain that are occupied by lysine and arginine and these locations are subject to attack by trypsin. The procedure is repeated with sickle-cell hemoglobin and the peptides of the normal and abnormal hemoglobin are then compared with respect to their rates of migration on filter-paper in an electric field. When this was done, one, and only one, of the peptides from the abnormal hemoglobin was found to have a migration rate different from that of its normal counterpart. This peptide was analyzed and was found to contain one extra valine and one less glutamic acid than the peptide from normal hemoglobin. Furthermore, it was possible to determine the exact position of the change as being at position 6 in the beta chain of hemoglobin. By a remarkable coincidence, another form of abnormal hemoglobin was discovered in some other patients in which the same glutamic acid fragment was replaced by lysine. The RNA codes for the three amino acids in Table I are as follows: glutamic acid is A, U, and G, valine is U, U, and G and lysine is A, U, and A. It thus appeared that the mutations were due to two different changes, A to U and G to A, in the same coding triplet, each change involving a different single base. The third letter, the U in the coding triplet, did not change. Other "single-amino-acid changes" soon came to light in newly-discovered mutational variations of human hemoglobin and all but one of these corresponded to single-base changes in the coding triplets in Table I.

In another series of investigations, an organism at the extreme opposite end of the biological scale was examined with respect to the properties of its protein content. This organism is *tobacco mosaic virus* (TMV) which is parasitic on tobacco and tomato plants. The virus consists of a long thread of ribonucleic acid surrounded by a protein coat. It multiplies within a tobacco leaf and, in this process, makes new virus RNA and proteins at the expense of its host. When the virus RNA, which behaves like messenger RNA, was separated from the protein coat and treated with certain mutagenic chemicals, especially nitrous acid, most of the virus particles were inactivated, but a few of them retained their infective property and proceeded to make a protein coat as usual when reconstituted with untreated protein and injected into a tobacco leaf. However, some changes in the amino acid content of the new protein coat had taken place. Upon comparing these changes with the amino acid codes in Table 1, it was noted by Speyer and co-workers [1962] that many of the amino-acid changes appeared to result from the typical reaction of nitrous acid in removing primary amino groups from two of the bases in RNA. By this deaminative reaction, cytosine is converted into uracil and adenine into hypoxanthine (H). Hypoxanthine is not present in RNA, but it is known to behave like guanine in forming hydrogen-bonded pairs with cytosine. The nitrous acid mutants of TMV could substitute, for example, leucine for proline, phenylalanine for serine, and valine for isoleucine in the TMV-protein. Assuming that the RNA strand of the virus functioned as messenger RNA, the substitutions correspond to deaminative changes as follows:

Proline 1U, 2C to leucine 2U, 1C
Serine 2U, 1C to phenylalanine 3U
Isoleucine 2U, 1A to valine 2U, 1G (equivalent to 2U, 1H)

In these changes, a pyrimidine is converted to another pyrimidine and a purine to another purine. Such changes are called *transitions*. Other changes, however, were observed in which purines apparently had interchanged with pyrimidines in the code. These changes are called *transversions* and examples are as follows:

Asparagine 1U, 1C, 1A to serine 2U, 1C(A to U)
Threonine 1U, 1C, 1A to methionine 1U, 1G, 1A(C to G)

Two possible explanations were open for the transversions: (i) Nitrous acid had behaved in an unexpected way, and had apparently caused a substitution rather than a deamination in the RNA; (ii) the apparent transversions were really not transversions at all but actually were transitional changes in coding triplets whose base composition had not yet been discovered. It seems, as is discussed later, that both possibilities exist.

It was found that nearly all of the mutations involving a single amino acid corresponded to single-base changes in the coding assignments in Table 1, if it was assumed that transitions and transversions were both possible. This comparison, shown in Table 2, enabled some inferences to be made with respect to the sequence of bases in each triplet. For example, lysine (1U, 2A) can be replaced by glutamic acid or aspartic acid, both of which are coded by 1U, 1A, 1G. Evidently the G in these two codes must be in two different positions; if

TABLE 2

Single Amino-acid Changes in Mutations Compared with Single Base Changes in Messenger RNA in Terms of the U-containing Triplets in Table 1

(Hb = hemoglobin, TMV = tobacco mosaic virus protein, TS = tryptophan synthetase, L = beta lactoglobulin, bovine)

Protein	Amino Acid Change	Corresponding Base Change	Protein	Amino Acid Change	Corresponding Base Change
Hb, TMV*	Lys/aspNH$_2$	A/C	TMV	Leu/phe	C/U
Hb, TMV	Lys/asp	A/G	Hb, TMV	Thre/ser	A/U
Hb	Lys/glu	A/G	TMV	Thre/met	C/G
Hb	AspNH$_2$/thre	A/C	TMV	Thre/ileu	C/U
TMV	AspNH$_2$/ala	A/G	TMV	Pro/leu	C/U
TMV	AspNH$_2$/ser	A/U	TMV	Pro/ser	C/U
TMV*	AspNH$_2$/arg	—	TMV	Ala/gly	C/G
Hb	His/tyr	C/U	L	Ala/val	C/U
Hb	His/arg	A/G	TMV	Ser/leu	C/A
TMV	GluN/val	—	TMV	Ser/phe	C/U
Hb, TS	Glu/ala	A/C	TMV	Asp/ala	—
Hb	Glu/gluNH$_2$	—	TMV, Hb, L	Asp/gly	A/G
Hb, TMV	Glu/gly	A/G	TMV, TS	Arg/gly	C/G
Hb	Glu/val	A/U	TMV	Arg/lys	—
TS	Tyr/cys	A/G	TS	Arg/ser	—
TMV	Tyr/phe	A/U	TMV	Ileu/met	U/G
TMV	Leu/ileu	C/A	TMV	Ileu/val	A/G

* Spontaneous changes in TMV.

the code for lysine is AUA and for glutamic acid is AUG then the code for aspartic acid is GUA. If however, lysine is UAA and glutamic acid is UGA, then aspartic acid should be UAG. By following this type of reasoning, it was possible to arrange the 22 triplet codes in Table 1 into interdependent sequences. There were six different ways of doing this, for example, if glutamic acid were written as AUG, AGU, GAU, GUA, UAG or UGA, the corresponding related ways of writing aspartic acid are GUA, GAU, AGU, AUG, UGA or UAG. However, experiments by Wahba and co-workers [1962] enabled the choice to be narrowed. They reasoned that if a single adenylate group was added in 3′, 5′ linkage to a polyuridylic acid chain, a poly-ribonucleotide could be formed with the abbreviated formula AUUU . . . U. When this preparation was used as a "template" for polypeptide formation, they obtained a polyphenylalanine chain terminating with a single tyrosine group which was joined by its amino group in peptide linkage to phenylalanine. This indicated that the sequence AUU was the triplet code for tyrosine, and that the RNA chain had been "read" from right to left during protein synthesis, because it was known from other investigations that the amino acid having a free carboxyl group is the last one to be "hooked up" when a protein is made. Their preparation of the polyribonucleotide also contained AAUU . . . U, but no amino acids other than tyrosine and phenylalanine were detected in the polypeptide product. It was also noted that GUUU . . . U and GGUU . . . U similarly incorporated cysteine in com-

TABLE 3

Sequences Proposed in Original Series of U-containing Triplets

AUA	Lysine	AUU	Tyrosine	UAA	Asparagine
CUC	Proline	UAU	Leucine	UGG	Tryptophan
GUG	Glycine	UUA	Isoleucine	UUU	Phenylalanine
AUC	Histidine	CUU	Serine	UCA	Threonine
CUA	Asparagine	UUC	Leucine	UGA	Methionine
AUG	Glutamic acid	GUU	Cysteine		
GUA	Aspartic acid	UGU	Leucine		
CUG	Alanine	UUG	Valine		
GUC	Arginine				

bination with phenylalanine, indicating GUU for cysteine. Smith and Dulbecco [1962] found that poly-U sequences terminated by one or more C residues at the 5'-end of poly-U would stimulate the incorporation of small amounts of serine into polyphenylalanine, perhaps indicating CUU or CCU for serine. These findings helped to support a proposal for a set of possible base sequences for the coding triplets containing U. This is shown in Table 3.

The reasoning used in assigning the sequences to the triplet codes in Table 1 was largely speculative. It could be argued that some or all of the mutations corresponded to single-base changes in undiscovered coding triplets differing entirely in composition from the combinations that were present in the synthetic polyribonucleotides. For example, the change in the codes from asparagine to serine, listed as CUA to CUU, might actually represent a change of A to G in, let us say, CAA to CAG. However, the agreement between the amino acid interchanges, which are summarized in Table 4, and single-base changes in the proposed triplet codes seemed far better than could be due to chance. Single-base changes are defined as changes occurring at the same location in two triplets. For example, AUC to GUC is a single-base change, but CUA to GUC is a two-base change. It was computed that, on a random basis, there was one chance in

TABLE 4

Single-amino-acid Interchanges Corresponding to Single-base Changes in Coding Triplets, in Mutations (or between Species as Indicated Below by Parentheses)

Serine:	Arg, aspNH$_2$, leu, phe, pro, thre (ala, glu, gly)
Alanine:	AspNH$_2$, glu, gly, val (pro)
Arginine:	AspNH$_2$, gly, his, lys (pro)
Glutamic acid:	GluNH$_2$, gly, lys, val
Asparagine:	Lys, thre
Glycine:	Asp
Isoleucine:	Leu, met, thre, val (phe)
Phenylalanine:	Leu, tyr
Threonine:	Met
Leucine:	Pro
Lysine:	Asp
Tyrosine:	Cys, his

Total: 38 (32 in mutations). "Nonfits" in mutations: 2. Possible in coding triplets: 77. Theoretical maximum: 190.

seven that an amino acid change would correspond to a single-base change in the 64 possible triplet sequences of A, C, G, and U. Against this, there was the very important objection that the average composition of the coding triplets in Table 1 included 48 per cent uracil. This was far higher than the uracil content of about 30 per cent found in various samples of natural messenger RNA. A possible explanation was that there were other triplet codes similar to those in Table 1, but in which the U was replaced by another base, perhaps C. This would reconcile the composition of the coding triplets with the composition of messenger RNA and would, at the same time, help to account for the agreement between the coding triplets in Table 1 and the mutations in Table 2. A clue pointing in this direction was that, in triplets containing a middle U, this base usually did not change when a mutation took place. Perhaps, in contrast, if the U in a triplet were changed to another base, such as a change of GUG to GCG, the coding function would remain the same. Answers to some of these questions soon appeared in publications from various laboratories describing the use of polyribonucleotides containing no uracil. It was reported by Bretscher and Grunberg-Manago [1962] that polyribonucleotides containing only A and C would direct the incorporation of proline, threonine, histidine and traces of glutamine into polypeptides. Jones and Nirenberg [1962] described experiments in which polyribonucleotides containing various combinations of A, C, and G without U were found to code a number of amino acids. Their conclusions from these results are summarized in Table 5 which is taken directly from their article.

TABLE 5

Tentative Summary of Code Words (from Jones and Nirenberg [1962])

C^{14}-Amino Acid	M-Code Words*			
Alanine	CCG			
Arginine	CGC			
Aspartic acid	ACA			
Asparagine	UAC or UAA†			
Cysteine	UUG or UGG‡			
Glutamic acid	ACA	AGA	AGU§	
Glycine	UGG			
Histidine	ACC			
Isoleucine	UUA			
Leucine	GUU	CUU	AUU†	(UUU)
Lysine	AAA	AAC	AAG	AAU
Methionine	UGA§			
Phenylalanine	UUU			
Proline	CCC	CCU	CCA	CCG
Serine	UCG	UCU		
Threonine	CAC	CAA		
Tryptophan	UCG			
Tyrosine	UAU			
Valine	UGU			

* Nucleotide sequence in code words is arbitrary.
† Proposed by Speyer, *et al.*
‡ We cannot differentiate between these possibilities at present.
§ It is not entirely clear whether these code words require U.

The table omits some of the U-containing triplets formerly listed by these authors, but in view of the experimental evidence it seems logical to include at least 25 triplets containing U. Simultaneously, Gardner and co-workers also described results with polyribonucleotides containing A + C and A + G; it was discovered that polylysine could readily be precipitated by 5 per cent tungstic acid from experimental preparations in which polyadenylic acid (poly-A) had been used as a template. This enabled these workers to employ poly-A in a procedure similar to that which had been used with poly-U, namely, to copolymerize poly-A with varying amounts of the other three ribonucleotides. The results with A + U (5:1) supported the conclusions that had been drawn with U + A (5:1) and led to the additional conclusion that 2A, 1U was a second code for isoleucine. The group then turned their attention to poly-C which had previously been found to incorporate small amounts of proline. The effectiveness of poly-C was increased by raising its ratio in proportion to the ribosome content of the experimental system. It was also found that polyproline was precipitated by raising the concentration of trichloracetic acid to 20 per cent. These observations made it possible to use poly-C for the testing of C + A copolymers. Difficulties due to strong cross-linking between C and G in C + G copolymers were ingeniously overcome by using hypoxanthine (H) instead of G, since it had been previously noted that H behaved similarly to G in coding experiments with U + H copolymers. Experiments were also carried out with copolymers containing A, C, and G. Alanine, aspartic acid, and serine were found to be incorporated

TABLE 6

Amino Acid Code Triplets
(from Wahba and co-workers [1963])

Amino Acid	U-Triplets	Non-U Triplets	Shared Doublets
Ala	CUG	CAG, CCG	C*G
Arg	GUC	GAA, GCC	G*C
AspN	UAA, CUA	CAA	*AA, C*A
Asp	GUA	GCA	G*A
Cys	GUU	—	—
Glu	AUG	AAG	A*G
GluN	UAC	AGG, AAC	*AC
Gly	GUG	GAG, GCG	G*G
His	AUC	ACC	A*C
Ileu	UUA, AAU, CAU	—	*AU
Leu	UAU, UUC, UGU, CCU	—	U*U
Lys	AUA	AAA	A*A
Met	UGA	—	—
Phe	UUU, UCU	—	—
Pro	CUC	CCC, CAC	C*C
Ser	CUU, UCC	ACG	—
Thre	UCA	ACA, CGC, CCA	*CA
Try	UGG	—	—
Tyr	AUU, ACU	—	A*U
Val	UUG	—	—

TABLE 7

Stimulation of Amino Acid Incorporation by Poly ACG

	46A:32C:22G*	4A:1C:1G†
Ala	123	121
Arg	128	550
Asp	167	78
Asp NH$_2$	—	354
Cys	—	16
Glu	326	431
Glu NH$_2$	—	620
Gly	5	69
His	71	261
Ileu	0	0
Leu	—	0
Lys	820	2060
Met	1	0
Phe	0	1
Pro	147	182
Ser	182	156
Thre	250	494
Try	1	0
Tyr	0	0
Val	1	0

* Jones and Nirenberg [1962]; $\mu\mu$ moles difference between C^{14} amino acid incorporation in the presence and absence of polynucleotides; base ratios determined by analysis.

† Wahba and co-workers [1963]; $\mu\mu$ moles incorporated per mg of ribosomal protein precipitated by trichloracetic acid + tungstic acid; base ratios calculated from input prior to synthesis of copolymer.

in ratios that indicated codes of 1A, 1C, and 1G. An interesting relationship was observed by comparing the various triplets; the assignments for the same amino acid in many cases contained two bases in common. These various findings were summarized by Wahba and co-workers [1963] in Table 6. A comparison of the results obtained by the two groups with ACG copolymers shows a striking qualitative agreement for all amino acids except glycine (Table 7). It is noteworthy that both groups failed to obtain incorporation of ileu, leu, met, phe, try, tyr, and val in the absence of U.

More recently Nirenberg [1963] has published a table of coding assignments which reconciles some of the differences between Tables 5 and 6. The new list included the following assignments which are the same as those published by Wahba *et al.* [1963] and which were omitted by Jones and Nirenberg [1962]; 1U, 1C, 1G, ala, arg; 2A, 1G, arg, glu; 2A, 1C, aspNH$_2$; 1U, 1A, 1G, asp; 1A, 2G, gly; and 1U, 2A ileu. Previously undescribed assignments were made [1963] of 2A, 1G and 1U, 1A, 1G, gluNH$_2$ and 1U, 2C ser; the latter has also been listed recently by Wahba and co-workers (in preparation). It seems reasonable to use the list in Table 6 until the remaining differences are resolved.

The "shared doublets" listed in Table 6 recall the proposal by Roberts [1962] that the RNA code could be written in the form of 16 "doublets" represented by the 16 possible 2-letter permutations of A, C, G, and U. Twelve of these were each assigned by Roberts to a single amino acid and the remaining 4 to 2 amino acids each. The proposal by Wahba, *et al.* [1963] modified this concept in that each "doublet" could be written in two forms based on its location within the coding triplet, for example, AA could be written as A*A or *AA, where * indicates a "variable" third base. Thirty-two such arrangements are possible. It was proposed that each such arrangement, termed a "modified doublet," was characteristic in most cases of the codes for each amino acid and that either of the two bases in the "modified doublet" could often be changed by mutations to produce a triplet with a different coding function. It was noted that the "variable" base could apparently be A, C, or U but not G, and that if the base in position 3 in the triplet was changed, the coding function of the triplet also was changed. These points are summarized in Table 8.

The proposal in Table 8 made it possible to revise (Table 9) some of the suggested base changes in Table 2. These revisions enable single-base changes to be correlated with all the described mutations except gluNH$_2$/val and asp/ala.

The revisions will also permit certain HNO$_2$-induced mutations in TMV to be written in terms of deaminative (A/G) changes in the coding triplets, but other such mutations correspond to transversions. Perhaps nitrous acid, in addition to deaminating A and C, may at times produce other changes which result in purine/pyrimidine substitutions. In this connection it has been reported that certain HNO$_2$-induced mutational changes in TMV, such as aspNH$_2$/ser, are produced also by other chemical mutagens which are not deaminative.

Single-amino-acid differences in the homologous proteins of various species in most cases correspond to single-base changes in the coding triplets but, in some cases, to two-base changes, such as phe/gly in cattle somatotropin/monkey

TABLE 8

Relations between "Modified Doublets" and the Proposed Messenger RNA Triplet Codes for the Amino Acids

	*=A	*=C	*=G	*=U		*=A	*=C	*=G	*=U
A*A lys	AAA	—	—	AUA	G*A arg/asp	GAA/	GCA	—	GUA
*AA aspN	—	—	—	UAA	*GA met	—	—	—	UGA
A*C his	—	ACC	—	AUC	G*C arg	—	GCC	—	GUC
*AC gluN	AAC	—	—	UAC	*GC thre	—	CGC	—	—
A*G glu	—	—	—	AUG	G*G gly	GAG	GCG	—	GUG
*AG glu	AAG	—	—	—	*GG try	—	—	—	UGG
A*U tyr	—	ACU	—	AUU	GG* gluN	GGA	—	—	—
*AU ileu/leu	AAU	CAU/	—	UAU	G*U cys	—	—	—	GUU
C*A aspN	CAA	—	—	CUA	*GU leu	—	—	—	UGU
*CA thre	ACA	CCA	—	UCA	U*A ileu	—	—	—	UUA
C*C pro	CAC	CCC	—	CUC	*UA ileu	—	—	—	''
*CC ser	—	—	—	UCC	U*C leu	—	—	—	UCC
C*G ala	CAG	CCG	—	CUG	*UC leu	—	—	—	''
*CG ser	ACG	—	—	—	U*G val	—	—	—	UUG
C*U ser	—	—	—	CUU	*UG	—	—	—	—
*CU leu	—	CCU	—	—	U*U phe	—	UCU	—	UUU
					*UU	—	—	—	—

TABLE 9

Certain Amino Acid Changes from Table 2 Revised in Terms of Single-base Changes in Coding Triplets in Table 7

Amino Acid Change	Corresponding Triplet Change
AspNH$_2$/arg	CAA/GAA
Glu/gluNH$_2$	AAG/AGG
Thre/ser	ACA/ACG
Ser/leu	UCC/UUC
Arg/gly	GAA/GAG
Arg/lys	GAA/AAA
Arg/ser	GCC/UCC

somatotropin which may reflect the evolutionary existence of an intermediate step, or an earlier "parent" molecule containing valine at this locus, so that the interchange could be represented by phe/val/gly, UUU/UUG/GUG.

Many assumptions were made in arriving at the proposal in Table 8, which should be judged in the light of their possible validity. The assumptions were as follows:

(*a*) The amino acid code consists of triplets.

(*b*) The coding assignments in the table represent the same amino acids in all biological systems. This does not preclude the possibility that certain codes may predominate differently in various organisms, for example, organism X may use principally GCG, CCG, and CCC for glycine, alanine and proline, while organism Y may use predominantly GUG, CUG, and CUC. This may be related to the observations by Sueoka [1961] who found a wide "spectrum" of variation in the DNA base composition of different microorganisms and a less wide variation in their amino acid composition.

(*c*) Single-amino-acid mutations in protein chains are due to single-base changes in the structural genes of DNA or to single-base changes in the protein coding regions of RNA viruses.

(*d*) The triplets are read from right to left in protein synthesis.

(*e*) In the case of amino acids with codes that contain "shared doublets," the relative positions of the two bases that form the "shared doublet" are the same in the codes for the same amino acid, so that if CUG is a code for alanine, its other two codes are CAG and CCG.

(*f*) The bases in the synthetic copolymers are in random, or almost random, sequences, and their base composition is approximately the same as the composition of the mixture used in their synthesis.

(*g*) The sequence in the 1A, 2U code for tyrosine is AUU, in the 1G, 2U code for cysteine is GUU and in the 1C, 2U code for serine is CUU, read from right to left in protein synthesis but from left to right in the usual convention for polynucleotides.

(*h*) The ratio of amino acids in the polypeptides formed by various copolymers of A, C, G, and U is a reflection of the frequency and coding assignments of the triplets in each copolymer. For example, the phe:glu:asp:met ratio incorporated by a copolymer prepared from 6U : 1A : 1G was 100 : 1.6 : 2.4 : 4.3, leading to the conclusion that glu, asp, and met were each coded by only one permutation of U, A, and G corresponding to a theoretical ratio of 100 : 2.8 : 2.8 : 2.8. If there were two codes for glu each containing U, A and G, the phe:glu ratio should be 100 : 5.6 in such an experiment. It is obvious that additional quantitative experiments in the incorporation of amino acids by coding triplets in the U, A, G; U, A, C; U, C, G; and A, C, G series would be valuable for further establishment of these coding assignments. Information from such experiments might well lead to the discovery that amino acids are coded by many of the triplets corresponding to unfilled spaces in Table 8.

The relatively high incorporation rate of methionine in the above results may suggest the existence of an additional coding triplet, such as GAU or AGU, for this amino acid. This would provide for a deaminative change of AAU/GAU or AAU/AGU to account for the nitrous acid mutation ileu/met in TMV protein.

The proposal in Table 8 should be regarded as speculative and subject to revision in the light of further experimental evidence. Rarely does Nature comply with predictions. Speculations are nevertheless useful for the stimulation of discussion and experimentation. Let us examine some of the probabilities which may have a bearing on the validity of the proposed coding assignments. One approach is as follows: Let us assume that the 64 possible permutations of A, C, G, and U in sequential triplets are indeed all codes for amino acids in naturally occurring messenger RNA. Let us also assume that the findings with synthetic polyribonucleotides in cell-free systems have no relationship to the codes occurring as messenger RNA in living cells. A random distribution of the possible interconversions between the 64 triplets provides for a ratio of 1:3:3 between single-base : two-base : and three-base changes. One sixth of all the single-base changes will be A/G, C/U, A/C, A/U, G/C, or G/U. Therefore, a random sample of 34 interchanges should contain 5 single-base changes, 1 of

TABLE 10

Illustrating the Number of Base Changes Required for Interconversion of the Various Triplets That Can Be Provided by A, C, G, and U

	GCG	AAA	AUC	UCC	GAU	(Etc.)	—
GUC	2	3	1	2	2	—	—
AUU	3	2	1	3	2	—	—
AAA	3	—	2	3	2	—	—
CUC	3	3	1	2	3	—	—
GGA	2	2	3	3	2	—	—
(Etc.)	—	—	—	—	—	—	—
—	—	—	—	—	—	—	—

Total possible interchanges: 4032, single base, 576; 2-base, 1728; 3-base, 1728. (1:3:3) Among single-base changes. A/C=A/G=A/U=C/G=C/U=G/U=96.

TABLE 11

Comparison of Mutational and Interspecies Single-amino-acid Changes in Proteins
on Basis of Code in Table 8 with Randomized Possibilities in Table 10

Base-change in Triplets	Occurring Only in Mutations		Total Changes	
	Found	Randomized Possibility	Found	Randomized Possibility
A/G	12	1	13	1.2
C/U	8	1	10	1.2
A/C	4	1	5	1.2
A/U	3	1	4	1.2
C/G	3	1	6	1.2
G/U	2	1	2	1.2
2-Base	2	15	8	21
3-Base	0	15	0	21

which should be A/G. The actual findings for the 34 described interchanges are that 32 of them correspond to single-base changes in the coding triplets obtained by an entirely different experimental procedure and that 12 of the changes correspond to A/G. This indicates a nonrandom correlation between the two sets of data. Thirteen of the 17 possible A/G interchanges between coding triplets and 10 of the 14 possible C/U interchanges have been reported in the literature. An additional statistic of interest is in the repeated occurrence of certain amino acid interchanges in numbers greater than the frequency predicted by the Poisson distribution. Ten interchanges, 8 of which can be attributed to A/G changes in the proposed coding triplets, occur 4, 5, or 6 times (Tables 10–13).

Several mutations have been reported in which more than one change can take place at the same coding site. It is most interesting that all of these correspond to single-base changes in the proposed coding triplets, as follows: val/ala/glu/gly/arg/ser in tryptophan synthetase can be written as UUG/CUG/AUG/GUG/GCG/GCC/UCC, including a "silent" mutation of GUG/GCG glycine; in human hemoglobin, lys/glu/val as AUA/AUG/UUG, tyr/his/arg as AUU/AUC/GUC, gluNH$_2$/gly/lys as AGG/AAG/AAA; in hemoglobin of various species, ala/gly/asp as C*G/G*G/G*A (*=C or U) and ala/glu/lys as C*G/A*G/A*A (*=A or U), in insulins, val/ileu/thre as UUG/UUA/UCA.

A large number of amino acid interchanges may be perceived by comparing the sequences in the polypeptide chains of α, β, and γ hemoglobin and sperm whale myoglobin. About 200 of these correspond to single-base changes in the coding triplets in Table 8. These changes have a considerable bearing on the validity of the coding triplets and the changes also tend to support the conclusion that these molecules originate in common from a primitive form of the gene.

There are 64 triplet permutations of the 4 code letters A, C, G, and U and only 48 of these were assigned to coding functions in Tables 7 and 8. The

TABLE 12

Probability of Repeated Occurrences of 100 Single-amino-acid Changes in Proteins as Compared with 190 Possible Amino-acid Interchanges on Basis of Poisson Distribution

No. of Times per Change	Anticipated by Poisson Distribution	Reported Occurrences
1	76	23
2	20	12
3	3.4	3
4	0.46	7
5	0.05	2
6	0.006	1

remaining 16 triplets may also be codes for amino acids which cannot be sorted out until further information is available on the incorporation of amino acids into polypeptides by polyribonucleotides in cell-free systems. There were complications in achieving the synthesis of poly-G; these have now been overcome, but this co-polymer readily forms secondary structures which may cause difficulties in its use as a "template." If the "shared doublet" concept is valid, it may well be that the future coding assignments to be made for the remaining 16 triplets will not greatly change the general pattern indicated by Tables 2, 7, and 8.

These various findings show that the coding triplet may be regarded as the model unit in genetic studies and the behavior of structural genes reflects the properties of long sequences of these units.

The number of different sequences in which a DNA molecule containing 10,001 base pairs can be arranged would be 4 to the 10,000th power, a number which is beyond the bounds of astronomical concepts. This makes theoretically possible the formation of a similarly vast number of protein molecules containing every conceivable sequence of amino acids. We may guess that, by random condensation occurring during the era when life originated, certain DNA strands were formed that contained sequences of bases that produce useful proteins. All living organisms depend for their existence on such sequences. These organisms are earmarked for survival. Other organisms die prematurely or fail to achieve an independent existence. These simple concepts appear to lie behind the origin of species and life. Moreover, the base sequence in DNA is subject to change. This has been shown experimentally in studies with nitrous acid, ultraviolet light and other mutagens. It seems evident that spontaneous mutations are produced by changes in the DNA strand similar to those occurring in such experiments. The change of a single base in DNA can in turn produce a change of an amino acid in an essential protein. The only result of such a change may be a slight alteration in the immunological specificity of the protein. However, if this change takes place at the functional site of an enzyme, the enzyme may be rendered inactive. This can lead to a lethal mutation, or a congenital disease, or perhaps idiocy in human beings due to poisoning of the central nervous

TABLE 13

Single-amino-acid Interchanges That Occur Most Frequently

Interchange	Occurrences	Base Change	Triplet Changes
Lys/glu	6	A/G	A*A/A*G[1]
Ileu/val	5	A/G	UUA/UUG
Arg/gly	5	A/G, C/G	GAA/GAG, G*C/G*G[2]
Asp/gly	4	A/G	G*A/G*G
Glu/gly	4	A/G	A*G/G*G
Lys/arg	4	A/G	AAA/GAA
Glu/gluNH$_2$	4	A/G, G/C	AAG/AGG, AAG/AAC
Thre/ser	4	A/G	ACA/ACG
Thre/ileu	4	C/U	UCA/UUA
Ala/gly	4	C/G	C*G/G*G[3]

[1] * = A or U.   [2] * = C or U.   [3] * = A, C or U.

system by a metabolite that can no longer be broken down. Evidently, lethal mutations are comparatively rare, because many species continue to reproduce and flourish for thousands of years. On the other hand, perhaps a new and useful protein may result from changes in DNA. At some time in the history of life, a strand of DNA appeared that enabled chlorophyll to be synthesized. Was this due to a lengthening of the strand by gene duplication or to changes in its sequence? Who knows how many million years of trial and error went by before this happened?

In one enzyme, pancreatic ribonuclease, which contains 124 amino acids, there are only two differences between the enzyme obtained from cattle and sheep. Both of them are attributable to A/G changes. This may imply that there have been only two changes in several million years in this piece of genetic DNA containing 372 bases.

Nothing is known of the base sequences and coding functions of those regions of the genetic DNA strand that contain the regulator and operator genes which regulate the production of messenger RNA.

The thread of life is thus revealed to us as being elementary in the simplicity of its fundamental structure, yet labyrinthine in its complexity, ageless in its continuity, and infinite in its variety. Surely there is no more impressive concept in Nature than the principle stating that a linear permutation of four variables is the storehouse of information giving rise to all the qualities that we associate with life. And one of these qualities is manifested in the prolonged and successful search that has enabled mankind, guided by the Promethean fire of radioactivity, to perceive, in 1963, the outlines of a genetic code that conveys the message necessary for the evolution and survival of all living creatures.

MICROBIAL STRUCTURE AND LIFE HISTORY

THE FORMATION OF BACTERIAL CELL WALLS

Since 1950 our knowledge of bacterial cell walls has been greatly enhanced by the development of several new preparative techniques. Among the earliest was the use of glass spheres or a ball mill to grind thick bacterial suspensions and thereby break bacterial cells into fragments. Suspension of ruptured bacterial cells in water or in sucrose solution, followed by separation in the ultracentrifuge, gave crude and impure cell-wall preparations. Repeated resuspension and centrifugation, carefully and painstakingly carried out, eventually yields pellets of relatively pure cell-wall material.

Chemical analysis of this highly complex material begins with breakdown into simpler materials. The cell-wall materials are proteins or mucopolysaccharides more or less impregnated with fatty materials—lipids or lipopolysaccharides. Over the years, microbial chemists have tried a large number of enzymes to break down bacterial cell walls. The ordinary proteolytic enzymes from the mammalian digestive tract—pepsin, trypsin, and chymotrypsin—have been relatively ineffective. Lipopolysaccharides are readily split by lysozyme, an enzyme or group of enzymes of widespread distribution, found in tears and in egg white. Some of the most useful enzymes employed in chemical analysis of bacterial cell-wall preparations are those obtained from the gut of snails.

Bacterial cell-wall preparations are turbid when suspended in water, but a turbid suspension may clear gradually upon addition of an enzyme. Optical devices such as the Klett-Summerson turbidimeter are useful in measuring the amount of suspended material, and hence the extent to which cell-wall material has been degraded by the enzymes employed. Microcurettes make possible the determination of enzymic efficiency on extremely small samples of cell-wall material.

Chemical analysis, by enzymic breakdown of complex cell-wall material and identification of the fragments, has given a great deal of information regarding the composition and structure of bacterial walls. Another approach to understanding the nature of the cell wall is to determine how bacteria synthesize these walls in nature. The article by Strominger reprinted below is an excellent review of the results obtained, mainly by detailed studies of the processes of cell-wall synthesis and of the nature of the chemical intermediates involved.

An insight into the chemical mechanism of the action of the antibiotics penicillin and oxamycin is a valuable and interesting by-product of the studies on bacterial cell-wall synthesis here reviewed.

Further information on the structure and composition of the bacterial wall may be obtained from the following sources:

Gerrit Toennies, Amino Acids in Bacterial Growth and Development, *Yale Alumni Magazine*, 38:20–22, 25, 1963. (An abridgment of this paper appears in this volume, pp. 133 to 141.)

Milton R. J. Salton, "Microbial Cell Walls," John Wiley & Sons, Inc., New York, 1960, 94 pp.

H. J. Rogers, The Surface Structures of Bacteria, *Biochem. Soc.* of London *Symp.*, No. 22. "The Structure and Function of the Membranes and Surfaces of Cells," Cambridge University Press, London, 1963, pp. 55–100.

Dr. Strominger is eminent for his work on the biochemistry of polysaccharide synthesis. He is Professor of Pharmacology at Washington University, St. Louis, Missouri.

From *Federation Proc.*,
21:134–143, 1962.

BIOSYNTHESIS OF BACTERIAL CELL WALLS

BY JACK L. STROMINGER

Current interest in bacterial cell walls stems from a number of sources. These substances are unusually complex organic molecules and of interest to biochemists and organic chemists, as well as to microbiologists. They are involved in a number of very interesting biological phenomena. The selective toxicity of some antibiotics is due to inhibition of bacterial cell wall synthesis. Animal cells do not possess structures which are morphologically or chemically equivalent to bacterial cell walls, and, therefore, the selective toxicity of these antibiotics is due to interference in a metabolic sequence, which is uniquely found in bacterial cells. Many of the specific toxic and antigenic responses of higher animals to infection with bacteria are reactions to bacterial cell wall components. Similarly, some of the defense mechanisms of the host are directed against the integrity of the bacterial cell wall. For example, there is widely distributed in nature a group of enzymes, termed lysozymes, which destroy invading bacteria by means of enzymatic attack on the bacterial cell wall, resulting in lysis of the microorganism.

Bacterial cell walls can be defined in a number of ways. First of all, they are well-defined morphological structures, and readily seen in electron micrographs of thin sections of bacteria. In the preparations from [*Escherichia*] *coli* of Kellenberger and Ryter [1958] several layers of the cell wall are evident, as well as an inner membrane, which is termed the cytoplasmic membrane.

Cell walls can be defined physiologically as well as morphologically. It has long been known that sensitive bacteria can be lysed by egg white lysozyme. However, Weibull [1953] observed that, if treatment with the enzyme was carried out, not in ordinary buffer, but in buffers containing hypertonic sucrose, the cells were not lysed. Instead they were converted to spherical forms, which Weibull termed protoplasts. The action of lysozyme is to digest the bacterial cell wall and these experiments then define the cell wall as the rigid outer membrane, which gives form and shape to the microorganism and serves to protect it from such deleterious influences as osmotic shock. If the fragile protoplasts, with their limiting cytoplasmic membranes, are centrifuged and resuspended in buffers of ordinary tonicity, they spontaneously lyse.

Cell walls are prepared by disruption of bacterial cells (e.g., with glass beads) followed by differential centrifugation of the cell wall fraction. Purification of this fraction is carried out by repeated centrifugation and/or digestion with proteases and nucleases. Electron micrographs of a cell wall preparation from a bacillus show that the cell wall has a sausage-like shape, while similar preparations from a coccus appear globoid. It is again evident, therefore, that the cell wall has the form and rigidity which are characteristic of the microorganism itself.

Interest in the mechanisms of bacterial cell wall synthesis was catalyzed by the observation that the selective toxicity of penicillin is due to inhibition of bacterial cell wall synthesis. Two independent lines of investigation first led to this hypothesis. Observations of the morphological effects of penicillin on bacteria had been made as long ago as 1946 by Duguid, who recognized their significance. Similar observations were made 10 years later by a number of investigators, particularly Lederberg [1957, 1958]. He observed that, in hypertonic sucrose broth, cells of E. coli underwent a transformation to spherical forms under the influence of penicillin and that, when the antibiotic was washed out of the culture, the organisms reverted to their normal bacillary forms. Therefore, under these conditions, penicillin had no lethal effect on the spherical form itself. In fact, the spherical forms from at least one bacillus species will grow and divide as spheres in the presence of penicillin. Lederberg recognized that the spherical forms induced by penicillin were analogous to the protoplasts formed under the influence of lysozyme. He, therefore, inferred that penicillin must be interfering either with the synthesis of the bacterial cell wall or with its maintenance.

The second line of investigation which also led to this hypothesis began with the observation of Park and Johnson [1949] that uridine nucleotides accumulate in [Staphylococcus] aureus inhibited by penicillin. The structure of the accumulated compounds is analogous to the structure of UDP-glucose. The principal nucleotide which accumulates (Fig. 1) contains uridine linked through a pyrophosphate bridge to a most unusual sugar. At the time of the isolation of this compound the structure of this sugar was not deduced. However, it was later found as a component of the peptide released during sporulation of bacilli and also as a component of bacterial cell walls. It was crystallized from a hydrolysate of spore peptide by Strange and Dark [1956], who then proposed that it was a 3-o-lactic acid ether of N-acetylglucosamine. Later, Kent and Strange [1959] synthesized the compound in confirmation of this structure. The lactic acid moiety in this sugar has the D-configuration, the opposite configuration from the lactic acid which is formed in fermentation. Attached to the lactic acid moiety of the nucleotide is a peptide, the sequence of which is L-ala · D-glu · L-lys · D-ala · D-ala. The occurrence of D-amino acids in the peptide is another very unusual feature of its structure.

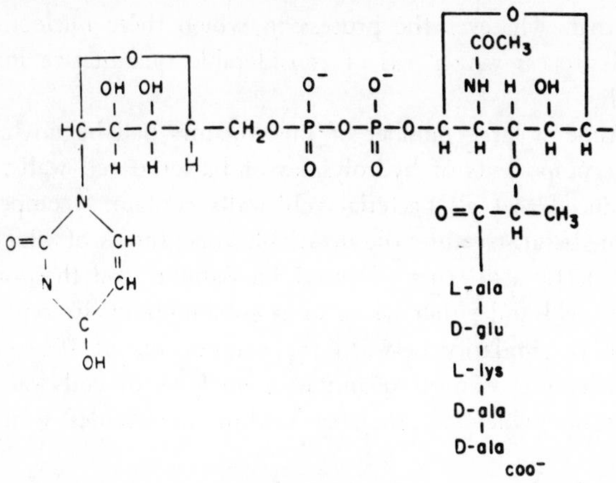

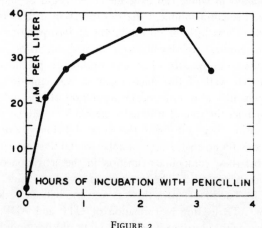

FIGURE 1

A uridine nucleotide from penicillin-treated *S. aureus.*

Although these unusual features were recognized at the time of the isolation of this compound, no data were available to suggest a function. However, a number of experiments suggested that the accumulation was not an accidental effect of the antibiotic, but might be very closely related to the mechanism by which the antibiotic was killing the bacterial cell. For example, the time course of accumulation of the nucleotide after the addition of antibiotic is a very early and striking effect (Fig. 2). The time for half-maximal accumulation is of the order of 15 min after the addition of penicillin. Maximal accumulation occurs at about 2 hr and at the point of maximal accumulation the amount of nucleotide is 50–100 times that found in the normal bacterial cell. In the best experiments, the total amount of nucleotide at this point of maximal accumulation amounts to 10% of the dry weight of the bacterial cell mass. These observa-

FIGURE 2

Time course of accumulation of uridine nucleotides in penicillin-treated *S. aureus.*

tions indicated that, whatever the process in which these nucleotides was involved, it was a process which was of considerable quantitative importance to the microbial cell.

At the same time, a large number of investigators had begun to investigate qualitatively the components of hydrolysates of bacterial cell walls. From their data, it was deduced that all bacterial cell walls contain a component which may be termed the basal structure, the invariable constituents of which are acetylglucosamine, the lactic acid ether of acetylglucosamine, and three amino acids, alanine, glutamic acid and either lysine or α,ϵ-diaminopimelic acid. These data indicated a striking similarity between the components of the cell wall and those of the nucleotide. Careful quantitative analyses of cell walls from two strains of *S. aureus* which accumulated uridine nucleotides were, therefore, carried out.

In the wall, as in the nucleotide, the molar ratios were, per residue of glutamic acid, one residue of lysine, three of alanine, and one of acetylglucosamine-lactic acid ether. Examination of the optical configurations of the amino acids indicated that 66% of the alanine residues were D-alanine residues, while 33% were L-alanine, both in the wall and in the nucleotide. That is, two of the three alanine residues are D-alanine residues and the other residue is an L-alanine residue. The glutamic acid is virtually 100% D-glutamic acid and the lysine is 100% L-lysine, both in the cell wall and in the nucleotide. These data, therefore, led to the hypothesis that the uridine nucleotide which accumulated in the penicillin inhibited cells was a precursor of the bacterial cell wall and that its accumulation was the consequence of inhibition of bacterial cell wall synthesis by penicillin.

This hypothesis is now also supported by direct isotopic measurements of cell wall synthesis. Such investigations have been carried out in a number of laboratories. For example, when C^{14}-lysine was employed as a precursor of the cell wall of *S. aureus* in whole cell experiments, it could be shown that, under conditions where penicillin inhibited the incorporation of this isotope into cell wall by 91%, there was little or no inhibition of incorporation of this isotope into cell protein. Similar experiments were carried out in *S. aureus* with P^{32}-inorganic phosphate. In *E. coli* when an appropriate precursor of the basal structure of the cell wall of this microorganism was employed (α,ϵ-diaminopimelic acid), penicillin also inhibited incorporation of this compound.

A few words about the role of uridine nucleotides in cellular metabolism will aid further discussion. Beginning with the work of Leloir [1960] and his collaborators, it has been found that a large number of UDP-sugar compounds occur in nature and that these compounds function in the activation of a sugar fragment for a synthetic reaction. The mechanism of glucuronide synthesis is an excellent example. The first step in this reaction mechanism is the phosphorylation of UDP by ATP leading to formation of UTP and ADP. In the second step, UTP reacts with glucose-1-P to give UDP-glucose and inorganic pyrophosphate. In the next step, the activated sugar fragment is modified, in this case by oxidation of the glucose moiety to glucuronic acid, to give UDP-glucuronic acid. The final step in this reaction cycle is transfer of the modified sugar fragment to an acceptor in the synthetic reaction leading to the formation of the glucuronide and of UDP. The essential features of this reaction cycle are *1*) phosphorylation; *2*) activation of the sugar; *3*) modification of the sugar; and finally, *4*) transfer of the modified sugar to an acceptor.

Exactly the same type of cyclic mechanism takes place in the synthesis of a part of the cell wall of *S. aureus* (Fig. 3). At the beginning of the cycle UDP is phosphorylated. Then a sugar fragment is activated, in this case acetylglucosamine, to form UDP-acetylglucosamine. Next, the acetylglucosamine moiety is modified in a very complex reaction mechanism in which, first, a three carbon fragment is added at the oxidation level of pyruvate, and then reduced to the oxidation level of lactate. Amino acids are then added in a step-wise fashion to give the peptide containing uridine nucleotide, the most complex of the known nucleotides which occurs in *S. aureus*. This cycle can be inhibited at a number of points by different agents. Penicillin, bacitracin, and novobiocin all inhibit at a late stage in the cycle by a mechanism which is not yet precisely known, leading to accumulation of the late intermediates. Earlier in the cycle the antibiotic oxamycin (D-cycloserine) inhibits the cycle leading to accumulation of earlier intermediates. Still earlier, lysine deprivation leads to accumulation of the uridine nucleotide containing the "incomplete" peptide, L-ala · D-glu, and an impurity found in one batch of gentian violet leads to accumulation of the earliest intermediates in the cycle.

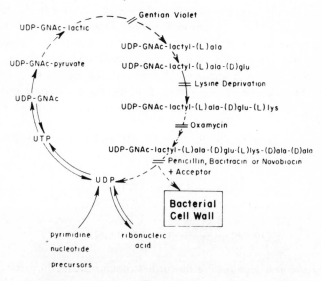

FIGURE 3
Pathway of synthesis of a part of the cell wall of *S. aureus*.

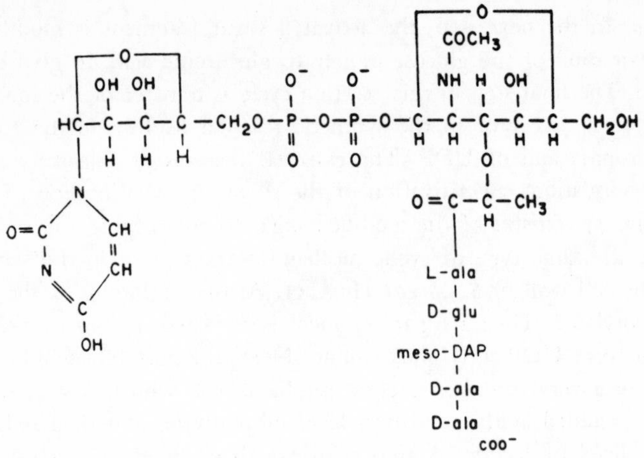

FIGURE 4

A uridine nucleotide from *E. coli.*

Before describing the reactions of this cycle in detail, it should be mentioned that modifications of cell wall structure in different microorganisms can be reflected by variations in the structure of uridine nucleotides which they contain. *E. coli* is an example of a microorganism which contains meso-diaminopimelic acid instead of L-lysine in the peptide of its bacterial cell wall. A uridine nucleotide has been isolated from *E. coli* which contains meso-diaminopimelic acid in the peptide sequence in place of L-lysine (Fig. 4). Some strains of *Streptococcus fecalis* contain a ratio of D-alanine to L-alanine in the cell wall of 1 : 1 rather than 2 : 1, as occurs in *S. aureus.* From one strain of *S. fecalis* a uridine nucleotide has been isolated which contains a peptide consisting of six rather than five amino acids. The "extra" amino acid is L-alanine, i.e., the nucleotide contains two L-alanine and two D-alanine residues, giving a 1 : 1 ratio of D- to L-alanine. It is believed that the extra alanine moiety of this nucleotide is substituted on the ε-amino group of lysine, forming a branched peptide (Fig. 5).

The first four reactions in the cycle of cell wall synthesis of *S. aureus* are represented by *equations 1–4.*

(1) $UDP + ATP \rightleftharpoons UTP + ADP$

(2) $UTP + GNAc\text{-}1\text{-}P \rightleftharpoons UDP\text{-}GNAc + PP$

(3) $UDP\text{-}GNAc + P\text{-}pyruvate \rightarrow UDP\text{-}GNAc\text{-}pyruvate + Pi$

(4) $UDP\text{-}GNAc\text{-}pyruvate \dashrightarrow UDP\text{-}GNAc\text{-}lactic$

The first two reactions require no further comment. The third reaction is the transfer of the pyruvate moiety of phosphoenol-pyruvic acid to UDP-acetyl-glucosamine, leading to formations of a pyruvate-enol-ether of UDP-acetylglu-

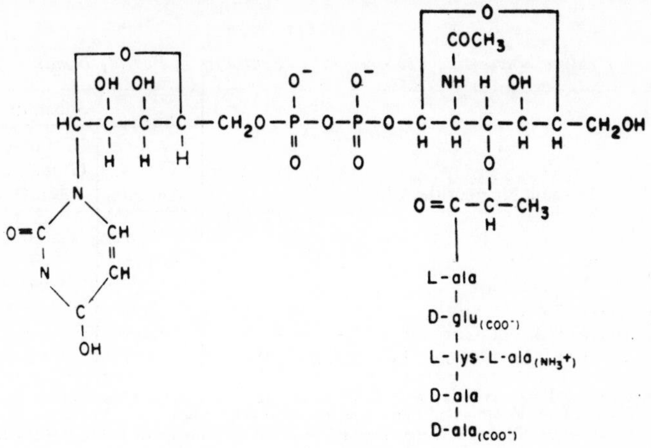

FIGURE 5

A uridine nucleotide from pencillin-treated *S. fecalis*. (P. Mandelstam, unpublished.)

cosamine and inorganic phosphate. The fourth reaction in the cycle is the least well studied of all of the group. It is the reduction of the UDP-acetyl-glucosamine-pyruvate-enol-ether to UDP-acetylglucosamine-lactic acid-ether. In a reaction mixture containing the enzymatically synthesized, C^{14}-pyruvate-labeled uridine nucleotide, formation of a compound with the electrophoretic mobility of the lactic acid ether derivative has been detected. However, the reaction product has not been definitely identified, and *reaction 4* should not be regarded as having been established. However, isotopic studies also support the conclusion that phosphopyruvate is the precursor of the lactic acid ether of N-acetylglucosamine.

The next reactions of the cycle are the sequential addition of the amino acids. In the first three reactions (*eq. 5–7*) L-alanine, D-glutamic acid, and L-lysine are added sequentially by separable enzymes, each of which requires ATP, Mn^{++} and a specific uridine nucleotide precursor.

$$(5) \quad \text{UDP-GNAc-lactic} + \text{L-ala} \xrightarrow[\text{Mn}^{++}]{\text{ATP}} \text{UDP-GNAc-lactyl} \cdot \text{L-ala}$$

$$(6) \quad \text{UDP-GNAc-lactyl} \cdot \text{L-ala} + \text{D-glu} \xrightarrow[\text{Mn}^{++}]{\text{ATP}}$$

$$\text{UDP-GNAc-lactyl} \cdot \text{L-ala} \cdot \text{D-glu}$$

$$(7) \quad \text{UDP-GNAc-lactyl} \cdot \text{L-ala} \cdot \text{D-glu} + \text{L-lys} \xrightarrow[\text{Mn}^{++}]{\text{ATP}}$$

$$\text{UDP-GNAc-lactyl} \cdot \text{L-ala} \cdot \text{D-glu} \cdot \text{L-lys}$$

TABLE I

Uridine Nucleotide Requirement in Synthesis of Peptide Bonds

Uridine Nucleotide Added	Substrate		
	C^{14}-L-Alanine	C^{14}-DL-Glutamic Acid*	C^{14}-L-Lysine
None	o	o	o
UDP-GNAc-lactic	1364	o	o
UDP-GNAc-lactyl · L-alanine		3720	o
UDP-GNAc-lactyl · L-Ala · D-Glu	8	o	3530
UDP-GNAc-lactyl · L-Ala · D-Glu · L-Lys	2200†	o	20
UDP-GNAc-lactyl · L-Ala · D-Glu · L-Lys · D-Ala · D-Ala	100	o	20

Reaction mixtures contained ATP as well as C^{14}-amino acids and uridine nucleotides indicated below. Data are recorded as c.p.m. incorporated into a charcoal adsorbable form.

* Although C^{14}-DL-glutamic acid was the substrate, it could be shown that only C^{14}-D-glutamic acid was enzymatically active.

† This result is known to be due to the occurrence of alanine racemase and the enzymes catalyzing *reactions 8* and *9* in the preparation.

The specificity of these three enzymes for the uridine nucleotide precursor is shown in Table I. With C^{14}-L-alanine as a precursor, L-alanine can be incorporated only into UDP-acetylglucosamine lactic acid ether. With C^{14}-DL-glutamic acid as a precursor, D-glutamic acid (but not the L-isomer) is incorporated only into UDP-acetyl-glucosamine-lactyl · L-ala; and with C^{14}-L-lysine as the precursor, L-lysine is incorporated only into the nucleotide containing the "incomplete" peptide, L-ala · D-glu.

The addition of the last two amino acids in the sequence occurs by a slightly different mechanism.

$$(8) \quad 2\text{D-ala} \xrightarrow[\text{Mn}^{++}]{\text{ATP}} \text{D-ala} \cdot \text{D-ala}$$

$$(9) \quad \text{UDP-GNAc-lactyl} \cdot \text{L-ala} \cdot \text{D-glu} \cdot \text{L-lys} + \text{D-ala} \cdot \text{D-ala} \xrightarrow[\text{Mn}^{++}]{\text{ATP}}$$

$$\text{UDP-GNAc-lactyl} \cdot \text{L-ala} \cdot \text{D-glu} \cdot \text{L-lys} \cdot \text{D-ala} \cdot \text{D-ala}$$

First, the dipeptide, D-alanyl · D-alanine, is formed from D-alanine. The dipeptide is then added as a unit to the uridine nucleotide. Again, each of these reactions is catalyzed by a separate enzyme, which requires ATP and Mn^{++} for activity. This sequence was discovered when it was found that, during purification of the enzyme, the ability to incorporate either D-alanine or L-alanine into the uridine nucleotide was completely lost. However, Ikawa and Snell [1958] had isolated the dipeptide, D-alanyl · D-alanine, from *S. fecalis*. This dipeptide was then isolated from lysine-deprived *S. aureus,* in which it accumulates, together with the uridine nucleotide. The isolated D-alanyl · D-alanine was fully

TABLE 2

Enzymatic Addition of D-Ala · D-Ala to UDP-GNAc-lactyl · L-Ala · D-Glu · L-Lys

Additions	c.p.m. in UDP-GNAc-lactyl · L-Ala · D-Glu · L-Lys · D-Ala · D-Ala
None	105
D-Ala · D-Ala (synthetic)	4,790
D-Ala · D-Ala (isolated)	6,600
L-Ala · L-Ala	20
D-Ala · L-Ala	56
D-Alanine	81
L-Alanine	37

The substrates were UDP-GNAc-lactyl · L-ala · D-glu · C[14]-L-lys (enzymatically synthesized), ATP, and dipeptides indicated. Radioactivity in the uridine nucleotide product was measured after separation of the products by paper chromatography.

active enzymatically, as was a synthetic sample of the dipeptide (Table 2). This reaction is highly specific for the stereoisomer of the dipeptide, since L-alanyl · L-alanine, D-alanyl · L-alanine and L-alanyl · D-alanine could not be added to the uridine nucleotide by this enzyme.

The dipeptide-adding enzyme can be utilized in an assay for the enzyme, which catalyzes the synthesis of the dipeptide. In this assay, in the first step, the radioactive dipeptide is formed from C^{14}-D-alanine, ATP and Mn^{++}. In the second step, the radioactive dipeptide, D-alanyl-D-alanine, is added to uridine nucleotide, in which form it can then be adsorbed on charcoal for subsequent measurement. The antibiotic oxamycin is included in the second stage of this assay, for a reason which will become apparent later.

The distribution of these enzymes has been measured in nine representative bacterial species. In general, these enzymes occur in all the bacterial species investigated with some interesting deletions and abnormalities, which may either represent proteins which are unstable under the conditions of extraction or true variations. The most interesting fact, however, which came out of this study of the comparative biochemistry of cell wall peptide synthesis relates to the occurrence of L-lysine in the basal structure of some bacterial cell walls and its replacement by a,ϵ-diaminopimelic acid in others. Those organisms, which contain lysine (e.g., *S. aureus* and *S. fecalis*), have a lysine-adding enzyme which is inactive with diaminopimelic acid as a substrate. On the other hand those organisms which contain diaminopimelic acid (e.g., *E. coli* and *C. xerosis*) have a diaminopimelic acid-adding enzyme which is inactive with lysine as a substrate (Table 3). The specificity of peptide sequence in this case is, therefore, determined by the specificity of a single enzyme, which is able to add either lysine or diaminopimelic acid to the growing peptide chain.

The separability of the enzymes, which catalyze these reactions, can be simply illustrated. These enzymes are all precipitated by protamine sulfate but at differ-

TABLE 3

Addition of Lysine or Diaminopimelic Acid to UDP-GNAc-lactyl · L-ala · D-glu

Extract from:	Substrate		Extract from:	Substrate	
	C^{14}-lys	H_3-DAP		C^{14}-lys	H_3-DAP
Staphylococcus aureus	0.95	0.01	Salmonella gallinarum	0	0.60
Micrococcus lysodeikticus	0.49	0	Bacillus cereus	0	0.42
Staphylococcus albus	0.36	0	Escherichia coli	0	0.20
Sarcina lutea	0.90	0.02	Corynebacterium xerosis	0	5.12
Streptococcus fecalis	1.25	0			

Extracts were prepared from logarithmic phase cells of the organisms listed. C^{14}-L-lysine and H^3-α, ϵ diaminopimelic acid (mixture of LL- and meso-isomers) were used as substrates. Radioactivity converted to a charcoal adsorbable form was measured, and data are expressed as mμmoles of amino acid added to the uridine nucleotide under the conditions of assay.

ent concentrations (Fig. 6). At low protamine concentrations, first, the D-ala · D-ala synthetase was precipitated. At higher concentrations the D-glutamic acid adding enzyme was precipitated, and at still higher concentrations the L-lysine-adding enzyme was precipitated. The precipitated enzymes can be eluted from the protamine proteinate with phosphate buffers of different ionic strengths. Fractional precipitation with protamine sulfate, followed by fractional elution with phosphate buffers, provides a convenient first step in purification of the various enzymes. Each of the six enzymes, including the diaminopimelic acid-adding enzyme, has been purified at least 30-fold. The L-lysine-adding enzyme has been purified about 400-fold. The adenine nucleotide products of these reactions have been identified so far in three cases, and in each of these the products are ADP and inorganic phosphate. These enzymes are the L-lysine-adding enzymes from *S. aureus,* the meso-diaminopimelic acid-adding enzyme from *C. xerosis* and the D-alanyl · D-alanine synthetase of *S. fecalis.**

In considering the mechanism of these enzymatic reactions, it was of interest to inquire as to whether or not ribonucleic acid might be involved in the synthetic mechanism, since RNA is an essential component of the synthesis of peptide bonds in proteins. Each of the five enzymes of *S. aureus* was incubated with ribonuclease. Four of them, (the L-alanine-adding, the D-glutamic acid-adding, the L-lysine-adding, and the D-alanyl · D-alanine-adding enzyme), were completely insensitive to preincubation with ribonuclease. The fifth enzyme, D-alanyl · D-alanine synthetase, was rapidly inactivated by incubation in buffer at pH 7.2 at 37° (and this inactivation was only slightly more rapid in the presence of ribonuclease than in its absence). However, if, after total inactivation of the enzyme, ATP and Mn^{++} were added at 37° and pH 7.2 in the absence of D-alanine, a rapid reactivation of the enzyme occurred. This reactivation did not occur at pH 8.7; the pH at which this enzyme is assayed. Furthermore, if ATP and Mn^{++} were added to enzyme at zero time, a similar activation of the enzyme

---

* Dr. S. Nathenson has also established that ADP and Pi [inorganic phosphate] are the reaction products of a purified glutamic acid-adding enzyme from *S. aureus* and Dr. N. Ishimoto has detected ADP as a reaction product of the D-alanyl · D-alanine synthetase in this organism (unpublished).

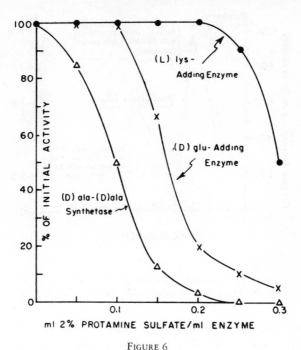

FIGURE 6

Separation of enzymes by protamine precipitation. Data are plotted as % of initial activity in the supernatant solution after addition of protamine sulfate. (E. Ito, unpublished.)

was observed. In addition to the requirement of ATP and Mn^{++} for reactivation of the inactivated enzyme, this reactivation also required a heat stable cofactor, which is found in extracts of *S. aureus*, as well as in other bacterial cells. The requirement for this cofactor was first observed with dialyzed enzyme preparations.

More recently, the enzyme and cofactor have been completely separated on a column of Sephadex-G-25 (Fig. 7). The protein peak from the Sephadex column showed no enzymatic activity when assayed directly, or when assayed after preincubation with ATP and Mn^{++} alone. However, when this protein was preincubated at pH 7.2 with ATP, Mn^{++} and supernatant solution from boiled *S. aureus* extract, activity was completely recovered. This preparation can therefore be used to assay for the cofactor. The cofactor followed the protein peak on the Sephadex column (Fig. 7), where it had a distribution similar to that of inorganic phosphate. From its dialyzability and distribution on the Sephadex column, it is apparent that the cofactor is a low molecular weight substance. It is RNAase insensitive and acid-labile (destroyed by 0.1 N HCl at 100° for 10 min) but alkali-stable. The substance cannot be adsorbed on charcoal, and the possibility that it is a cation such as Mg^{++} or K^+ has been ruled out. Further investigation of the properties of this substance are being carried out, as are attempts to purify it.

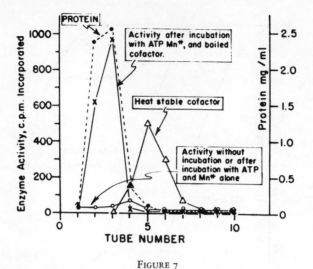

FIGURE 7

Resolution of D-alanyl · D-alanine synthetase from *S. aureus* by
Sephadex G-25 chromatography. (N. Ishimoto, unpublished.)

Finally, the antibiotic, oxamycin, inhibits bacterial multiplication by inhibiting
enzymes in the pathway of cell wall peptide synthesis. Ciak and Hahn [1959]
had observed that oxamycin, like penicillin, induced uridine nucleotide accumulation in *S. aureus* and protoplast formation in *E. coli*. However, it was observed
that one of the compounds, which accumulated in the presence of oxamycin, had
a slightly different position on 2-dimensional paper chromatography than one
of the compounds which accumulated in the presence of penicillin. This compound was isolated in larger amounts and subjected to degradation and analysis.
It differed from the compound obtained from penicillin inhibited cells in containing one alanine rather than three alanine residues; this alanine was an
L-alanine residue. The structure UDP-GNAc-lactyl · L-ala · D-glu · L-lys could,
therefore, be assigned to this nucleotide. It is missing the terminal two D-alanine
residues from the peptide sequence. This fact, as well as the knowledge that the
antibiotic contains an asymmetric carbon atom with the D-configuration, suggested the possibility that the antibiotic might be a competitive antagonist of the
incorporation of D-alanine into the uridine nucleotide. It was readily demonstrated
that D-alanine in increasing amounts would prevent accumulation of nucleotides
induced by oxamycin. L-Alanine was completely ineffective in substituting for
D-alanine in this effect. Not only did D-alanine prevent nucleotide accumulation
induced by oxamycin, but it also reversed uridine nucleotide accumulation previously induced by the antibiotic.

For this experiment, cells were incubated with the antibiotic for 45 min
at which time they had accumulated 20 μmoles of nucleotide (per liter of cul-

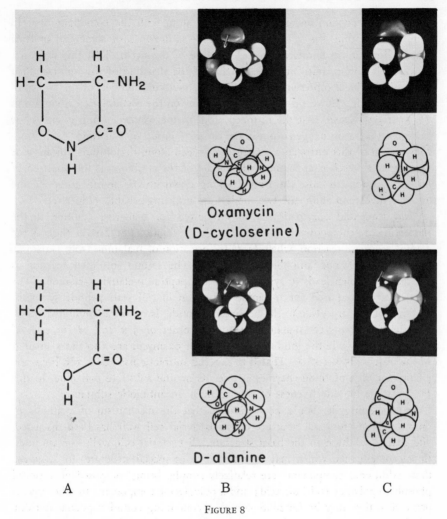

Oxamycin
(D-cycloserine)

D-alanine

A   B   C

FIGURE 8

Structures (*A*) and molecular models, (*B, C*) of D-alanine and oxamycin (D-cycloserine).

ture). If incubation was continued for an additional 45 min the amount of nucleotide increased to 30 μmoles. However, if during the second 45-min incubation, D-alanine was added to the culture, the amount of nucleotide, rather than increasing, decreased to 12 and 7 μmoles with increasing amount of D-ala-nine. L-Alanine, DL-alanyl · DL-alanine and D-serine were completely ineffective in replacing D-alanine in this phenomenon. More extensive kinetic analysis of this phenomena showed that the relationship between D-alanine and oxamycin was a true competitive one. The molecular basis for this phenomenon is apparent in consideration of the structures of the two compounds (Fig. 8*A*). Both antibiotic and substrate contain an asymmetric carbon atom with the D-configuration. In this representation, the structure of D-alanine is drawn in a somewhat unusual way to illustrate its similarity to the structure of oxamycin. That this structure, however, is a more faithful representation of the structure of this subtrate than the ordinary linear representation is shown by molecular models of the two compounds. Looking down on the hydrogen atoms on the asymmetric carbon atoms (Fig. 8B) it is seen that the nitrogen atom in the oxamycin ring occupies the same position as an oxygen atom in the carboxyl group of D-alanine. Aside from substitution of this nitrogen atom for the oxygen atom, the only modification of the substrate which is apparent in the model of the antibiotic is the insertion of an oxygen atom to close the ring. Looking down on the amino group on the asymmetric carbon atom, the two models are indistinguishable (Fig. 8C).

Two sequential enzymatic reactions required for D-alanine addition to the nucleotide are competitively inhibited by the antibiotic. The first of these is the alanine racemase reaction, which leads to formation of D-alanine from L-alanine, discovered by Wood and Gunsalus [1951]. The second inhibited reaction is the reaction which leads to synthesis of the dipeptide D-alanyl · D-alanine. (The third reaction required for D-alanine utilization in cell wall peptide synthesis, addition of the dipeptide to the uridine nucleotide, is not at all inhibited.) The Michaelis constants for D-alanine are of the order of 5×10^{-3} M for each of these enzymes while the inhibitor constants for oxamycin are 100 times smaller, of the order of 5×10^{-5} M. That is to say, the antibiotic has about 100 times the affinity for each of these enzymes as does its natural substrate D-alanine. In this fact must lie the effectiveness of this agent as an antibiotic substance.

In concluding, it should be mentioned that the mechanism of synthesis of only a part of the basal structure of the bacterial cell wall has been discussed, and that in addition to the basal structure, all bacterial cell walls contain additional components, which may be referred to as special structure. In S. aureus these additional components are relatively simple, being composed of a ribitol phosphate polymer (teichoic acid) and a polyglycine component. In other microorganisms, they may be far more complex, containing complex polysaccharides, which carry determinants of antigenic specificity, and proteins. In gram-negative bacteria, where the protein-lipopolysaccharide conjugates are components of the special structure, the cell wall has a very great complexity. These substances are among the most complex polymers known to occur in nature, and are determinants of many of the responses of man to bacterial infection. The mechanisms of their synthesis are exceedingly intriguing problems. Some beginnings in this direction have already been made.

The structural relationship of the various components of the wall of S. aureus, and the mechanisms by which these various components are put together to form the wall are still largely unknown. A present proposal of the structure of the cell wall of one strain of S. aureus (Fig. 9) will serve to emphasize the fact that so far the mechanism of synthesis of only a very small fragment of the cell wall,

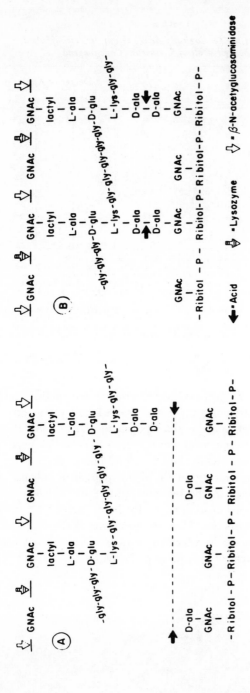

FIGURE 9

Two possible structures of the cell wall of *S. aureus* (Copenhagen). In both structures the glycopeptide (polymer of N-acetylglucosamine and N-acetylglucosamine-lactyl-peptide) is shown cross-linked by a polyglycine component, linking the lysine of one peptide chain and the glutamic acid of another. In *structure A*, two species of peptides occur in the glycopeptide, and the means of attachment of the ribitol phosphate polymer (teichoic acid) to the rest of the wall is not specified. In *structure B*, the ribitol phosphate polymer is shown attached to the glycopeptide through the peptide. The antigenic component in the wall is an α-acetylglucosaminyl-ribitol grouping in the teichoic acid. These structures were derived from studies of fragments obtained after treatment with acid and with enzymes and from studies of the structure of the teichoic acid; points of cleavage are shown by *arrows*.

TABLE 4

Identification of the Serologically Active Group in Teichoic Acid from the Cell Wall of S. Aureus (Copenhagen)

Additions	Final Conc., M	Degree of Agglutination			
		5 min	1 hr	2 hr	24 hr
None		4+	4+	4+	4+
Acetylglucosamine	0.01	0	0	1+	3+
α-phenyl-acetylglucosaminide	0.0025	0	0	1+	3+
β-phenyl-acetylglucosaminide	0.0025	4+	4+	4+	4+
Teichoic acid	0.0013	0	0	1+	3+
Alanine-free teichoic acid	0.0008	0	0	1+	3+
Teichoic acid (limit β-acetylglucosaminidase) *	0.0003	0	0	0	0
Acetylglucosaminyl-ribitol phosphates†	0.003	0	0	2+	4+
Acetylglucosaminyl-ribitol†	0.003	0	0	2+	4+
D-Ribitol-5-phosphate	0.01	4+	4+	4+	4+
Normal rabbit serum substituted for antiserum		0	0	0	0

Rabbit antisera prepared against *S. aureus* (Copenhagen) agglutinated purified cell walls of this strain. To investigate the chemical basis of the immunological reaction, specific inhibition of agglutinations by haptenes derived from or related to the cell wall was examined. All compounds active as inhibitors and several inactive ones are listed. A large number of other compounds not listed did not inhibit agglutination. Data shown indicate that an α-acetylglucosaminyl-ribitol linkage in the teichoic acid is the serologically active group.

* Prepared from alanine-free teichoic acid by treatment with a β-acetylglucosaminidase. The reaction stopped when about 85% of the acetylglucosamine was liberated. The resulting polymer was isolated and contained 12% of the acetylglucosamine found in the teichoic acid. The remaining acetylglucosamine was slowly released by treatment with an α-acetylglucosaminidase but not by further treatment with β-acetylglucosaminidase.

† Prepared by ion-exchange chromatography and selective N-acetylation of the glucosaminyl-ribitol phosphates formed on strong alkaline hydrolysis of teichoic acid. Acetylglucosaminyl-ribitol was obtained by dephosphorylation with a phosphomonoesterase.

the GNAc-lactyl-peptide fragment, is known, although one might speculate that CDP-ribitol and UDP-acetylglucosamine are also cell wall precursors. The cell wall of this microorganism contains three polymeric threads, the glycopeptide backbone; the polyglycine component which appears to cross-link peptide chains through the ε-amino group of lysine; and the ribitol phosphate polymer. Among these substances, only the structure of the ribitol phosphate polymer (teichoic acid), which is the antigen in the cell wall (Table 4), is fairly completely known, although a great deal of information has been obtained about the glyco-peptide in other bacterial species. The exact structure of the cell wall of this organism and the mechanism by which the various pieces are put together in this mosaic represent extremely interesting problems for the future.

Nearly all known bacteria are minute rods or spheres which are usually quite uniform in size and shape because of their tough, rigid cell walls. Bacteria devoid of cell walls are osmotically fragile structures, often flattened and pancake-shaped, easily destroyed by pressure or by slight variation in the osmotic pressure of the suspending liquid. It is well known that the cytoplasm within the bacterial membrane contains in solution nutrients, including sodium and potassium ions and free amino acids, in such concentration that their osmotic pressure may be as high as 20 atmospheres. An extremely tough wall structure, affording protection against osmotic explosion, is necessary for the survival of such bacteria.

The enzyme lysozyme, which is present in egg white, in tears, and in most body fluids, catalyzes the digestion of bacterial cell walls and is important in the defense against bacterial infection. Bacteria subjected to lysozyme are generally killed, possibly as a result of osmotic bursting after the dissolution of their walls. However, if bacteria are grown in fairly concentrated liquid culture media containing a small amount of lysozyme, bacterial cells devoid of walls may be obtained and, with care, may be kept alive in culture. Such bacterial cells, known as *protoplasts,* are useful in the study of the precise role of the bacterial wall and in studies of bacterial physiology, biochemistry, and genetics.

The bacterial protoplasts described in the following paper are laboratory artifacts. There are, in nature, a number of bacteria comprising the genus *Mycoplasma,* consisting of cells without walls and in most respects resembling bacterial protoplasts. The first member of this group to be described was the organism that causes bovine pleuropneumonia. Other species, originally referred to as *pleuropneumonia-like organisms* (PPLO), are responsible for several diseases of domestic animals and man. Also, some species of bacteria give rise in culture to abnormal forms, known as *L forms,* which are very similar to, or identical with, bacterial protoplasts.

Drs. Zinder and Arndt, the authors of the paper presented below, are on the staff of the Rockefeller Institute for Medical Research. Both are active, extremely capable research scientists who have made important contributions to our present-day knowledge of microbiology.

From *Proc. Nat. Acad. Sci.*,
42:586–590, 1956.

PRODUCTION OF PROTOPLASTS OF ESCHERICHIA COLI BY LYSOZYME TREATMENT

BY NORTON D. ZINDER AND WILLIAM F. ARNDT

Recently, investigators of some biochemical problems have made use of subcellular elements of bacteria in an attempt to study systems more highly integrated than soluble extracts but more amenable to external manipulation than intact cells. Cells which either have been sonically disrupted or have had their cell walls removed (protoplasts) have been used. Protoplasts have hitherto been prepared only from gram-positive organisms. Treatment of *Bacillus megaterium* with lysozyme in hypertonic media brings about a change from its normal rodlike form to a spherical one and results in its susceptibility to lysis upon suspension in hypotonic media. These altered properties are presumed to result from dissolution of the cell wall, the cytoplasmic contents then being retained by the cell membrane. Unfortunately, little is known of the genetics of the gram-positive organisms, and the fruitful concomitant biochemical and genetic attack is thus restricted. For this reason it would be of obvious advantage to obtain protoplasts of such organisms as *Escherichia coli,* which has been the subject of detailed genetic and physiological investigation. This report details the development of such a technique which also involves the use of lysozyme.

Our thinking on the problem of obtaining protoplasts of *E. coli* was influenced by the report of Hirsch [1956] that some material isolated by him from rabbit leukocytes (phagocytin) would kill *E. coli* strains. Phagocytin had chemical properties similar to, but not identical with, those of lysozyme. When *E. coli* cells were treated with crude phagocytin (kindly provided by Dr. Hirsch) in hypertonic media at pH 5, they became susceptible to lysis upon dilution into distilled water. However, only a rare cell was morphologically identifiable as a protoplast. The difficulty in obtaining phagocytin in sufficient quantity for detailed investigation caused us to seek another source of active material. On the hypothesis that phagocytin was a lysozyme of different specificity, hen egg albumen, a rich source of lysozyme, was tested. Treatment of cells with a one-to-four dilution of fresh albumen resulted in the rapid conversion of cells to protoplasts at pH 5 and 9. At pH 5 the spheres were badly agglutinated. All further experiments, unless otherwise noted, were therefore done at pH 9. No activity of albumen was detected at pH 6–8. Crude fractionation of egg albumen revealed that the activity was associated with the lysozyme fraction. Commercial lysozyme (Armour Chemical Company) was equally effective.

CONVERSION OF CELLS TO PROTOPLASTS

The following procedures for the efficient conversion of cells of *E. coli* strains K12 and B, and their derivatives, were empirically developed. Overnight broth cultures of cells are diluted tenfold in Difco Penassay broth and incubated with aeration for 90 minutes. This takes the culture just out of logarithmic growth phase (cells less fragile) and gives a titer of $4-5 \times 10^8$ cells per milliliter. The culture is washed once in saline by centrifugation and resuspended in saline. After 3 minutes of incubation at 37° C., sufficient tris buffer (Sigma Chemical Company) and lysozyme are added to make the final concentrations 1 M and 200 μg/ml., respectively. Further incubation for 5 minutes converts the cells to protoplasts. Other supporting media that can be used are sucrose 0.6 M with 0.1 M carbonate buffer, pH 9, or $M/2$ NaCl with carbonate buffer, or 0.3 M NH_4Cl brought to pH 9 with NaOH. In these latter two media the cells will cytolyze upon dilution into hypotonic media but do not assume a spherical shape. Centrifugation of the preprotoplasts and resuspension in 0.6 M sucrose will cause their immediate swelling into spheres.

With regard to these procedures, some points need be mentioned: (1) At pH 8–8.8, protoplasts are formed but are badly agglutinated. This agglutination can be prevented by the addition of 0.1 per cent Mg^{++}; however, some 10 per cent of the cells retain their rodlike shape and are not subject to cytolysis. (2) It is requisite that the cells be washed and starved slightly for quantitative conversion to occur. Perhaps they can heal the lysozyme-induced lesions if they are able to grow. (3) Certain strains will not form spheres in the treatment medium but will do so when resuspended in other media. In order for the cells to form spheres, they apparently must imbibe some water and swell—in a sense, hatch out of their cell walls. As yet there is no rationale for the preferential use of any medium, other than its empirical success with the strain in question.

PROPERTIES OF PROTOPLASTS OF *E. COLI*

1. General.—Growing cells of *E. coli* are generally in a doublet condition. Each doublet gives rise to two protoplasts, with separation occurring at the point of incipient division. Motile strains lose their motility when converted to protoplasts. The spheres do not detectably adsorb bacteriophage. The protoplasts readily reduce methylene blue.

When protoplasts are suspended in broth media, they lyse no matter how high the osmotic pressure of the medium and whether it is maintained by sucrose,

TABLE 1

Growth of Bacteriophage T4 in Protoplasts and Cells of E. coli B

(Number of Plaques per Plate, Had Equivalent Volumes
of Equivalent Dilutions Been Plated)

	Incubation Time			Incubation Time	
	0 Min.	90 Min.		0 Min.	90 Min.
Cells	350	21,100	Lysed protoplasts	3	12
Protoplasts	83	15,500			

NaCl, or dextran. Addition, to a final concentration of 2 per cent, of bovine serum albumin prevents their lysis and makes further study possible. The following medium (P-broth) was used to study the growth of bacteriophage by, and the viability of, the protoplasts: Difco Penassay broth was supplemented with 0.6 M sucrose, 2 per cent serum albumin, and 0.1 per cent Mg^{++} (this prevents agglutination at the lower pH of this medium and may be required for growth processes).

2. *Growth of Bacteriophage.*—Protoplasts of *E. coli* B will grow bacteriophage T4. Cells were grown as described, and suspended, after washing, in saline containing 100 μg/ml. *l*-tryptophan (necessary for phage adsorption). Phage was added so as to give one particle per hundred bacteria, and after 5 minutes of incubation for adsorption and injection the cells were converted to protoplasts in tris buffer. Infective center titers (plaques) were obtained for protoplasts, lysed protoplasts, and cells by plating in $M/2$ NaCl phage agar (8 per cent tryptone, 0.1 per cent glucose, and agar) with an excess of *E. coli* B. Suitable samples were incubated in P-broth to determine final yields. Table 1 shows the results of such an experiment. About 20 per cent of protoplast infective centers are recovered directly. Only 1 per cent of infective centers are recovered from lysed protoplasts. These probably represent unadsorbed and desorbed phage, as there is little rise in the titer with time. Protoplasts give almost as large a yield as the untreated cells, indicating that the initial loss of protoplast infective centers is due to their premature lysis on the plates rather than to inability to grow phage.

3. *Viability.*—For 4 hours after suspension and incubation in P-broth, protoplasts exhibit no gross morphological changes as observed by phase-contrast microscopy. At this time, the majority of the protoplasts start to shrink, become highly refractile at their periphery, and assume a coccobacillus form. Their fate is still uncertain, but they probably represent a degenerate state. On the other hand, about 10 per cent of the protoplasts increase in volume and form a large vacuole. From the side distal to the vacuole, finger-like processes appear which grow into rods. The mother protoplast becomes extremely distorted, and a wide variety of morphological abberations are observed, reminiscent of the growth of L-forms from large bodies. Direct demonstration of the viability of the proto-

plasts has been obtained by plating them in P-broth to which sufficient agar to just solidify the mixture was added. The equivalent of from 2 to 20 per cent (different experiments) of the treated cells formed normal colonies. On no other solid media have the protoplasts returned to the actual bacillary form.

DISCUSSION

Although lysozyme has been claimed to be without effect on *E. coli* cells, it was known to be bound by them. In our studies it was clear that at pH 6–8 lysozyme was without effect, whereas its activity was extremely rapid at pH 8 and above. It is interesting to note that suspension of *E. coli* in the alkaline treatment medium, in the absence of lysozyme, brings about, within 30 minutes, the slow lysis of the cells upon their suspension in hypotonic media. This action may be analogous to, though less efficient than, that of lysozyme, which is itself a basic protein. Certain classes of bacteriolytic agents may have as their primary site of activity the cell-wall substance, with the lysis of the cell being due to secondary osmotic effects following the dissolution of the cell wall. In the course of these investigations it was noted that the lysis of *E. coli* by phage ghosts (phage membranes obtained by osmotic shock) went through a protoplast stage. However, no suitable stabilizing medium for such protoplasts was found. Thus three biological reagents—phagocytin, lysozyme, and phage ghosts—are available for efficient lysis of *E. coli* cells for preparation of bacterial enzymes, nucleic acids, cell membranes, etc.

The protoplasts of *E. coli* have retained—as had their predecessors, the protoplasts of *B. megaterium*—sufficient of their synthetic capacities to synthesize bacteriophage. This may be taken as a general indication of their biochemical integrity. The difference in the viability of *E. coli* and *B. megaterium* protoplasts may be only a reflection of the different media used in the different studies. As pointed out, there has been considerable variation in the viability of the *E. coli* protoplasts. This may depend on the amount of residual cell-wall substance left on the protoplast and/or the soluble materials lost during the conversion process.

With the ready accessibility of protoplasts of *E. coli,* investigation of their genetic potentialities is under way.

THE STRUCTURE OF VIRUSES

Even today the structure of viruses is not completely understood. Early studies by microbiologists who had only the light microscope at their disposal revealed very little: even the largest of the viruses lie at the threshold of visibility, and internal structure could not be seen.

With the invention of the electron microscope and with the practice of coating surfaces of particles with a thin layer of metal, it became possible to see virus particles clearly enough to distinguish their shapes and sizes. Techniques of sectioning, first using freshly broken glass and later using the sharp edges of diamonds as microtome knives, gave considerable information concerning the internal structure of the viruses. X-ray diffraction techniques were applied to the study of virus structure by Bernal and Fankuchen in 1940–1941. These and other techniques of observation and interpretation are at last giving a clear and, hopefully, a reasonably accurate picture of the structure of the viruses, which is reviewed in considerable detail in the paper that follows.

Because of space limitations, some of the text and several of the illustrations in the original paper have been omitted. The reader is advised to consult the original source.

We owe a great deal of our present knowledge of virus structure to the painstaking studies carried out by Dr. Horne, presently at the Cavendish Laboratory, Cambridge University, and Dr. Wildy, now at the Institute of Virology, University of Glasgow, and to their capacity to synthesize information obtained by a variety of methods into a consistent and verifiable picture.

Additional information may be found in Heinz Fraenkel-Conrat, "Design and Function at the Threshold of Life," Academic Press Inc., New York, 1962, 118 pp.

From *Virology*,
15:348–373, 1961.

SYMMETRY IN VIRUS ARCHITECTURE

BY R. W. HORNE AND P. WILDY

INTRODUCTION

. . . The fine structure of virus particles concerns the chemical, serological and morphological features of their components. . . . Recently a number of important advances in this field have so transformed our ideas of virus particles that the rather indefinite blobs of a few years ago begin to appear as intricate esthetically satisfying structures belonging to a number of geometrical families.

The modern concept of the infective virus particle or *virion* is that it consists fundamentally of a core composed of or containing one kind of nucleic acid which is encased in a protein shell or *capsid*. The capsid is built from a number of morphological subunits, the *capsomeres* (for general discussion and terminology see Lwoff *et al.*, 1959). It must be made clear that the capsomere may be composed of a number of smaller chemical or structural subunits and need not be equivalent to the crystallographic subunit. . . . Larger, more complex virions may also contain accessory structures, such as envelopes surrounding their capsids or specialized structures such as tails. . . .

SYMMETRY AND "SUBUNITS" IN THE VIRION

The Requirement for "Subunits" and Symmetry.—Arguing largely from general principles, Crick and Watson (1956, 1957) advanced two major propositions applicable particularly to small virions. First, they pointed out that the ribonucleic acid (RNA) in such particles was probably insufficient to code for more than a few sorts of protein molecules of limited size. The only reasonable way to build a protein shell was, therefore, to use the same type of molecule over and over again, hence the identical subunits.

It will be noted that these are *chemical subunits* and need not be equivalent to capsomeres as will appear later.

The second part of Crick's and Watson's argument concerned the way the subunits must be packed in the protein shell or capsid. On general grounds it was expected that identical subunits would be packed so as to provide each with an identical environment; this is possible only if they are packed symmetrically. It is essential to consider the predictions of Crick and Watson in terms of *symmetry elements* rather than particle shapes.

The validity of their predictions is becoming increasingly apparent, and it is found that they apply to virions of all sizes and of very different character. Moreover, it is in the capsid that the symmetry is found.

Methods of Looking for Symmetry.—Two experimental tools have been valuable in showing up the symmetry of virus particles. (1) X-Ray diffraction techniques first used by Bernal and Fankuchen (1941) have now become capable of very delicate analysis. Some of the results obtained by this method have been discussed in detail by Klug and Caspar (1961). (2) Electron microscopy at first gave little evidence of symmetry, though from the beginning the general shapes of the particles at least indicated what type of symmetry might be present (cf. Kausche *et al.,* 1939). Refinements in fixation procedures and shadowing methods have, however, allowed such precise determinations of the shapes of particles that their symmetry is self-evident. . . . More recently the negative-staining procedure of Brenner and Horne (1959) has revealed not only the over-all shapes of particles, but the symmetrical arrangement of their components. This technique is reviewed in detail by Horne (1961).

Types of Symmetry Found in the Virion.—We have precise data on the virions of very few species; these, however, include representatives with widely different characteristics. The symmetry patterns found in the capsids fall into two major groups: (1) those with helical (screw) symmetry and (2) those with cubic symmetry. Most virions are found in one or other of these groups. We shall discuss each at length and will subsequently deal briefly with symmetry in elongated capsids and with complex virions which have more than one pattern of symmetry.

CAPSIDS WITH HELICAL SYMMETRY

Tobacco Mosaic Virus.—The best-studied virions with helical symmetry in the capsid are those of tobacco mosaic virus (TMV). The combined results of chemical and X-ray diffraction analyses on whole virus and reaggregated capsids have provided a clear picture of the structure of TMV. In the interests of brevity we shall simply summarize the essential features (for evidence and references see Franklin *et al.,* 1957; Klug and Caspar, 1961) (see Fig. 1):

1. The virion is in the form of a hollow rod 3000 A long and 170 A wide. Its molecular weight is 39.2×10^6.

2. It is built from 2130 helically arranged crystallographic subunits.

3. There are $3n + 1$ subunits in every three turns of the helix. The value of n is now accepted as 16.

4. There are 2130 identical protein molecules (mol. wt. 17,420) in each rod. Each molecule contains one cysteine residue.

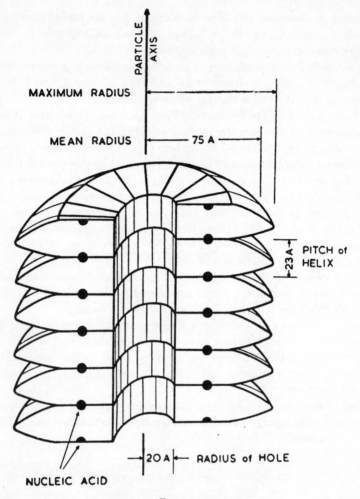

PARTICLE AXIS

MAXIMUM RADIUS

MEAN RADIUS |———— 75 A ————|

PITCH of HELIX

23 A

←|20 A|← RADIUS of HOLE

NUCLEIC ACID

FIGURE 1

Diagram showing helical arrangement of capsomeres in tobacco mosaic virus and their relation to the nucleic acid. After Franklin *et al.* (1957).

5. The crystallographic and chemical subunits are equivalent.

6. The RNA, amounting to 5.2% of the particle, appears to lie in a helical groove between the protein subunits. Its molecular weight is 2.06×10^6.

Extensive studies by electron microscopy have been made on TMV, using several preparative techniques, and these at first led to a somewhat different concept of its structure. Shadow-casting methods revealed apparently rigid rods about 3000 A × 150 A, but no evidence of substructures was found (Williams and Steere, 1951; Hall, 1958). Micrographs made of the protein component obtained by alkaline degradation (Schramm, 1947) revealed circular disks with a central hole about 50 A in diameter (Schramm *et al.*, 1955; Fraenkel-Conrat and Williams, 1955). This led to the suggestion that the central region was where the RNA was located—a supposition which was strengthened by Hart's (1955) finding on RNase-sensitive core (50 A in diameter) protruding from the rod after controlled degradation from sodium dodecyl sulfate.

Replica methods showed some evidence of periodic structure in the form of a "herringbone" arrangement along the rod axis, but the obscured spacing of 45 A was twice that inferred from X-ray diffraction studies (Matthews *et al.*, 1956).

More recently, electron microscope findings have been more in accord with the concept summarized in Fig. 1. The hollow central region was first directly observed by Huxley (1957) using negative staining and more recently studies of reaggregated capsids have revealed a periodic structure which accords well with the X-ray results (Nixon and Woods, 1960).

These workers also found that, when negatively stained rods were viewed along their axes, radially disposed capsomeres were clearly seen, there being 16 and a bit per turn. This finding leads to the conclusion that the capsomere, the crystallographic subunit and the chemical subunit are equivalent in this virus. Further confirmation of the X-ray work has been found in negatively stained preparations of intact rods (Naginton and Horne, unpublished). In these preparations, a periodic structure was seen with a mean spacing of about 25 A and some rods were seen to be disrupting. In them the helix was extended and elongated capsomeres were revealed.

Tobacco Rattle Virus.—Studies on tobacco rattle virus show that it is probably structurally similar to TMV. It appears as a rigid helix whose capsomeres may be disposed in much the same way (Nixon and Woods, 1959).

Sugar Beet Yellows Virus.—Electron micrographs made on preparations of sugar beet yellows virus reveal long slender filaments 100 A in diameter and of variable length. . . . High-resolution studies using negative staining have been made in material from infected sugar beet. They show filaments with regular periodicity along their axes (mean spacing = 26–30 A). The filaments had a central hollow region 30–40 A in diameter and the width of the capsomeres was reported to be about 20 A. Unlike the rigid looking rods of TMV, these filaments appeared to be flexible and were interpreted as being loose helixes (Horne *et al.*, 1959), which are shown in Fig. 2.

The Myxoviruses.—Until 1960 the only known examples of virions with helical symmetry were those of plant viruses. At the same time, the architecture of the myxoviruses was poorly understood. It was known that they were highly pleomorphic and relatively complex structures containing RNA, protein and a large proportion of lipid. The experiments of Hoyle (1950, 1952) and of Schäfer (1957) showed that the virions of influenza and fowl plague virus could be broken down by ether treatment releasing hemagglutinin and "soluble" antigen. It was shown that the RNA was located in the "soluble" antigen,

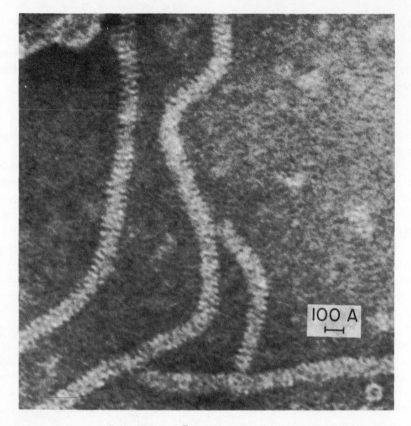

FIGURE 2

Sugar beet yellows virus filaments showing a loose helical structure. The particle bottom right is a fragment from a filament viewed along the axis revealing the hollow central region. After Horne *et al.* (1959).

which contains 5% RNA for influenza strains (Ada, 1957), 10–15% for fowl plague (Schäfer, 1957) and about 6% for Newcastle disease virus (NDV) (Schäfer and Rott, 1959).

Earlier electron micrographs of shadow-cast preparations revealed particles of varying shape and size, but little detail was reported from observing intact particles. . . . Valentine and Isaacs (1957) examined particles with and without chemical and enzymatic treatments and found evidence of a rind of protein material surrounding a ring or horseshoe of RNA-containing material.

The split products of fowl plague virus and NDV were examined by Schäfer (1957) and Schäfer and Rott (1959). After ether splitting, the hemagglutinin and "soluble" antigen were examined. The most interesting findings from our present standpoint were that the RNA-containing material from fowl plague virus appeared as small, apparently spherical particles 100–150 A across which often appeared in chains. That from NDV appeared as flexible cylindrical structures about 200 A in diameter and of variable length.

The most revealing studies have been made with negatively stained material (Horne et al., 1960; Horne and Waterson, 1960). In the strains examined the particles were seen to consist of two main parts: (1) an outer envelope studded with periodic projections and (2) an inner component which often presented a whorled appearance. Studies made on degraded influenza virus have shown that the spiky projections are present in fractions containing the hemagglutinin component (Hoyle et al., 1961). These do not seem to correspond with any precise symmetry arrangement though there is evidence of some regularity, and after ether splitting they appear as well-defined rosettes which are similar in size and shape to the shadowed preparations of fowl plague hemagglutinin (Schäfer, 1957).

When released from the particle, the inner components are seen either as filaments or fragments of filaments about 170 A in diameter. These are formed from helically arranged capsomeres (Horne et al., 1960; Horne and Waterson, 1960). There is no doubt that these structures are "soluble" antigen and are seen abundantly in purified preparations of influenzal "soluble" antigen (Hoyle et al., 1961). It follows that the helixes represent the site of viral RNA and we may legitimately regard them as capsids.

Helixes from different myxoviruses differ considerably in appearance. Those from influenza and fowl plague are found as a large number of short pieces of about the size noted by Schäfer (1957). It is presumed that helixes from these viruses are readily broken by the procedures that release them. Helixes from mumps virus, Sendai virus and NDV are long (the last example fits well the data of Schäfer and Rott [1959]), but differ somewhat from each other in appearance. The capsid of mumps virus shown in Fig. 3 has features in common with that of TMV but resembles sugar beet yellows virus in its flexibility (cf. Fig. 2). The capsid of Sendai virus appears to be much more rigid and looks as though it possesses more than one helical component. We shall return to this question presently. The capsid of NDV seems to be much more tightly packed than the other two, making detailed interpretation difficult.

Though the resemblance between the capsids of myxoviruses and the rod-shaped plant viruses is striking, it would be foolish to suggest that their capsomeres are necessarily packed in the same way as in TMV. At present there is no good evidence either of how these are packed or of their relationship with the RNA. However, the flexibility of the mumps capsid and the way it seems to unravel, forming long slender strands, suggest a different arrangement. It is as though the capsomeres were strung together with the RNA.

Little need be said about the geometry of helical structures; the symmetry arrangements in fibrous molecules have been discussed by Klug et al. (1958). We feel, however, that it is important to discuss briefly the interpretation that the capsids of Sendai virus and possibly also influenza virus comprise more than

FIGURE 3

Capsids from disrupted mumps virus. These structures bear a striking resemblance to the TMV capsids. . . . After Horne and Waterson (1960).

one helix. If this interpretation is correct, it strongly suggests (though it does not demand) more than one strand of RNA per capsid; this obviously has important genetic implications. The decision to be made is whether the appearance of more than one apparent strand of capsomeres means that there is more than one fundamental helix. Unfortunately, whenever like units are packed corkscrew fashion, a series of crisscross helixes arises. The phenomenon is well known in phyllotaxis and has been admirably dealt with by D'Arcy Thompson (1942). The scales of a fir cone, for example, usually seem to be arranged in several opposing helixes (there may be three left handed, and five right handed), yet there is only one fundamental helix. It is unnecessary to give all the mathematical laws governing the possible numbers of helixes that may be generated in this way (see D'Arcy Thompson, 1942). The important rule to state is that which decides the number of fundamental helixes. If the numbers of opposing helixes have a common factor n, there must be n fundamental helixes. Thus, if the numbers of helixes are prime to one another, there can be only one fundamental helix. In the case of the capsid of Sendai virus, two helixes are clearly seen running in opposite directions; this strongly supports the idea of two fundamental helixes.

The essential architecture of the myxoviruses thus seems fairly clear; it is shown in Fig. 4. The RNA lies in helical capsids. These are bundled up in envelopes with no evident symmetry which are probably derived partly from host cell material (Hoyle, 1954). This concept does much to explain how the filamentous forms of influenza virus are related to the "spherical" forms.

In spite of their pleomorphism and difference in size from strain to strain (influenza and fowl plague viruses are 800–1000 A in diameter, and NDV, Sendai virus, and mumps virus are 1000–5000 A), the appearance of the myxovirus particle is characteristic. It is therefore very interesting to find that Rous sarcoma virus particles have somewhat similar features (Dourmashkin and Simons, 1961). As yet there is no hint as to the nature of the internal component of this virus and it will be interesting to see if this too will prove to have helical symmetry.

CAPSIDS WITH CUBIC SYMMETRY

Symmetry.—In their discussions on "spherical" viruses, Crick and Watson (1956, 1957) pointed out that the only way to provide each subunit with an identical environment was by packing them to fit some form of cubic symmetry. A body with cubic symmetry possesses a number of axes about which it may be rotated to give a number of identical appearances. Figure 5 illustrates a model of an icosahedron whose axes of symmetry are represented by pegs. It will be seen that when viewed down a fivefold axis for example, there are five positions in which the model can be rotated giving identical appearances. It is important to note that the symmetry operation is rotational, hence the members of a figure

FIGURE 4

Schematic model constructed to show possible arrangement of components forming myxovirus particles. The precise way in which the capsid material
is wound is not known. (Horne, Hoyle, and Waterson, unpublished).

must be identical but need not themselves be symmetrical. Thus the fylfot
symbol 卐 possesses fourfold symmetry.

Three types of cubic symmetry are recognized. The simplest is that of a
regular tetrahedron which has threefold and twofold axes of rotational symmetry (written 3:2 symmetry). The cube and the octahedron have 4:3:2 symmetry and the regular dodecahedron and icosahedron have 5:3:2 symmetry.
Besides the five Platonic bodies just mentioned, these symmetry patterns are also
found in their derivatives. Some of these bodies also have mirror symmetry,
others do not.

Pure cubic symmetry has now been demonstrated in virions of ten species.
These have been investigated by three different methods and all appear to have
5:3:2 symmetry (see Table 1). Although ten species is a small sample on
which to base generalizations, it is emphasized that this sample includes viruses

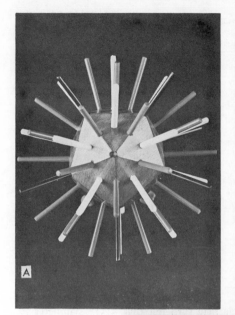
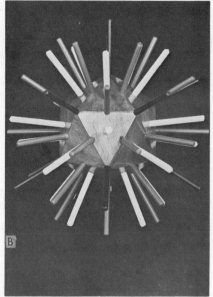
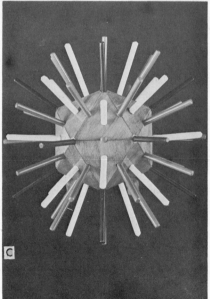

FIGURE 5

Icosahedral model showing axes of symmetry. A. Viewed down fivefold axis. B. Viewed down threefold axis. C. Viewed down twofold axis. It will be seen that when the body is rotated about an axis there are 5, 3, or 2 positions in which it appears identical. The axes are shown as follows: black = fivefold axis; white = threefold axis; gray = twofold axis.

TABLE I

The Evidence for 5:3:2 Cubic Symmetry

Method	Reference
X-Ray diffraction studies	
Bushy stunt virus	Caspar (1956)
Turnip yellow mosaic virus	Klug *et al.* (1957); Klug and Finch (1960)
Poliomyelitis virus	Finch and Klug (1959)
Southern bean mosaic virus	Magdorff (1960)
Electron microscopy (shadow casting)	
Tipula iridescent virus	Williams and Smith (1958)
Bacteriophage φX174	Hall *et al.* (1959)
Electron microscopy (negative staining)	
Adenovirus type 5	Horne *et al.* (1959)
Polyoma virus	Wildy *et al.* (1960)
Herpes virus	Wildy *et al.* (1960)
Tipula iridescent virus	Smith and Hills (1960)
Turnip yellow mosaic virus	Huxley and Zubay (1960); Nixon and Gibbs (1960)
Wart virus (Verruca vulgaris)	Williams *et al.* (1961)
Bacteriophage φX174	Tromans and Horne (1961)

of widely differing characteristics and it may turn out that 5:3:2 symmetry is preferred by viruses.

Before we leave this question we must briefly mention the conflicting interpretation of Andres and Nielsen (1960), who found that adenovirus type 3 appeared hexagonal in cross section (cf. also Valentine and Hopper, 1957). Their thin sections suggested that the particle possessed the features of a rhombic dodecahedron (i.e., 4:3:2 symmetry). The work of Horne *et al.* (1959), however, leaves us in no doubt that adenovirus type 5 has axes of fivefold symmetry which are clearly discerned in the micrographs, and it seems reasonable to suppose that adenovirus of other types is similar. There is some evidence that other viruses not mentioned in Table 1 may also have 5:3:2 symmetry. The simian virus SV39 (Archetti *et al.,* 1961), three plant viruses—tomato black ring virus, raspberry ring spot virus, and arabis mosaic virus (Harrison and Nixon, 1960)—and the particles of foot-and-mouth disease described by Bradish *et al.* (1960) have all been found to possess hexagonal profiles and some evidence of triangular facets suggesting icosahedral shape.

Cubic symmetry combined with some other patterns is also seen in some bacterial viruses (Bradley and Kay, 1960) and in some of these there is evidence of 4:3:2 symmetry. These will be considered later; for our present purpose it will be sufficient to consider only 5:3:2 symmetry and how subunits and capsomeres may be packed to fit it.

The Relation of Capsomeres with Subunits.—In their discussions, Crick and Watson (1956, 1957), Caspar (1956), Klug *et al.* (1957), and Finch and Klug (1959) were thinking in terms of asymmetrical protein subunits packed so as to provide each with an identical environment. It was pointed out that

5:3:2 symmetry required a multiple of 60 subunits to cover the surface completely. Such an arrangement is shown in Fig. 6A, where it will be noted that (1) each unit is related identically and asymmetrically with its neighbors, and (2) none of the units coincides with an axis of symmetry. A glance at Table 2 shows that this pattern is not seen in the electron micrographs of capsids. In no instance has the deduced number of *capsomeres* been a multiple of 60. Furthermore, the capsomeres themselves appear to be symmetrical. First, capsomeres have been found located on symmetry axes and consequently must themselves be symmetrical, e.g., polyoma virus (Wildy *et al.*, 1960), herpes virus (Wildy *et al.*, 1960), turnip yellow mosaic virus (TYMV) (Nixon and Gibbs, 1960). Secondly, in some instances they appear as symmetrical hollow prisms or disks, e.g., herpes virus (Wildy *et al.*, 1960), polyoma virus (Wildy *et al.*, 1960), turnip yellow mosaic virus (Nixon and Gibbs, 1960), papilloma virus (Williams *et al.*, 1960). It is therefore clear that with capsids of cubic symmetry the capsomeres are not equivalent to the subunits of Crick and Watson (1956, 1957). An obvious solution to the problem is provided by supposing that the symmetrical capsomeres are built from a number of asymmetrical subunits held together in the form of a faggot (Wildy *et al.*, 1960).

The geometrical evolution of capsids resulting from the above operation has been described previously (Wildy, 1960; Wildy and Horne, 1960), and is summarized in Table 3 and Fig. 6. Here we see subunits being combined two at a time, three at a time, and five at a time to give capsomeres with rotational symmetry which may be placed over appropriate symmetry axes, thus giving three basic patterns, the simple capsids, comprising 30, 20, and 12 capsomeres (Fig. 6B–D).

TABLE 2

The Numbers of Capsomeres Reported for Virions with 5:3:2 Cubic Symmetry

| Virus | Capsomeres | Capsomeres situated on | | | Reference |
		(a) 5-fold axis	(b) 3-fold axis	(c) 2-fold axis	
Bacteriophage φX174	12	12	—	—	Hall *et al.* (1959); Tromans and Horne (1961)
Turnip yellow mosaic virus	32	12	20	—	Huxley and Zubay (1960); Nixon and Gibbs (1960)
Polyoma virus	42	12	—	30	Wildy *et al.* (1960)
Wart virus	92	12	20	—	Williams *et al.* (1961)
Herpes virus	162	12	—	30	Wildy *et al.* (1960)
Adenovirus type 5	252	12	—	—	Horne *et al.* (1959)
	362	12	20	30	
	492	12	—	—	
	642	12	—	30	
Tipula iridescent virus	812	12	20	—	Smith and Hills (1960)
	1002 etc.	12	—	30	

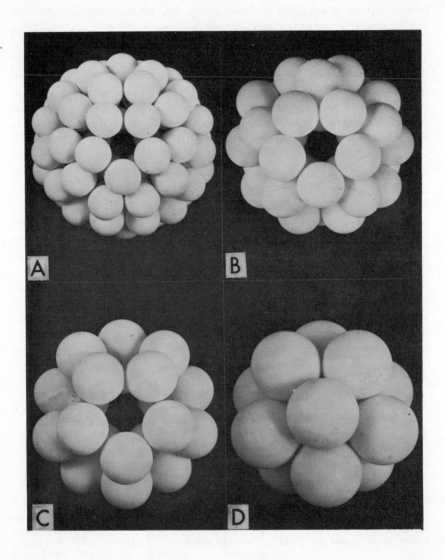

FIGURE 6

Four models illustrating the ways in which identical units can be packed in accordance with 5:3:2 symmetry. All models are viewed down an axis of fivefold symmetry. A. Model composed of 60 spheres, each representing an asymmetric unit. B. Model composed of 30 spheres, each representing a unit with twofold symmetry. C. A model composed of 20 spheres, each representing a unit with threefold symmetry. D. A model composed of 12 spheres, each representing a unit of fivefold symmetry. Wildy (1960); Wildy and Horne (1960).

TABLE 3

The Relationship between Capsomeres and Structural Subunits in Bodies with 5:3:2 Cubic Symmetry

	Number of capsomeres			Number of subunits
	5-fold	3-fold	2-fold	
Initial conception	—	—	—	$60n$
Simple capsids:				
(a)	12	—	—	$60n$
(b)	—	20	—	$60n$
(c)	—	—	30	$60n$
Composite capsids:				
(a)	12	20	—	$120n$
(b)	12	—	30	$120n$
(c)	12	20	30	$180n$

Composite capsids may be derived by combining different types of capsomere; for example, fivefold and threefold capsomeres may be arranged to give a capsid consisting of 32 capsomeres (see Fig. 7).

It is obvious that fivefold capsomeres must be located on axes of fivefold symmetry, but if we introduce sixfold (potentially hexagonal) capsomeres, they may be situated (1) on axes of twofold symmetry, (2) on axes of threefold symmetry, or (3) in indifferent sites where they are admirably suited to hexagonal packing. In this way it is possible to build a variety of complicated bodies in which 5:3:2 symmetry is preserved and in each of which the number of Crick's and Watson's subunits is a multiple of 60. Some of these are seen in Fig. 7.

An alternative hypothesis has been considered (Klug and Finch, 1960; Klug and Caspar, 1961) in which protein subunits are grouped together in the form of identical asymmetrical building blocks. These are packed symmetrically about the axis of symmetry but may not lie over them. The component parts of these asymmetrical building blocks might well give the appearance of symmetrical capsomeres.

The electron micrographs strongly support the existence of capsomeres. Not only have symmetrical structures been seen lying on the axes of symmetry in different capsids (Horne *et al.*, 1959; Wildy *et al.*, 1960; Huxley and Zubay, 1960; Nixon and Gibbs, 1960), but they have been found to retain their configuration after disruption of the capsid (Wildy *et al.*, 1960; Macpherson *et al.*, 1961). This evidence does not however exclude the possibility that asymmetrical building blocks may coexist with capsomeres. Although it contravenes the principle of economy, it is possible that asymmetrical building blocks, which for some reason are not resolved in the micrographs, are packed between the capsomeres.

There is direct evidence that capsomeres of hexagonal and pentagonal section exist. The best samples are found in the capsid of herpes virus, which has rel-

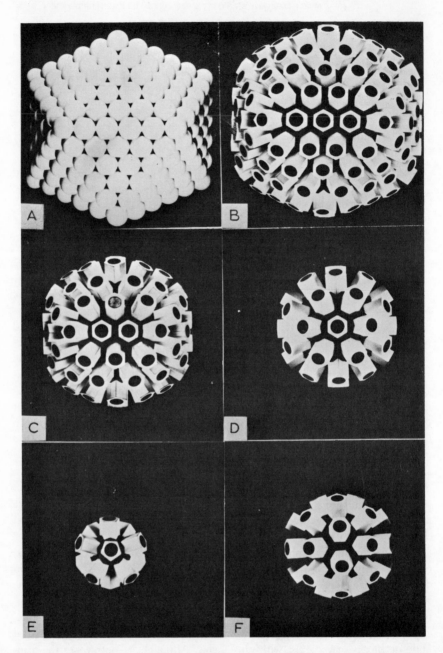

FIGURE 7

Six models constructed from pentagonal and hexagonal members arranged in accordance with 5:3:2 symmetry. All fall into the series $10x(n-1)^2 + 2$ for models A–E, $x = 1$; for F, $x = 3$. The numbers of members are as follows: A, 252; B, 162; C, 92; D, 42; E, 12; F, 32.

atively large capsomeres (Wildy *et al.*, 1960). Here all the capsomeres appear to be hollow prisms which, in favorable circumstances, were five or six sided. The conception also fits well with chemical data, discussed by Klug and Finch (1960) and Harris and Hindley (1961), that the 32 capsomeres of TYMV may be composed of 12 capsomeres each with 5 protein subunits and of 20 capsomeres each with 6 subunits, though at present this is not the only possible interpretation.

It is interesting to compare the morphological appearance of the capsomeres of herpes with annelid hemoglobin (Roche *et al.*, 1960) and with hemocyanin (van Bruggen *et al.*, 1960). Both these protein molecules appear as pentagonal or hexagonal prisms. This configuration is also seen in other situations. Unpublished work on the structure of isolated cell walls has clearly revealed hexagonal units (Thornley and Horne, unpublished; Tromans and Horne, 1961).

Arrangement of Capsomeres in Capsids with 5:3:2 Symmetry.—We are led to consider how pentagonal and hexagonal capsomeres may be combined to give bodies with 5:3:2 symmetry. For this purpose it is convenient to think of the capsid as a polyhedron defined by f_5 pentagons and f_6 hexagons (representing the faces of the capsomeres). Here we are concerned with similar problems to those considered by D'Arcy Thompson (1942) in connection with radiolarians and, more recently, by Smith and Littan (1960) in connection with brochosomes. The value of f_5 may at once be fixed at 12 by applying Euler's theorem: corners − edges + faces = 2.

This result is independent of the existence of 5:3:2 symmetry, but shows that hexagons and pentagons may be packed to comply with it because the 12 pentagons may fit over the 6 fivefold axes. The values taken by f_6 are harder to define, but it may be shown that they are limited if 5:3:2 symmetry is to be preserved. The hexagons may be placed in three situations: (1) over axes of twofold symmetry, (2) over the axes of threefold symmetry, and (3) in indifferent sites. Thus the values for (1) may be 0 or 30, for (2) 0 or 20, and for (3) must be a multiple of 60 to comply with symmetry requirements. This procedure limits the numbers of polygons which may be packed on a polyhedron with 5:3:2 symmetry but unfortunately does not lead to a general equation for such bodies since it predicts solutions which cannot exist. It has, however, been useful in directing our attention to four series of bodies that can exist; these are listed in Table 4.

The first two, which have previously been noted by Fuller (1960), have the general formula $10x(n - 1)^2 + 2$, where x has the values 1 or 3. When $x = 1$, a series of icosahedral bodies results in which the capsomeres on the edges are shared between faces, and in which the *sides* of the fivefold members are opposite (cf. Fig. 7A–E and Fig. 8A). Here n = the number of capsomeres on the edge of the body (including those situated over fivefold axes). This series, as has previously been noted (Wildy and Horne, 1960; Wildy, 1960) is the commonest so far encountered in viral capsids. The second series in which $x = 3$ and n = the number of capsomeres between and including those over

TABLE 4

The First Few Solutions of Four Series of Bodies Having 5:3:2 Symmetry That Are Built Entirely from Hexagons and Pentagons[a]

$10x(n-1)^2 + 2$		$10(n^2 + n) + 12$	$30n^2 + 12$
$x = 1$	$x = 3$		
12	—	12	12
—	32	32	—
42	—	—	42
—	—	72	—
92	—	—	—
—	122	—	—
—	—	132	132
162	—	—	—
—	—	212	—
252	—	—	—
—	272	—	—
—	—	—	282
—	—	312	—
362	—	—	—

[a] The values shown represent the total number of polygons on the surface. Compare with Table 2.

the threefold axes, describes a series of triacontahedral bodies whose edges are also shared capsomeres. Interestingly, the fivefold members are rotated about the fivefold symmetry axes and therefore the corners of these are opposite (cf. Fig. 7F and 8B). In the remaining two series described by $10(n^2 - n) + 12$ and $30n^2 + 12$, the fivefold members do not form part of the triangular or rhombic facets. In the higher members of these series, the polygons are rotated so that neither the sides nor corners of the fivefold capsomeres are opposite one another (see Fig. 8C). In consequence, like the snub dodecahedron, these bodies are enantiomorphic (i.e., they can exist in left- and right-handed configurations).

So far all the capsids whose structure has been elucidated may be described by the formula $10x(n - 1)^2 + 2$ (compare Tables 2 and 4), a result suggesting that these forms perhaps have some selective advantage. It is believed that they have, because they are relatively unstrained.

It has previously been pointed out (Horne *et al.*, 1959) that the icosahedral form $10(n - 1)^2 + 2$ is ideally suited to hexagonal packing in the equilateral triangular facets. Some strain must occur at the edges where, although the pattern is retained, it extends to a new plane. With the second series $30(n - 1)^2 + 2$, additional strain is imposed (in all except the 32 solution) owing to the fact that the rhombic faces of a triacontahedron do not have angles of $60°$ and $120°$. It is therefore a less likely solution than the icosahedral form. Finally, the remaining two series impose a great deal of strain giving rise to bodies with puckered surfaces. It is not surprising then, that the examples of capsids with cubic symmetry belong to the first two series only. It is interesting that these were considered by Fuller (1960) in connection with his icosogeodesic domes.

SYMMETRY IN ELONGATED CAPSIDS

Brief attention must be paid to two configurations which have not been covered so far. These include the elongated forms found in some virus preparations and the poxviruses.

Elongated Forms.—Elongated forms have been found in preparations of polyoma virus (Howatson and Almeida, 1960) and of Shope papilloma virus (Williams *et al.*, 1960). With polyoma these forms are found in the nuclei of some infected cells, and thin sections stained with uranyl acetate suggest that

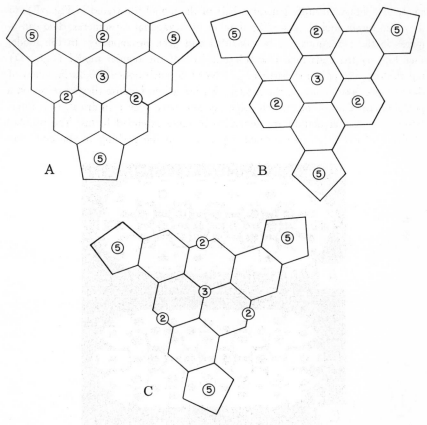

FIGURE 8

Diagrams showing packing arrangement of hexagons and pentagons on part of the surface of a body having 5:3:2 symmetry. The axes of symmetry are appropriately labeled.

A. From icosahedral body belonging to the series $10(n-1)^2 + 2$. This example would have 92 polygons. Note that edges of pentagons are opposite.

B. From triacontahedral body belonging to the series $30(n-1)^2 + 2$. This example would have 122 polygons. Note that corners of pentagons are opposite.

C. From body falling in both series $10(n^2 + n) + 12$ and $30n^2 + 12$, having 132 polygons. Note that pentagons are oriented so that neither corners nor edges are opposite.

the central portion is occupied by nucleic acid. Negatively stained preparations reveal hollow elongated capsomeres in regular array. These structures are provisionally interpreted as aberrant forms. However they are interpreted, it is clear that they are closely related to the more commonly encountered "spherical" forms.

If it is assumed that these forms are covered entirely with the same hexagonal and pentagonal capsomeres as the commoner capsid, there must be exactly 12 pentagonal capsomeres (from formula 2). And if the elongated capsids are symmetrical, there must be 6 pentagonal capsomeres at each end. There are a number of ways in which the ends could thus be formed. They could be made solely of pentagonal units (imagine half of the model illustrated in Fig. 7F), or they also might include a specific number of hexagonal capsomeres. The capsomeres in the sides must all be six-sided and pack hexagonally. In the model (see Fig. 9) the ends each resemble one half of the regular model (Fig. 7D) representing the polyoma particle. . . . Not too much notice should be taken of the tilting of the prisms in the model; this has arisen because they were set on a pentagonally shaped core which might as well have been cylindrical. It is interesting to note that helixes are generated in these extended forms. The number of fundamental helixes so formed depends upon the packing in the ends and

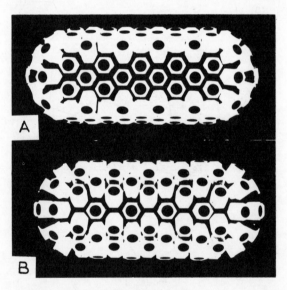

FIGURE 9

Model showing how hexagonal and pentagonal prisms may be packed to form elongated structures. The prisms have been set on a structure of pentagonal section. View A looks down at a face, and view B at an edge. Note that the hexagonal packing extends over the edges of the core, generating a number of helixes.

must be a multiple of five or six depending upon whether there is five- or six-fold rotational symmetry about the long axis of the particle.

Capsids of the Poxviruses.—Extensive electron microscope studies have been made on members of the pox group (Dawson and MacFarlane, 1948; Gaylord and Melnick, 1953; Epstein, 1958; Peters, 1956, 1960; Stoeckenius and Peters, 1955) from which it is evident that their structure is complex. The particles appear to consist of a number of "membranes" surrounding a central nucleoid. Little is known at present about the symmetry or of how the capsomeres are packed. Some preliminary unpublished studies by the Cambridge workers, which were made with the negative staining technique, suggest that underlying the outer envelope is a structure composed of a number of elongated tubular components. There is no clear indication of how these are packed, though the considerations in the last section may obviously be pertinent.

SYMMETRIES IN COMPLEX VIRIONS

The foregoing discussions have concerned virions with relatively simple symmetry arrangements, which may be seen primarily in their capsids. We now come to consider the patterns found in the tadpole-shaped bacteriophages. Here it is common to find two distinct patterns of symmetry in the head (capsid) and in the tail. These we shall consider separately.

Symmetry in the Bacteriophage Head.—Electron micrographs, made on material prepared in various ways, have revealed that the heads of different phages assume a number of geometrical forms. Some, such as the T-even coliphages, appear to be bipyramidal hexagonal prisms. . . . Others, such as Vi 1 phage and a phage of *B. megatherium,* clearly have icosahedral heads. . . .

Typhoid phage 2 has been reported to have octahedral heads, and in other phages variously ovoid heads have been noted (Bradley and Kay, 1960).

So far there has been little indication of the shape or packing of capsomeres, but Bradley and Kay (1960) have reported hollow capsomeres (100 × 50 A) in the capsid of T5. These structures were only seen when negative contrast was obtained using uranyl acetate at pH 3.5, and then only in empty capsids. There is as yet no indication as to how these are packed. With these phages whose heads have 5:3:2 symmetry, we should not be surprised to find an arrangement of hexagonal and pentagonal capsomeres packed in one of the patterns we have discussed. From similar geometrical reasoning, the octahedral heads could be built from 6 tetragonal and n hexagonal capsomeres. It would be foolish however, to predict that the capsids of phages necessarily resemble those of other viruses. Nevertheless, the well-defined symmetrical shapes of their heads indicate that they possess an orderly arrangement of substructures.

The Tail Structures.—The comparative studies of Bradley and Kay have clearly indicated that some bacteriophages have a clearly defined injection mechanism whereas others do not. In all of them, however, the micrographs suggest

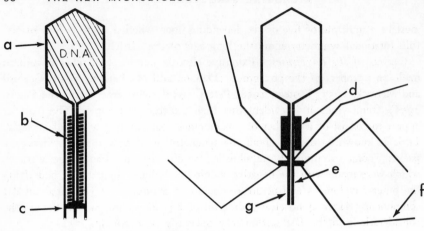

FIGURE 10

Diagram of bacteriophage T2 summarizing the essential features of the intact (left) and triggered (right) virus. Total length of phage = 2200–2300A; total length of tail = 1100–1150A. Intact phage: *a*, Head; length = 950–1050A, width = 600–800A, membrane thickness = 25–30A. *b*, Sheath (extended); length = 750–800A, diameter = 160–175A, striations (number) = 25–28, striations (width) = 25–28A, striations (spacing) = 35–40A. *c*, Plate (hexagonal structure); across = 300–350A, length = 200–250A. Triggered phage: *d*, Sheath (contracted); length = 330–350A (shortened by 350–450A), diameter = 200–300A (increased by 45–50A), hole diameter = 90–110A. *e*, Core (whole); length = 900–950A, diameter = 75–80A, hole diameter = 18–20A. *f*, Tail fiber (6 in all); length = 1400–1600A; length to bend = 700–800A, diameter = 20A. *g*, Core (exposed after contraction); length = 550–600A.

that the tails possess some form of rotational symmetry, and often morphological subunits may be discerned.

The tail structures at the T-even coliphages have been specially well studied, and it is interesting to examine them with function in mind. It is well known that in the process of infection most of the phage protein remains outside the bacterial host (Hershey and Chase, 1952) in the form of empty ghosts (Kellenberger and Arber, 1955). The DNA is squirted into the bacterial cell as though the phage were a microsyringe. The mechanism responsible for thrusting the tail into the bacterium may equally well be likened to that of a spring gun.

The tail comprises three main components, the tail sheath surrounding the rigid tail core on the end of which is a diffuse structure from which fibers protrude. These structures have been revealed in shadow-cast electron micrographs after chemical and physical treatments which cause the sheath to contract (Kozloff and Henderson, 1955; Kellenberger and Arber, 1955; Williams and Fraser, 1956).

More recently Brenner *et al.* (1959) have examined the tail structures in detail. The negative staining method was applied in parallel with chemical studies and the results are summarized in Fig. 10, which should be compared with the micrographs, Figs. 11 and 12. The important findings are then (1) the

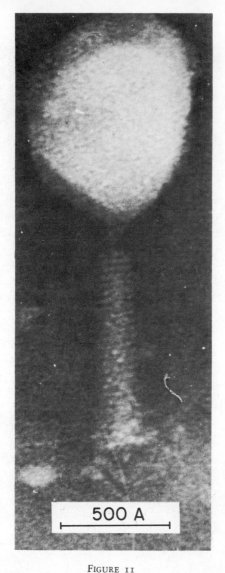

500 A

FIGURE 11

Negatively stained particle of bacteriophage T2. Note helical arrangement of tail
sheath.

tail is attached to the capsid on an axis of sixfold symmetry; (2) the tail core
is hollow; (3) the core is surrounded by a contractable sheath. In the intact
state, the sheath is seen to be composed of morphological subunits arranged
helically. There appears to be one fundamental helix spaced at 30 A. There are
about 24 turns to the helix. Where purified preparations of sheaths were exam-

1000 A

FIGURE 12

Negatively stained particle of bacteriophage T2 after triggering. Note contracted sheath and splayed tail fibers.

ined, they were found to consist of 12–15 radially disposed morphological sub-units when seen end on. The sheath contracts after appropriate chemical or physical treatment or after attachment to the bacterial cell. (4) At the end of the sheath there is a hexagonal plate structure from which six prongs protrude. During sheath contraction, the plate moves, always toward the head, and six tail fibers become visible, splaying out from the plate.

This type of structure has been described for all the T-even coliphages, for phages P1 and P2, and for typhoid phages 2, 3T⁺, C4, 11F, 66F, and V11 (Anderson, 1960; Bradley and Kay, 1960). For all three phages the mechanism for piercing the host cell wall may be explained thus. The tail plate (and/or fibers) become firmly attached to the cell wall, and by sheath contraction the tail core is forced into the cell. It was pointed out by Brenner *et al.* (1959) that the contraction of the sheath could result from an alteration in the number of subunits comprising one turn of the helix.

A host of other phages described by Hall *et al.* (1959), Anderson (1960), and Bradley and Kay (1960) have no morphological evidence of an injection mechanism though some of them have plates or "knobs" on the ends of their tails.

Finally, it is unknown exactly how the symmetry of the tails of phages is related to the head. In the T-even coliphages, the evidence suggests sixfold symmetry about the long axis of the virion which is reflected both in the tail and the head. There is some evidence that the hexagonal plate structure pos-sessing six tail fibers is located in certain positions on the particle axis with respect to the head symmetry. It would thus be difficult to relate tail components possessing sixfold symmetry with head structures of fivefold symmetry. In the instances where the phage head is a regular polyhedron, one might expect a similar homogeneity; those with an icosahedral head might have a fivefold tail protruding from one vertex, and with an octahedral head, a fourfold tail. There is so far no evidence at all, and much work obviously remains to be done.

GENERAL COMMENTS

The most natural way to build a structure is to consider it from a mathe-matical point. Unfortunately whenever mathematics enters a biological field, there is a danger that its fascination will compete with and usurp biological interest. This is particularly so in the present context. It should be remembered, however, that although the possible packing arrangements and the symmetry are geometrically interdependent the original requirement for symmetry and "subunits" was a biological one. It is interesting to find how well the predic-tions of Crick and Watson (1956, 1957) have stood up to subsequent investi-gation, even to their suggestion that the myxoviruses might be found to have symmetrical capsids. Their insistence that bodies with 5:3:2 symmetry must have a multiple of 60 "subunits" is a mathematical necessity; all the solutions given in Table 4 comply with this.

The finding of hexagonal and pentagonal capsomeres has led us to extend the arguments of Crick and Watson in a particular direction and suggests that the pattern given by $10(n - 1)^2 + 2$ may occur most commonly because it involves least strain. We would emphasize that we have explored only one channel, i.e., bodies with 5:3:2 symmetry which are composed of pentagonal and hexagonal capsomeres. Other channels may be equally well worth exploring.

Functional Aspects.—The important question to ask is: how does the architecture of the virion fit with its function? Obviously the patterns we have considered are likely to form stable structures in which the genetic material may be protected from the environment. Of much greater interest are the questions of how the genetic material of the virus is made available to the cell and of how the virion is assembled from its components. We have already discussed the first question in relation to the bacteriophages. With other viruses, nothing is known of the way nucleic acid is released. It is felt that the techniques now available may provide some useful information.

The second question of what specifies the correct assembly of virions has been discussed before (Wildy, 1960). It is assumed that nucleic acid and protein are synthesized independently and are subsequently assembled to form complete virions. Probably the best evidence for this is the phenomenon of phenotypic mixing. The question is whether the symmetry and packing arrangements in the capsid are specified (1) by the nucleic acid-containing core, (2) by the configuration of the capsomeres, or (3) by both.

There can be no doubt that the capsomeres of TMV may specify capsid formation *in vitro* for protein obtained from virus, or X protein may readily be made to form rods morphologically similar to the virion. These may be empty capsids (RNA-free) or contain RNA from the same or a different but related virus, in which case they are infective (Fraenkel-Conrat and Williams, 1955; Lippincott and Commoner, 1956; Fraenkel-Conrat, 1956; Fraenkel-Conrat and Singer, 1957; Takahashi, 1955).

This is the only virus in which this phenomenon has been observed, and it is not known whether it applies to synthesis *in vivo*. It has been suggested that the appearance of empty capsids in preparations of a number of viruses reflect a similar specificity in the protein subunits. The classic example is the top component of TYMV (Markham and Smith, 1949). Similar forms have been seen with poliovirus (Horne and Nagington, 1959), herpes virus (Wildy *et al.*, 1960) and some others. In many instances (herpes is one) these forms probably represent originally complete virions which have discharged their core. This type of evidence therefore testifies to the stability of the capsid rather than to its self-assembly. Again the observation that these forms are more abundant early in the multiplication cycle with tipula iridescent virus (Smith, 1958; Hills and

Smith, 1959) and poliovirus (Horne and Nagington, 1959) may reflect greater instability of the virion at this stage. The evidence that these forms are abundant in cells infected with poliovirus in the presence of proflavine (Ledinko, 1958; Nagington and Horne, unpublished) is a little more convincing but is not conclusive.

The most critical work of which we are aware leads to a contrary conclusion. Careful studies by the Geneva group (reviewed by Kellenberger, 1959) show that the DNA of bacteriophage T2 is laid down in particles of characteristic shape before it becomes invested in the protein capsid. This strongly suggests that the symmetry is already determined before the capsomeres are applied. Thin-section studies on animal viruses (Morgan et al., 1954, 1958; Dourmashkin and Negroni, 1960; Howatson and Almeida, 1960; and others) in general support this view that the core is laid down first.

Returning to the primitive condition of a capsid with 5:3:2 symmetry having 60 identical asymmetrical subunits, it is easy to imagine each having a conformation such that it inevitably links with its neighbors to give a specific configuration. This is also true with the simpler capsids we have examined (i.e., these composed of 12, 32, or 42 capsomeres). The more complex the capsids become, the harder it is to see how specific assembly could arise. A large pool of hexagonal capsomeres could as well pack to form sheets or tubes of indefinite length, or alternatively might form capsids of different sizes and shapes. In fact, such capsomeres might be capable of packing in a limited number of configurations, where size and possible symmetry was dictated by the sizes and shapes of preformed cores. In general, where the cores were standard, the "normal" packing arrangement would be the only one possible. Abnormal cores might then result in abnormal capsids, and a deficiency of cores in sheets or crystals of capsomeres. Though such a hypothesis explains the finding of (1) crystals of specific protein with adenovirus (Pereira, 1960); (2) tubular forms (Howatson and Almeida, 1960; Williams et al., 1960) and the small-headed bacteriophage (Anderson, 1960), we do not pretend that it is the only way of explaining such structures.

Classification.—In conclusion we would like to consider how morphological criteria may be useful for classification. Obviously any classification must be based upon a number of quite different criteria and should reflect a natural taxonomic grouping. We are anxious to make plain that the remarks which follow are meant to point out *how* morphological features may be used in classification and do not necessarily indicate at what level they should be used. Moreover, our omission of antigenic, biochemical, and biological characteristics must not be taken to mean that we ignore their importance.

Size and shape of the virion have so far been the only morphological characteristics used to classify viruses. These attributes are both unreliable and misleading as criteria and we suggest that they be abandoned forthwith. It is now

TABLE 5

Symmetry as a Criterion for Classification

| Symmetry | Nucleic acid | |
	DNA	RNA
Helical	—	Tobacco mosaic virus, sugar beet yellows virus, myxoviruses
Cubic	Adenovirus, herpes virus, polyoma virus, φX174	Turnip yellow mosaic virus, poliovirus
Other	Most bacteriophages, pox virus	—

clear that the over-all size of the virion may be very variable, as is evident with the myxoviruses (Horne *et al.*, 1960) and with herpes virus (Wildy *et al.*, 1960). The capsid, on the other hand, appears to be remarkably uniform and it is suggested that the size of the capsid is a much better criterion for classification.

Similarly, the over-all shape of the virion may be misleading. Not only may it be variable and subject to artifactual deformation, but it is now clear that the shape of the virion is the result of (1) the symmetry of the capsid and (2) the presence or absence of such accessory structures as envelopes or tail structures. If shape must be used at all, the only meaningful shape is that of the capsid; we would go further and abandon shape in favor of the symmetry of the capsid. Studies on several viruses have provided clear indications of the symmetry of the capsid and of the arrangement of capsomeres in it, but have given only poor evidence on its shape; we have previously discussed this (Wildy *et al.*, 1960). A particularly illuminating example is also provided by two excellent studies made simultaneously on turnip yellow mosaic virus by different groups (Huxley and Zubay, 1960; Nixon and Gibbs, 1960). Both studies clearly indicate the same symmetry, the same number of capsomeres, and the same essential packing arrangement, but the shape of the capsid was interpreted as a rhombic triacontahedron by the first group and as an icosahedron by the second.

Three other morphological features appear valid as criteria for classification and may prove to be useful. The first is the number of capsomeres; this is particularly applicable to capsids with cubic symmetry. We have seen that capsids of this type belong to one of two families having 5:3:2 symmetry. It is interesting that both adenovirus type 5 and GAL virus (Horne *et al.*, 1959; Macpherson *et al.*, 1961), which have many biological features in common, have been reported to have 252 capsomeres. Some doubt has, however, been cast on this by Davies and Englert (1961), who have deduced 162 capsomeres for GAL virus. It is not yet clear whether the different numbers are due to interpretation or the fact that two viruses have in fact been studied. The second point concerns capsids with helical symmetry. Here the nature of the helix might be useful. For example, TMV has a rigid capsid built as a single helix and containing $16\frac{1}{3}$ capsomeres per turn. Beet yellows and the myxoviruses have flexible capsids, and there is a strong possibility that the capsid of Sendai virus is a double helix. Third, the presence of accessories, such as an envelope or tail structures, might be valuable criteria for classification. There is one reservation that must be made, however; in some instances, for example the envelope of herpes, the structure may be irrelevant and inessential to the virion.

In general, we are impressed by the over-all applicability of the above criteria which cut right across the existing animal (including insect), plant, and bacterial divisions of virology. However, it must be remembered that the information we have at present is limited to very few viruses. It would therefore be prudent to devise a classification which is elastic enough to allow additions and which will accord with other characteristics. Such a scheme is suggested in Table 5. It is emphasized that this could form the basis for an all-embracing classification or could equally well be applied within the various divisions. . . .

The bacteriophages described by Twort (1915) and d'Herelle (1917) were lethal and comparatively virulent. Infection of a susceptible, uninfected bacterial culture in a liquid medium was quickly followed by "clearing," i.e., loss of turbidity due to the death and disruption of the suspended bacteria. As soon as perfection of electron microscopy made it possible to observe what was happening, it was found that the bacteriophages (of *Escherichia coli* and many other bacterial species) are minute tadpole-shaped organisms which attach to the bacterial surface by their "tail" and inject the contents of the "head" into the bacterial cell. The injected substance disappears, but after a few minutes many new bacteriophage particles are observed forming within the infected bacterium; the infected bacterial cell ruptures, releasing the newly formed bacteriophage particles into the surrounding medium, where they attach to neighboring uninfected bacterial cells. The process of injection, disappearance of injected substance, formation of new bacteriophages, and their escape continues until the initially turbid bacterial suspension is "cleared," all the bacteria having ultimately been destroyed.

Other situations were soon observed. In some cases, after a bacterial culture was inoculated with a suspension of bacteriophages, attachment and infection might proceed normally, but only a few of the bacterial cells would rupture and release bacteriophage particles; the culture might survive indefinitely, a few cells in each generation spontaneously rupturing and releasing virus particles. It was found that treatment of an apparently uninfected bacterial suspension with any one of a number of agents, notably a brief exposure to ultraviolet radiation, would trigger the rupture of bacterial cells, with release of bacteriophages. It seemed clear that the cultures were infected with a nonlethal or comparatively avirulent bacterial virus. Cultures of bacteria so infected, mostly capable of growth, survival, and reproduction with little or no indication that they are bacteriophage-infected, and capable of releasing bacteriophages spontaneously or after application of a triggering stimulus, are said to be *lysogenic*. Bacteriophages capable of initiating lysogenic infections are said to be *temperate*.

The events that occurred between attachment and injection of viral substance and the release of new virus were unknown until recently. The injected virus substance disappeared from view: it obviously did not maintain its structural identity, as a foreign cell within the invaded cell, or propagate by fission or mitosis or by any observable process. Within recent years, however, more expert use of the electron microscope, together with a wide variety of ingenious experiments, has provided considerable information on the structure of the bacteriophage and its behavior in the infected bacterial cell. It is now known that the substance in the head of the bacteriophage, which is injected into the bacterial cell, is a long double strand of deoxyribonucleic acid (DNA), the linear polymer that transmits genetic traits from generation to generation in the higher forms of life. It is clearly established that during the period after infection, when no bacteriophage substance can be detected within the bacterial cell, the injected substance (bacteriophage DNA) is in fact closely associated with the DNA of the bacterial chromosome. The invading double-strand helix of bacteriophage DNA appears to attach to the strand of bacterial DNA, at least in certain regions along their length where the composition of the bacteriophage DNA resembles that of the bacterial DNA.*

These and other findings, by many investigators, have provided a clear, detailed picture of the processes of infection of cells by viruses and multiplication of viruses in the infected cell. One of the scientists who has contributed notably to this development is Dr. Andre Lwoff, of the Institut Pasteur, Paris, the author of the paper that follows.

---

* Interchange of segments may occasionally take place. When "peaceful coexistence" has run its course and new bacteriophage particles are formed, these sometimes contain segments, or genes, of bacterial DNA. A form of hybridization of bacteria may be carried out as follows: Suppose that it is desired to transfer a character, *a*, from a strain A that possesses it to another strain, B, that does not. If strain A is infected with a suitable bacteriophage and then strain B is infected with the progeny of that bacteriophage from infected A cultures, the resulting substrain of B may possess the *a* trait in some cases. This method of genetic transfer is called *transduction*.

From *Proc. Roy. Soc.* (London), *Ser. B,*
154:1–20, 1961.

THE DYNAMICS OF VIRAL FUNCTIONS

BY A. LWOFF

THE PROBLEMS

The ultimate aim of biochemistry, wrote Sir Frederick Gowland Hopkins
(1933), should be an adequate and acceptable description of molecular dynamics in living cells and tissues. My ambition, in this eleventh Leeuwenhoek
Lecture, is to describe some aspects of the molecular dynamics of viral functions.

A specific entity which is unable to multiply could not be a virus. The proper
activity of a virus, the viral function par excellence, is consequently reproduction. Yet viral reproduction involves, not one, but a whole set of functions, for
viruses, despite their reputation, are highly complex structures. In order that
the lecture should not appear as the expression of an esoteric and impervious
doctrinal corpus, we have to state first what we understand by the term virus,
a necessary step in view of the fact that this is the fifth Leeuwenhoek Lecture
dealing with viruses. It will also be necessary to explain the meaning of a very
few unfamiliar terms. This done, a virus will be introduced into a cell and we
shall try to understand how it develops. An infected cell may either die or
survive. Sometimes a new balanced cell-virus system emerges, such as a lysogenic
bacterium or a malignant cell. The complex interplay of cellular and viral functions will be analyzed. Then the current views concerning the mechanisms by
which a cell regulates its functions will be summarized. This will lead finally
to a discussion of the relation of viruses to regulating systems in general.

VIRUSES

Viruses represent a specific category of infectious agents which may exist in
three states: infectious, proviral and vegetative. The viral infectious particle or
virion is composed essentially of a condensed genetic material surrounded by a
coat or *capsid* formed essentially of proteinic subunits, the *capsomeres.* The
virion is, structurally and physiologically, different from any cellular organelle

and from any micro-organism. It is devoid of metabolism, unable to grow and to undergo binary fission.

An entity can be recognized as viral only if an infectious phase has been disclosed in its life cycle. As everyone knows, an infection is the introduction into a cell or an organism of an entity, the infectum, able to multiply and to reproduce infectious entities. In the cases of viruses, the infectum is the genetic material, for viruses are reproduced from their genetic material only. A virus is necessarily the sum of its various phases and can be visualized as the life cycle of an abnormal genetic material. Abnormality here refers to the ability to produce a unique type of structure, the infective particle or virion.

A virus can thus be considered either as an infectious entity able to reproduce from its genetic material only, or vice versa, as a genetic material able to produce a virion.

INFECTION AND DEVELOPMENT

Structure.—Bacteriophage *T*2, a parasite of the bacterium *Escherichia coli,* has been selected as a suitable material for the analysis of viral development.

The virion possesses a head and a tail. The head is a hexagonal proteinic prism topped by two hexagonal pyramids. It encloses the genetic material which is a desoxyribonucleic acid, and also two non-genetic substances, a polypeptide and the internal protein. The tail itself is built of a series of structures: (1) the outer sheath which is a contractile myosin-like protein, containing some 110 molecules of ribo– and deoxyribo–adenosine–triphosphate, (2) the core which is an inner tube, (3) a plate with spikes present at the tip, (4) a few molecules of endolysine, a lysozyme-like enzyme, (5) a series of fibres wound around the distal end.

Infection.—When the tip of the tail comes into contact with the wall of a receptive bacterium, it is attached to it, first reversibly, then irreversibly. The thiolester bonds of the fibres are oxidized by the zinc present in the bacterial wall. The endolysine is thus unmasked, and depolymerizes the mucopolysaccharides of the bacterial wall. The contraction of the sheath is triggered, possibly by the SH groups which have been freed. As a result of the contraction, the core of the tail penetrates deeply into the wall, and pierces the bacterial membrane. Then, the injection of the DNA is triggered, perhaps by glucosamine, one of the products of the hydrolysis of the mucopolysaccharide. Finally, the DNA is injected into the bacterial cytoplasm.

In the inert virion, the infective functions exist only as potentialities. The infection, the penetration of the genetic material of a bacteriophage into its host, involves the expression of numerous functions. It comprises a well-ordered sequence of events stemming from the interaction between the bacterium and the virion.

The genetic material of the virus has now penetrated into the cytoplasm of its host. Twenty minutes later, the bacterium will lyse and liberate a few hundred

TABLE I

*% Nucleic Bases in the DNA of Phage T2 and in the RNA of the Normal
and in the Phage RNA of T2 Infected Bacteria*

(From the data of E. Volkin.)

	RNA of normal bacteria	Phage RNA of T2 infected bacteria	DNA of phage T2
5-hydroxymethyl cytosine (in DNA) or cytosine (in RNA)	25	18	16.7
guanine	25	18	18.2
thymine (in DNA) or uracil (in RNA)	25	32	32.6
adenine	25	32	32.5

infectious particles. How does the genetic material multiply, how are viral structures produced and assembled, and why does the bacterium lyse?

Vegetative Phase.—Soon after infection, an active desoxyribonuclease is at work in the bacterium. Its activity seems to be the result of the unmasking of a pre-existing bacterial enzyme. The bacterial chromosome anyhow disintegrates and this destruction of the genetic information accounts for the fact that the infected bacterium stops synthesizing bacterial nucleic acids and bacterial enzymes.

The enzymic machinery of the infected bacterium, however, continues to function: amino acids and nucleic bases are synthesized at the normal rate, but they will be turned into phage material.

The first event in phage multiplication is the production of a specific phage *RNA*. In the nucleic acid of *Escherichia coli,* whether *DNA* or *RNA,* the four nucleic bases are present in the same proportion. In the *DNA* of phage T2, the proportion of the nucleic bases is markedly different. Soon after infection, a new *RNA* appears in the bacterium which has the same base ratio as the phage *DNA*. It can only be the phage *RNA* which, as will be seen later, represents the specific templates on which the phage proteins will be synthesized. The phage *RNA* also provides the building blocks for the synthesis of phage *DNA*. A powerful depolymerase degrades this phage *RNA* into ribonucleotides. These are then converted into deoxyribonucleotides. It happens that the *DNA* of phage T2 contains 5-hydroxymethyl-cytosine instead of the universal, 'normal', base, cystosine. A set of four new phage enzymes will produce the deoxyribohydroxymethyl-cytosine triphosphoric acid out of deoxyribocytosine triphosphate. They are deoxyribocytosine triphosphatase, deoxyribocytosine monophosphate hydroxymethylase, deoxyribohydroxymethyl-cytosine mono- and diphosphate kinases (figure 1).

In addition, a new deoxyribocytosine monophosphate deaminase will deaminate this compound into the corresponding uracil compound which, in turn will be methylated by a bacterial thymidylate synthetase into the corresponding thymine compound. Then a *DNA* polymerase assembles the four nucleotides. The bacterial *DNA* polymerase can produce a *DNA* including 5-hydroxymethyl-cytosine. It could be, however, that in T2 infected bacteria a completely new phage *DNA* polymerase is present and responsible for the reproduction of phage *DNA* proper. Finally, two new additional phage enzymes are synthesized which are responsible, respectively, for mono- and di-glycosylation at the hydroxymethyl group of deoxyribo-5-hydroxymethyl cytidylic acid of the newly formed phage *DNA*.

It was stated that, soon after the infection, the bacterial chromosome is destroyed by a desoxyribonuclease. The infected bacterium containing an active *DNA*ase nevertheless, synthesizes phage *DNA*. This looks paradoxical until one knows that phage *DNA* is much less sensitive to desoxyribonuclease than the bacterial *DNA*.

During the first 7 min following infection, almost all the proteins synthesized by the infected bacterium are phage enzymes necessary for the synthesis of phage *DNA*. However, one among the early proteins appearing after 2 or 3 minutes has not been recognized as an enzyme. It has been identified only thanks to its antigenic specificity, and will be found later to be present in the head of the bacteriophage particle. Because this protein is located inside the head, it is generally called internal protein. Sometimes, for reasons unknown, it is referred to as gut-protein.

The synthesis of phage *DNA* starts at the 7th minute, and its condensation at the 9th minute. At this time, the synthesis of more new proteins is initiated: the protein of the head and the various proteins of the tail, including the lyso-

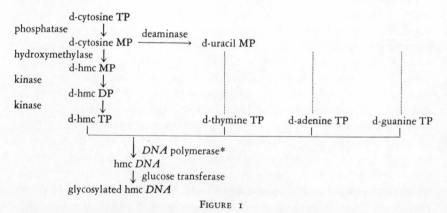

FIGURE 1

Enzymes in the life cycle of bacteriophage T2 (modified from S. S. Cohen). MP, DP and TP, mono-, di- and triphosphoric acid; d = deoxyribose; hmc = hydroxymethyl-cytosine.

* The phage nature of the *DNA* polymerase has not yet been ascertained (see text).

TABLE 2

Sequence of Events in the Life Cycle of Bacteriophage T2

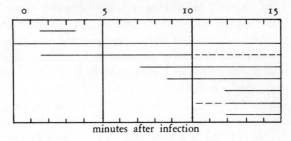

breakdown of bacterial nucleus
synthesis of phage *RNA*
synthesis of phage enzymes
synthesis of phage *DNA*
condensation of phage *DNA*
S.B.P. protein
head protein
infective particle

minutes after infection

(From an unpublished chart of E. Kellenberger.)

zymelike enzyme endolysine. The first infective particle appears around the 12th minute. How its various pieces are assembled remains completely mysterious.

The synthesis of endolysine continues. It is responsible for the depolymerization of bacterial mucopolysaccharides and consequent bacterial lysis which liberates the virions. The vegetative phase has come to its end and the life cycle has now been completed.

LYSOGENY

A bacteriophage such as T2 which always kills the bacterium it infects is called virulent. Infection by certain other phages is compatible with bacterial survival and such phages are called temperate.

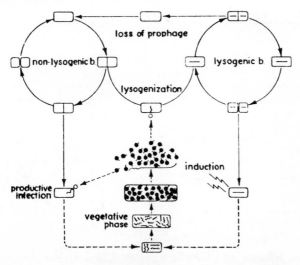

FIGURE 2

Diagrammatic representation of lysogeny. (After Lwoff 1953.)

When a temperate virion infects a bacterium it sometimes enters the vegetative phase which inevitably culminates in the production of infectious particles and bacterial death. However, the vegetative phase is sometimes not initiated. In this even the bacterium remains alive and becomes lysogenic.

Each lysogenic bacterium possesses and perpetuates the potential capacity to produce bacteriophage particles in the absence of infection. When this potentiality is not expressed, the bacterium grows and divides. Obviously we can know that this potentiality exists only if it is manifested. And indeed, from time to time, the vegetative phase is initiated in a few bacteria and those bacteria produce virions and die. We have to know why viral functions are sometimes expressed and sometimes not. The current hypothesis—the leitmotiv—of the chapter is that viral functions are not expressed in a lysogenic bacterium because they are blocked by a repressor.

The Prophage.—Lysogenic bacteria perpetuate a specific non-infectious structure called the prophage. A number of experimental data have led to the following conclusions concerning this structure.

(1) The prophage is the genetic material of the bacteriophage. It carries the information for the production of infectious particles.

(2) There is only one prophage per bacterial chromosome.

(3) Each specific prophage is always attached to a specific and unique locus of the bacterial chromosome.

(4) The prophage does not, as prophage, express its potentialities: no viral proteins are to be found in a lysogenic bacterium, and of course, no infectious particles.

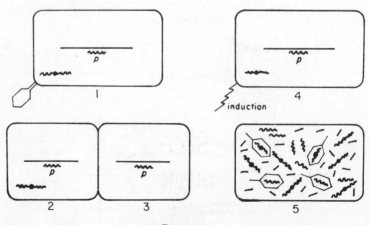

FIGURE 3

Immunity and induction. 1, A lysogenic bacterium is superinfected with a mutant of the homologous virion. 2–3, The prophage *p* divides, the autonomous genome of the superinfecting phage does not divide. 4–5, If the superinfected bacterium is induced, both prophages and the superinfecting mutant enter the vegetative phase. ⋀⋀⋀ prophage (*p*) or corresponding autonomous *DNA*, ⋀⋀ ● ⋀⋀, *DNA* of homologous superinfecting phage.

During the vegetative phase, the viral genome multiplies at its own pace; it duplicates every 2 or 3 min. The prophage of a lysogenic bacterium duplicates together with the bacterial chromosome, once in each generation, the length of which is determined by the bacterial species, and the nature of the environment, etc. Thus during the vegetative phase the phage genome is autonomous, whereas in a lysogenic bacterium, as prophage, it behaves as if it were a bacterial gene. How is it possible that one and the same structure exhibits such a dual behaviour? Why is it sometimes subject to the bacterial system of control, why does it sometimes escape this control? In order to provide an answer it is necessary to consider first immunity, then induction and finally lysogenization.

Immunity.—Thanks to the presence of the prophage, the lysogenic bacterium is endowed with the so-called immunity. A lysogenic bacterium perpetuates a prophage A. It is now superinfected by a mutant A' of the homologous virion. The genetic material of the infecting virion A' penetrates into the lysogenic bacterium. The vegetative phase, however, is not initiated, viral functions are not expressed, phage proteins are not produced. Moreover, the superinfecting genetic material of phage A' does not multiply and is diluted out in the course of bacterial multiplication. It behaves as an inert particle. Immunity is specific. A bacteriophage B, not genetically related to bacteriophage A can multiply vegetatively in the lysogenic bacterium, just as if prophage A were not present. It is as if a specific repressor exists in the cytoplasm of the lysogenic bacterium which blocks specifically the initiation of the vegetative phase of the homologous phage only.

Induction.—The probability for a lysogenic bacterium to produce infectious particles spontaneously varies with the strains from 10^{-2} to 10^{-7} per generation. In some strains, called inducible, the production of bacteriophage can be induced at will in practically the whole population.

An inducible lysogenic bacterium exposed to an inducing agent such as ultraviolet light continues to grow for about an hour and then lyses, each bacterium liberating some 100 infectious particles. This is most extraordinary. A bacterium lives in harmony with its prophage which behaves as if it were a normal bacterial gene. And suddenly, the vegetative phase of the bacteriophage is initiated, the lysogenic bacterium produces bacteriophage and dies. The problem of the control of viral development is thus posed in the most dramatic way.

Bacteria exhibit sexual processes. When male and female bacteria are mixed, they conjugate and the male injects its chromosome into the female. The prophage λ of *Escherichia coli* K 12 is located on the bacterial chromosome close to one of the genes controlling the utilization of galactose which, after conjugation, enters into the female at about the 25th minute.

If both male and female are lysogenic, nothing abnormal happens. If the female only is lysogenic, nothing happens either. But if a lysogenic male mates with a non-lysogenic female, the outcome is quite different. As soon as the prophage attached to the chromosome of the lysogenic male has penetrated into the non-lysogenic female the vegetative phase is initiated, bacteriophage particles are produced and the female is lysed. Thus, phage development is induced when, as a consequence of conjugation, an inducible prophage penetrates into a non-lysogenic bacterium. This is 'zygotic induction'.

These data are again consistent with the hypothesis that, in the lysogenic male bacterium, the expression of the viral functions is blocked by a cytoplasmic repressor. When the prophage of the lysogenic male enters the non-lysogenic female, repression ceases because the cytoplasm of the female is devoid of repressor, and viral functions are expressed.

The antibiotic chloramphenicol is known to block the synthesis of proteins. If bacteria conjugate in the presence of chloramphenicol, zygotic induction fails to take place in a large fraction of the zygotes. It could well be that the viral function necessary for the onset of the vegetative phase is the synthesis of a protein. This hypothesis will be discussed later. If the interpretation is correct, it should apply to infection and lysogenization.

Lysogenization.—A non-lysogenic bacterium infected by a temperate phage may, as already stated, either produce infectious particles and lyse, or become lysogenic. The fraction of the infected bacteria which will become lysogenic

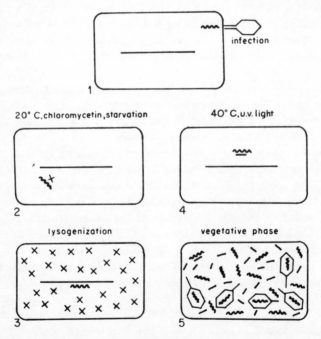

FIGURE 4

Evolution of an infected non-lysogenic bacterium. 1, Infection. 2, The synthesis of a repressor is the primary event and the bacterium (3) is lysogenized. 4, The primary event is the synthesis of a protein and the vegetative phase is initiated. ⌇⌇⌇ phage *DNA*, ——— phage proteins, × repressor.

varies from less than 1% to more than 99%. The fate of the bacterium/phage system depends on the genetic constitution of the temperate bacteriophage, and for a given phage, on extrinsic factors. For example, a high temperature (40° C), favours the establishment of the lytic cycle, whereas a low temperature (20° C), or the addition of chloramphenicol which blocks protein synthesis, favours lysogenization. The extrinsic factors act only during the first 7 min following infection. After the 7th minute, the decision has been made and cannot be modified: something irreversible has happened. What is the nature of this primary determining event?

One hypothesis accounts for all the data. If the primary event is the synthesis of a protein, the vegetative phase is initiated and the process is, from now on, irreversible: more proteins will be synthesised, the phage genome will multiply and virions will finally be manufactured. If the primary event is the production of a repressor, the synthesis of the protein and the expression of other viral potentialities are blocked and the vegetative phase cannot be initiated. The phage genome attaches itself to its chromosomal receptor and the bacterium becomes lysogenic. What is the nature of the repressor? The antibiotic mitomycin which blocks the synthesis of *DNA* induces the development of the prophage. Thus the repressor could be a nucleic acid.

In last analysis the agents favouring the lysogenic response would be those which block the synthesis of the primary vegetative protein, and thus increase the probability that a repressor is produced first. The agents which favour the lytic response would be those which block the synthesis of a repressor and thus increase the probability that the primary vegetative protein is manufactured first. The inducing agents would act by blocking the synthesis of a labile repressor with a short half-life, thus allowing the expression of viral vegetative functions.

VIRAL FUNCTIONS AS AFFECTED BY MUTATIONS

The genetic material of a phage may undergo mutations affecting various functions such as inducibility, the power to lysogenize, virulence and the vegetative development. The study of these mutants has provided useful data concerning viral functions and a few of them will be discussed.

Mutations Affecting Inducibility.—The wild type of phage λ is inducible with u.v. [ultraviolet] light. A mutant was discovered which has lost its original inducibility with u.v. light. This mutant is, however, sensitive to zygotic induction and is therefore called 'semi-inducible.' Double lysogenic strains can be obtained which carry two prophages: an inducible and a semi-inducible. When these strains are irradiated with u.v. light, neither of the bacteriophages develops. In the presence of the semi-inducible prophage λ, the inducible one cannot be induced. The semi-inducible mutation is dominant.

When a bacterium carrying the inducible prophage is irradiated with u.v. light, the vegetative phase is initiated. This inducing effect can be suppressed

TABLE 3

*Position of Inductive, Semi-inductive and Non-inductive Phages
towards Inducing Agents and Interpretative Hypotheses*

	Inducibility		Interpretations	
			Repressor	
	By u.v.	Zygotic	Liability	Affinity for operator
inducible	+	+	+ + +	+
semi-inducible	o	+	+ +	+ +
non-inducible	o	o	+	+ + +

by superinfection with the semi-inducible phage. Three hypotheses can account for these data: (1) the semi-inducible bacteriophage produces more repressor than the wild type, (2) it produces an altered repressor which could, for example, be more stable, (3) it produces a repressor possessing a higher affinity for the genetic material of the bacteriophage.

Mutations Affecting the Power to Lysogenize.—The ability of a given phage to lysogenize a bacterium under a fixed set of conditions can be modified by mutations. Some mutants of a temperate phage are unable to lysogenize. Whereas an infection by one category of such mutants ends in bacterial lysis, a double infection sometimes ends in lysogenization. Some mutants therefore can complement each other. Lysogenization obviously involves a sequence of steps and the genetic information for the completion of the different functions involved does not need to be carried by the same genome.

Mutations Affecting Virulence.—Lysogenic bacteria are immune towards some of the bacteriophage mutants unable to lysogenize. These mutants are therefore repressible, that is sensitive to the repressor, and it is tempting to suppose that the mutation has affected only the ability to manufacture the repressor. These repressible mutants can give rise to a more extreme type, unable to lysogenize, and, moreover, in contrast to their ancestor, able to develop in a lysogenic bacterium carrying the original prophage. It is as if they had become *insensitive to the repressor* produced by the prophage.

In the evolution of a temperate bacteriophage towards virulence, two steps

TABLE 4

A Temperate Phage and Its Mutants Leading to Virulence

	Bacteriophage		
	Normal temperate	'Clear' mutants	Virulent mutants
ability to lysogenize	+	o	o
ability to develop in a lysogenic bacterium	o	o	+
repressor { production of	+	o	o
repressor { sensitivity to	+	+	o

have thus been recognized. The first is the loss of ability to produce a repressor. The second is the loss of the sensitivity to the repressor.

It has been proposed that the prophage does not enter the vegetative phase because it is subject to the action of a repressor which blocks one primary function necessary to initiate the vegetative phase, and consequently the expression of all potential viral functions. If this hypothesis is correct, the virulent mutant, insensitive to the repressor, which does multiply autonomously, should be able to initiate the vegetative development of the otherwise repressed prophage. If a lysogenic bacterium is infected with a virulent non-repressible phage, genetically related to the prophage, the prophage does enter the vegetative phase. The non-repressible phage has introduced the hitherto repressed function.

Mutations Affecting the Vegetative Phase.—In a normal inducible lysogenic population, any bacterium is potentially able to produce bacteriophage and will do so and lyse, if induced. In some strains of lysogenic bacteria, all bacteria lyse after induction, but only one out of 10^5 or so will produce virions. The absence of bacteriophage production is due to a genetic defect of the prophage. Defective lysogenics belong to different categories. In some of them the defect has not been identified. They manufacture the proteins which have been looked for and the genetic material multiplies. In other defectives the synthesis of one or more phage proteins does not take place, the genetic material does not multiply autonomously.

It appears that though the vegetative phase is characterized by a series of sequential events, some have to be completed before a following one can be initiated. This conclusion is reinforced by the observation that superinfection of some *defective* lysogenic bacteria by a *normal* genetically related phage determines the vegetative multiplication of the otherwise blocked defective phage genome.

In a defective prophage, the capacity to multiply as an autonomous unit may be missing. But the genetic alteration does not affect the ability to multiply as

TABLE 5

Some Defective Lysogenic Bacteria

	I	2			
autonomous multiplication of the genome	+	o (A)	o (A)	o	o
synthesis of endolysine	+	o	o	+	+
synthesis of the tail protein controlling adsorption	+	o	+	o	+
synthesis of the protein controlling host range	+	o (A)	+	o (A)	o
ability to lysogenize	+	o	o	o	o
production of virions after superinfection with a normal phage	+	+	+	+	

A = possible with the assistance of a superinfecting normal bacteriophage.
(From the data of F. Jacob, C. R. Fuerst and E. L. Wollman.)

prophage, that is as an integrated unit. This conclusion poses the problem of the interrelation between bacterial and viral functions.

INTERACTIONS OF CELLULAR AND VIRAL REPRODUCTIVE FUNCTIONS AT THE GENETIC LEVEL

Cellular Control of the Reproduction of a Virus.—It is often stated in textbooks or reviews that viruses are able to multiply in a cell only because they are not submitted to the regulating mechanisms of their host. This certainly does not apply always to those mechanisms which control the replication of the genetic material.

In a lysogenic bacterium the genetic material of the phage is attached to the bacterial chromosome. It behaves as if it were a bacterial gene, since it duplicates in harmony with the chromosome.

We know that the autonomous multiplication of the phage genome requires the expression of a series of functions. How is the replication of the bacterial chromosome controlled?

In a cell, in a micro-organism, all the chromosomes divide at the right time and also at the same time. Chromosomal multiplication is in harmony with cellular growth and reproduction. Some system of regulation must be at work which controls the duplication of the genetic material.*

In a lysogenic bacterium the functions necessary for the autonomous reproduction of the phage genome are not expressed and the prophage nevertheless multiplies. The prophage is obviously subject to the unknown mechanism which controls the duplication of the bacterial chromosome.

When a lysogenic bacterium is infected with an homologous phage, the genetic material of this phage does not multiply. The autonomous phage genome is not subject to the action of cellular control systems whereas the prophage, the integrated phage genome, is subject to this system. The logical conclusion is that the prophage divides in synchrony with the bacterial chromosome because it is attached to it. Thus the behaviour of one and the same entity, namely, the genetic material of a virus, can differ according to its position in the bacterium.

The conclusion that attachment or binding of two structures may play a determining role in their functional interrelations is reinforced when one considers related situations.

In a bacterium, some elements called episomes, such as the sexual element *F,* are either free in the cytoplasm, or attached to the bacterial chromosome. When free they multiply autonomously. When attached they multiply in harmony with the chromosome. The chromosome/episome system behaves as a unit.

Sometimes the genetic material of the phage is not attached to the bacterial

---

* The genetic material has a dual function: (*a*) production of *RNA* messengers, (*b*) replication. The *RNA* messengers could be produced on the *DNA* double helix. But replication necessarily implies a separation of the two chains for which a specific disjunctive function could be needed.

chromosome but to the autonomous sexual episome. When this happens, the prophage multiplies in harmony with the episome. Thus, two otherwise independent structures, when bound to each other, may behave as a unit.

In all the cases discussed up to now it is the virus which is subject to the regulating mechanisms of its host. As will be seen next, a cellular gene can be under viral command.

Viral Control of the Reproduction of a Gene.—The prophage is attached to a specific receptor site of the bacterial chromosome. A part of the receptor of prophage λ is the gene which carries the information for galactokinase, the enzyme which phosphorylates galactose. It happens that this gene 'galactokinase' can be exchanged with a part of phage λ. The gene galactokinase is now part of phage λ: and when this phage multiplies vegetatively, the gene galactokinase multiplies too.

In one case, the prophage behaves as if it were a bacterial gene. In the other case, a bacterial gene behaves as if it were a viral gene. All this means that, so far as replication is concerned, a given genetic material whether cellular or viral, and the 'foreign' structure it may carry, constitute a unit subject to one and the same regulating mechanism.

Before any further discussion it is necessary to summarize the current views concerning the regulating mechanisms of the cell.

REGULATING MECHANISMS OF THE CELL

Cellular growth and multiplication depend on the balanced completion of a large set of reactions.

(1) A series of enzymes secure energy in the proper form.

(2) Other enzymes manufacture the amino acid and nucleic bases, the building blocks of macromolecular compounds.

(3) A series of specific templates is responsible for the assemblage of the building blocks into the specific sequences, proteins and nucleic acids. This is *diataxy*.*

The cell has to cope with the variation of its environment and has to adjust its enzymic equipment according to its needs. And the machine must be regulated in such a way that each one of the four nucleic bases, and each one of the

---

* Biosyntheses comprise two different types of process. The synthesis of building blocks, amino acids or nucleic bases, which involve only enzymes and the manufacture of proteins and nucleic acids which requires a template, the ribosome/messenger system.

This process is often referred to as *patternization* which I had utilized. A British friend who read the manuscript of this lecture expressed a profound reluctance at the idea of seeing this word printed in the *Proceedings of the Royal Society*. I was told that the verb 'to patternize' does not exist and that patternization is most horrible. Proteins and nucleic acids are sequences, but if a sequence is necessarily a pattern, a pattern is not necessarily a sequence and 'sequentialization' sounds as ugly as patternization. Finally, I was urged to propose a new term, hence *diataxy*, from the Greek διαταττεῖν (*diatattein*), to put in order. Diataxy, diatactic, refer to the ordering of building blocks into specific sequences.

twenty amino acids is manufactured in the right amount and proportion. More-over, a balance has to be maintained between the desoxyribonucleic acid, the ribonucleic acid and the proteins, for an imbalance means waste and disease.

How does the genetic material know what happens in the cytoplasm and in the environment? How are the orders transmitted from one molecule to an-other? Let us consider, as a model, the synthesis of tryptophan. The information for the synthesis of each specific enzyme responsible for one specific reaction in the chain of biosynthesis is contained in the genetic material, that is in *DNA*.

So far as we know each structural gene produces a specific ribonucleic messen-ger which becomes attached to a non-specific cytoplasmic ribosome (Gros, Watson & Wally, 1960). This ribosome/messenger system is the enzyme-forming machine. It manufactures one or a very few molecules of protein and the *RNA* messenger is then destroyed. Enzymes are thus manufactured, perform their functions and tryptophan is synthesized. If all the tryptophan is utilized, enzymes continue to be synthesized and to work. If an excess of tryptophan is produced, two regulating mechanisms are set in action.

(1) Tryptophan inhibits the *activity* of the first enzyme and the functioning of the whole chain is thus brought to a standstill.

(2) Tryptophan inhibits the synthesis of the enzymes. This is a complex process. A specific regulating gene produces an apo-repressor. Tryptophan acts as a co-repressor which combines with this apo-repressor and a complete re-pressor is thus formed. The repressor acts on an operator gene which controls all the linked structural genes involved in the synthesis of tryptophan enzymes. When no repressor is present the operator gene is in position *go*: the structural genes manufacture their *RNA* messengers and enzymes are synthesized. When a repressor is present the operator gene is in position *stop*: no messengers are produced and no enzymes are synthesized.

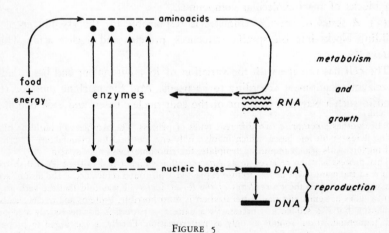

FIGURE 5

General scheme of metabolism, growth and reproduction.

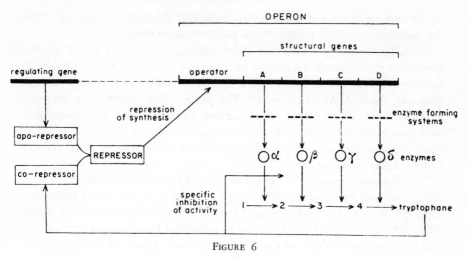

FIGURE 6

The regulating mechanism of the cell. (From the data of F. Jacob, J. Monod *et al.*). The existence of an operator gene in the tryptophan system is for the time being hypothetical.

Thus the phenotypic expression of a structural gene, which is essentially the manufacture of an enzyme, is subject to an elaborate regulative feedback mechanism. It involves a regulating gene, an operator gene, a few structural genes, a ribonucleic messenger, a ribosome, the end product of enzymic activity and a repressor.

The cell is an integrated system of interdependent structures and functions. Each enzyme or group of enzymes possesses its own regulating device. The regulation of the cell as a whole is the result of the interaction of all the individual regulating systems. These regulating systems are essentially genetic, and consequently can undergo mutations. In a bacterium, as a result of a mutation, an operator gene can become insensitive to the repressor. Virulent phage mutants were mentioned which are insensitive towards the repressor produced by the prophage. This loss or repressibility seems to be due to a mutation of a viral operator gene, which in fact, has been localized on the phage genome.

Viruses are strict intracellular parasites and we have already learned that the prophage is subject to the mysterious system which commands the duplication of its host's chromosome. We have to go further and try to learn what the position of the virus is towards the other cellular regulating mechanisms.

BACTERIUM AND BACTERIOPHAGE

Co-operation.—The bacteriophage makes use of the enzymic machinery of its host. More precisely it utilizes the energy and the activated building blocks synthesized by the bacterium. In a bacterium the sequential ordering of the amino acids takes place on a ribonucleic messenger attached to a ribosome. The first question is: where are the phage proteins manufactured?

It has been recently shown that *RNA* messengers produced by the genetic material of the phage are captured by bacterial ribosomes. Each hybrid ribosome/ messenger system produces one—or a very few—molecules of phage protein, (Brenner, Jacob & Meselson 1961). The phage *RNA* messenger is then degraded whereas the ribosomal *RNA* remains intact. Thus the production of a viral protein depends on the intimate association between a viral and a bacterial structure. This was an unsuspected type of co-operation between two foreign entities at the molecular level.

The ribosome seems to be devoid of an independent functional regulating system. Its activity depends: (*a*) on the availability of the *RNA* messenger coming from the structural genes, (*b*) on the availability of activated amino acids. Both factors are in the last analysis controlled by a feedback mechanism. Are viral functions subject to the cellular feedback systems of control and do viruses themselves possess such a feedback system?

The Problem of Phage-controlled Feedback Systems.—The virulent bacteriophage destroys the chromosome of its host and thereby ruins the whole genetic feedback system. The temperate bacteriophage does not alter the bacterial chromosome and the bacterial feedback system continues to work. It controls the synthesis of the essential metabolites utilized by the phage, and, as a consequence, viral reproduction. This is, however, an overall regulation and not a specific regulation of the individual functions of the phage.

The bacterial feedback mechanism controls enzyme synthesis because the product of enzymic activity participates in the formation of a repressor. A theoretical possibility exists that, in the phage T2 which manufactures 5-hydroxymethyl cytosine, the synthesis of the responsible enzymes is controlled by a phage-made repressor system. It is, however, difficult to conceive of a feedback system dealing with those proteins of the head and of the tail which are devoid of enzymic activity. It has been stated again and again that the onset of the vegetative phase can be blocked by a specific phage repressor. The current hypothesis is that when this repressor is present the synthesis of an essential protein cannot take place. But when this protein has been manufactured, the whole set of vegetative functions is initiated, and the process continues unabated until the bacterium lyses.

It should not be forgotten that the production of each of the phage proteins during the vegetative phase is accurately timed. It is as if a sequential inductive system was at work.*

---

* After an infection, the phage genome produces *RNA* templates and viral proteins are synthesized. The replication of viral *DNA* starts after a 'negative period' of a few minutes. If only those phages containing 5-hydroxymethyl cytosine were considered the conclusion could be reached that the delay corresponds to the synthesis of the new base. But the delay is the same for the conventional phages containing cytosine. Moreover, in a bacterium infected by a temperate phage the synthesis of bacterial *DNA* continues; this excludes the synthesis of deoxynucleotides as the cause of the 'negative period'.

INTERACTIONS BETWEEN CELLULAR AND VIRAL FUNCTIONS

The analysis of the interactions between cell and virus should reveal some other aspects of viral functions. A non-lysogenic *Salmonella* produces a given somatic antigen 10. If lysogenized with a given phage *epsilon* 15, it stops producing the antigen 10, and starts to produce another antigen 15. The mechanism by which a phage can control the synthesis of a bacterial antigen is still a mystery. A possible hypothesis is that one of the phage genes carries the information for the synthesis of antigen 15. In any case the virus has introduced a new function into its host, which has become modified.

Typically, when a virus infects a cell, the vegetative phase is initiated and virions are produced. The study of a few animal cell/virus systems will disclose to what extent the expression of viral functions may depend on the host cell.

The influenza virus develops normally in the allantoic cells of the chorioallantoic membrane of the chick embryo. The viral genetic material multiplies to viral proteins, the *S* antigen and the haemagglutinin are synthesized, and virions are finally formed. In the chorionic cells virions are not produced. The manufacture of virions is controlled by the nature of the differentiation undergone by the cell. The responsible process is not known, but the viral development is clearly controlled by the host cell. More complex cases of interactions will now be briefly analyzed.

Let us consider first the rabbit infected with Shope's papilloma virus. No viral antigens are detectable in the cell of the basal layer of the skin and the virus perhaps exists in the form of its genetic material only. Whatever the situation may be, the virus is responsible for an increased rate of cellular proliferation, hence the papilloma. The multiplication of the basal cells results in non-dividing keratohyaline cells. The first signs of the presence of a virus are abnormal structures in their nucleolus. It is as if the alteration correlated with cellular differentiation were responsible for the initiation of the vegetative development of the virus. Virions are finally produced, but only in the cotton-tail rabbit. In the domestic rabbit, the great majority of the keratohyaline cells produces only viral antigens and no virions.

Here the virus modifies the cell and the genetical and phenotypical constitution of the cell control viral development. In the case of the Polyoma virus the interaction is even more complex.

The fibroblasts of the mouse infected by the Polyoma virus either produce virions and die, or do not produce virions, survive and multiply. These surviving cells perpetuate the potentiality to produce viral antigens and infective particles but this potentiality is expressed in only a small fraction of the cells. Moreover, the surviving cells are immune towards superinfection by the homologous Polyoma virus. The viral genetic material might be multiplied in the mouse cells as a provirus, and it could be that the expression of the viral functions is blocked by a repressor responsible for immunity.

A similar situation exists in the hamster. Here also the cells which survive an infection by the Polyoma virus are immune and they perpetuate the potentiality to synthesize viral antigens. But they never produce a virion. The genome of the virus might be present in the hamster cells in some altered form, which could be a defective provirus. The important fact is that, whether mouse or hamster cells are concerned, those cells which have survived an infection by the Polyoma virus are malignant.

When the fibroblasts of the chick are infected by the virus of the Rous sarcoma, the virus enters the vegetative phase and virions are produced. The development of the virus is not lethal, perhaps because it is limited by some yet mysterious regulating process. Whatever the case might be the fibroblasts survive and are malignant.

In the case of the Rous sarcoma virus the malignant change takes place in a cell in which viral functions are expressed. The example of the Polyoma virus shows, however, that a cell may be malignant in the absence of any sign of vegetative viral development.

Finally, a last case of interactions between cellular and viral functions should be mentioned. Under certain conditions infected animal cells produce a protein called interferon which depresses or prevents viral development. Cellular populations treated with interferon become unable to produce virions, or the viral production is greatly decreased. This is true whether or not the infecting virus is genetically related to the original virus. Interferon acts by inhibiting the oxidative phosphorylation of the host cell. It seems as if the genetic information for its synthesis pre-exists in the chromosome of the cell, and that its production is either considerably enhanced or perhaps even initiated by the viral infection. Whether or not interferon intervenes in the regulation of normal cellular function is not known. Anyhow, as the result of a viral infection, a protein may be produced by the host cell which blocks a cellular function necessary for viral development.

CONCLUSION

As previously stated, my ambition was to describe some aspects of the molecular dynamics of viral functions. Now that the lecture has reached its end, I would like to sum up the main conclusions.

Viruses being reproduced from their genetic material only, it is a truism to state that the viral genome must carry the information, the structural genes, for the synthesis of the specific viral proteins. As viral functions can be blocked by specific viral inhibitors the viral genome has to contain also regulating genes and perhaps an operator gene.

The life cycle of a virus involves a sequence of developmental functions, as does the morphogenesis of an animal. Viruses being strict intracellular parasites, the cell as a whole necessarily controls the viral life cycle.

As a result of a viral infection, new cell/virus systems sometimes emerge. The analysis of such integrated systems shows that cellular mechanisms can control viral functions and that viral mechanisms can control cellular functions. It is anyhow essential to recall that the activity and behaviour of a given molecule may depend on its association with another molecule and that cellular and viral structures may form hybrid organelles which behave as units. To disclose the intimate structural and functional secrets of these hybrid entities is a task of the utmost importance for those who, as a result of the modern trend of science towards unification, have, willingly or not, become molecular biologists.

MICROBIAL BIOCHEMISTRY

Proteins, when digested either by acids or by enzymes, yield amino acids. Individual microbial proteins, such as those from animal and plant tissues, vary considerably in amino acid composition, but in general the 21 common amino acids—glycine, alanine, valine, leucine, isoleucine, serine, threonine, cysteine, cystine, methionine, aspartic acid, asparagine, glutamic acid, glutamine, lysine, arginine, proline, histidine, phenylalanine, tyrosine, and tryptophan—or at least a wide assortment of these, are found to be present.

For protein synthesis, hence growth, to take place, all the amino acids characteristic of the protein being synthesized must be simultaneously present (or capable of being made on the spot in adequate amount). In most mammalian species, most of these amino acids can be made *in situ,* from the corresponding organic (keto-) acids (formed by metabolism of carbohydrates), or transformed one into another. For growing humans, the following amino acids cannot be synthesized in adequate amounts and must be present in the diet: lysine, tryptophan, phenylalanine, threonine, valine, methionine, leucine, and isoleucine. Most of these are present in normal diet, but lysine, tryptophan, threonine, and methionine may occasionally be absent or deficient, requiring dietary supplementation. Usually amino acids are synthesized by multistep metabolic pathways, each step being enzyme-catalyzed. Mutational loss of capacity to synthesize one of the enzymes requisite for a chain reaction (metabolic pathway) is sufficient to block the synthesis of that amino acid; in such a case, the amino acid, if essential for the growth of the bacterium, must be supplied, directly or indirectly, in the culture medium.

Most gram-positive bacteria and some gram-negative organisms are auxotrophs; i.e., they require the presence of at least some of the preformed amino acids in their culture medium. When so supplied, some of the amino acids, such as lysine and tyrosine, appear to enter the bacterial cell by simple diffusion. Others, such as histidine and glutamic acid, require special biochemical processes to facilitate their entrance into the bacterial cell and their diffusion within the cell.

Much can be learned about the individual functions of the several amino acids by rearing bacteria in chemically defined media, supplying all but one of the amino acids required for growth. For instance, in studies on *Streptococcus faecalis,* valine is one of the 12 amino acids essential for growth and cell multiplication. When *S. faecalis* is grown on liquid media containing ample quantities of all the other requisite nutrients, with valine present in small (growth-limiting) amounts, the bacterial cells will grow and divide until the valine in the medium is exhausted. After the valine is completely exhausted, the cultures will *appear* to continue their growth: turbidity of the cell suspension will increase, as if cell multiplication were actually taking place. However, careful studies of the number of cells present will show that the bacterial cells no longer divide and cell number remains stationary. The bacterial cell walls, on the other hand, continue for a time to increase in thickness, accounting for the enlargement of the cells and the continuing increase in turbidity of the culture. Apparently valine, though necessary for the synthesis of some of the essential proteins of the streptococcal cell, is not an essential component of the cell wall, and cell-wall "growth" may continue even after the valine in the culture medium is exhausted. Threonine, likewise essential for some of the bacterial proteins but not a component of the wall, behaves in the same fashion.

Dr. Toennies, a biochemist famous for his work on bacterial nutrition, is Research Professor of Microbial Physiology in the Department of Microbiology, Temple University School of Medicine, Philadelphia. Most of the work reported in the following paper was done while he was Head of the Department of General Biochemistry in the Institute for Cancer Research, Philadelphia.

From *Yale Sci. Mag.*,
38:20–22, 25, 1963.

AMINO ACIDS
IN BACTERIAL GROWTH AND DEVELOPMENT

A Study of Production of Anatomically Modified Cells Offers Insight into the Differentiation of Cells, and the Specific Synthetic Processes Underlying the Formation of Cell Components

BY GERRIT TOENNIES

Among the infinite variety of existing microbial forms one finds a major class of bacteria which is of special biochemical interest, and which is found in the normal intestinal flora of higher animals: the lactic acid-forming *Streptococci*. They are round bodies about one-thousandth of a millimeter in diameter, which weigh about one one hundred million billionth as much as a man. They resemble man in that, among the twenty-odd different kinds of protein building-blocks known as amino acids, they can synthesize only those amino acids of simpler design. Since all of the amino acids are needed for protein synthesis, both man and streptococcus depend on outside sources for the more complicated ones. While man and coccus resemble each other in amino acid requirements they differ profoundly with regard to power economy. Streptococci degrade simple sugars with the aid of enzymes to lactic acid:

$$
\begin{array}{ccc}
\begin{array}{c}
\text{H H H H H H} \\
\text{C--C--C--C--C--CH} \\
\text{O O O O O O} \\
\text{H H H H H}
\end{array}
&
\rightarrow
&
\begin{array}{c}
\text{H H} \\
\text{2 HC--C--CO} \\
\text{H O O} \\
\text{H H}
\end{array}
\quad + \quad \text{Energy}
\\
\text{Sugar} & & \text{Lactic Acid}
\end{array}
$$

This process, which actually involves many intermediate steps, is known as lactic acid fermentation, and is the principal energy source of the cocci.

Sugar can also supply the energy needs of man, but in this case the enzymatic process resembles ordinary combustion in its end results, in that it leads to carbon dioxide and water instead of lactic acid:

$$C_6H_{12}O_6 + 6 O_2 \rightarrow 6 CO_2 + 6 H_2O + \text{Energy}$$

The possession of the mechanism for the complete 'combustion' of sugar to CO_2 and H_2O with the help of the oxygen of the air enables the respiring organisms to obtain from a sugar molecule 10 or more times as much energy as the more simply equipped fermenting organisms. In other words, lactic acid is a product of *incomplete* sugar degradation which still contains the major part of the potential energy of sugar unutilized.

In order to avoid complexities, we shall present, from the array of more than 20 different amino acids which enter into protein construction, just one example of a "simple" and one example of a "complicated" amino acid.

A "simple" amino acid is here defined as one which can be obtained with the aid of one or very few enzymes from compounds which occur as intermediates in the energy-yielding degradation of sugars. An example is alanine which is easily visualized as a derivative of lactic acid:

$$
\begin{array}{ccccc}
\text{H H} & & & \text{H H} & \\
\text{HC--C--CO} & + & \text{NH}_3 & \rightarrow & \text{HC--C--CO} & + & \text{H}_2\text{O} \\
\text{H O O} & & & \text{H N O} & \\
\text{H H} & & & \text{H}_2\text{ H} & \\
\end{array}
$$

$$
\quad \text{Lactic Acid} \qquad \text{Ammonia} \qquad \text{Alanine}
$$

The amino acids (protein building blocks) differ from the compounds of carbohydrate (sugar) metabolism by the presence of nitrogen, in addition to the carbon, hydrogen and oxygen atoms of the carbohydrates. The resulting amino ($-NH_2$) group is basic, and is capable of joining with the acidic ($-COOH$) group of another amino acid in a neutral "peptide" linkage which represents the backbone linkage of protein molecules:

$$
-NH_2 \;+\; HOOC- \;\rightarrow\; -NH \cdot CO- \;+\; H_2O
$$

$$
\text{peptide}
$$

All amino acids contain the grouping $HOOC-\overset{|}{C}-NH_2$ shown above in the case of alanine. The existing two dozen different varieties are characterized by different molecular configurations in the place of $-CH_3$ of alanine. If we designate these different configurations as R_1, R_2, R_3, etc., we can schematically describe a protein molecule as:

$$
\begin{array}{cccc}
R_1 & R_2 & R_3 & R_n \\
| & | & | & | \\
H_2N-C-CO-NH-C-CO-NH-C-CO \ldots NH-C-COOH \\
H & H & H & H
\end{array}
$$

When we realize that there are some twenty "R" forms available, that several hundred amino acids combine to make one protein molecule, and that the R's may be lined up in any conceivable sequence of alternation or repetition, we see that the number of conceivable protein species is immense, and it becomes plausible to consider this immensity as the basis of the vast variety of living forms.

An extreme example of a "complicated" amino acid would be tryptophan:

$$
\begin{array}{c}
\text{CH} \qquad \text{NH} \\
\text{HC} \qquad \text{C} \qquad \text{CH} \\
\text{HC} \qquad \text{CH} \text{---} \text{C} \\
\text{C} \qquad \text{HOOC} \text{--} \text{C} \text{--} \text{NH}_2 \\
\text{H} \qquad \qquad \text{H}
\end{array}
$$

More than a dozen different enzymes are probably involved in assembling this show-piece of molecular architecture. An enzyme may be likened to an assembly line worker endowed with the ability of performing one specific step of a biochemical program. Each enzyme is itself a protein molecule which has to be assembled on the basis of directives issued by the genetic control center of the cell, and which draws upon the spatial, material and energy resources of the cells. It is not surprising, therefore, that in the design of the more complex living forms nature has found it expedient to omit machinery for the production of those parts which can be obtained ready made from other organisms. The more complicated amino acids, commonly referred to as the essential ones, are examples of this tendency. The higher animal has dispensed with the dozens of enzymes involved in their synthesis, and, therefore, needs these amino acids in its food. Plants, which do possess the large array of these enzymes, supply the essential amino acids, either directly or via the flesh of other, herbivorous, animals.

NUTRITION AND ANATOMY OF A STREPTOCOCCUS

Streptococcus faecalis is a microorganism which will not grow (multiply) when any one of 12 different amino acids is absent from an otherwise adequate medium. Let us imagine 12 different "basal" media, each lacking one of the 12 essential amino acids. The amount of growth which can be supported by each of these media will obviously depend on the amount of the missing amino acid which one might add to it. The amounts of the different amino acids needed as protein building blocks differ, but identical growth responses may be expected if each of the 12 different media is supplemented with the appropriate amount of the missing amino acid. In order to determine the composition of actively growing bacteria, a growing culture is rapidly chilled, the bacteria are collected by centrifuging them down, and after thorough washing are dried. By suitable analytical methods it is found that 100 milligrams dry weight (about 1/300 ounce) of rapidly growing cells of *Streptococcus faecalis* contain the amounts of essential amino acids shown in Table 1.

Accordingly, if one-liter portions of each of the 12 deficient media (which

TABLE I

Essential Amino Acids in 100 mg. Rapidly Growing
Streptococcus faecalis Cells

	milligrams		milligrams
Tryptophan	0.7	Arginine	2.8
Histidine	1.1	Isoleucine	3.4
Methionine	1.6	Valine	3.7
Tyrosine	1.8	Leucine	3.9
Phenylalanine	2.3	Lysine	5.9
Threonine	2.7	Glutamic acid	8.3

in each case contain all other nutrients in large excess) were supplemented
with the listed amount of the corresponding amino acid, the resulting bacterial
growth may in each case be expected to be limited to 100 mg. of dried bacterial
substance. Actually, in almost each case that was investigated, substantially
more bacterial substance was obtained; a finding which demanded explanation.
It was known that in higher animals (mice or rats) analogous experiments tend
to give the opposite result: essential amino acids are not only utilized as protein
building blocks, but are in part converted into other compounds or completely
oxidized as cellular "fuel." What happens in streptococci may conveniently be
explained with the aid of two examples. Fig. 1 describes experiments in which
the medium contains 3.7 mg. valine per liter in one case, and 2.7 mg. threonine
in the other case, with all other nutrients being present in excess. The two
curves show how on continued incubation the bacterial concentration increases
in the two inoculated cultures. According to calculation, as outlined, growth
should cease at the level of 100 mg. dry weight per liter. Actually, the final

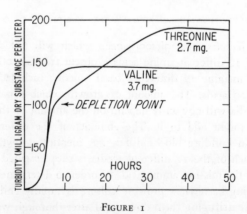

FIGURE I

Growth curves of cultures of *Streptococcus*
faecalis which contain the amounts of valine or
threonine that are found in 100 mg. of cells
collected during the phase of rapid growth
(the first 8-10 hours).

level attained is higher by 45 and 90 per cent, respectively. When during the early, rapid phase of growth consecutive samples of the culture are analyzed, one finds that there is a steady disappearance of the limiting amino acid (valine or threonine) from the liquid medium, and an exactly corresponding increase in the amount of the same amino acid that has become part of the newly formed bacterial substance. The data indicate that at the expected 100 mg. level the limiting amino acid actually has been completely removed from the medium (depletion point). Similar experiments with other essential amino acids showed similar but individually characteristic patterns of growth. While generally the depletion point is followed by further slow growth which has its own character- istics for each amino acid, it was unexpected to find in the experiment with lysine that the turbidity level corresponding to the depletion point was barely attained, and that immediately there followed a steady decrease in turbidity, so that after 20 hours of incubation the medium was again clear.

CELL WALL

As mentioned earlier, bacteria generally has an outer shell, the bacterial cell wall. The wall of *Streptococcus faecalis* and related organisms does not contain any protein, but is constructed of large carbohydrate-like molecules into which a few species of amino acids are built as cross-links or side-chains. The only essential amino acids which participate in the wall structure are glutamic acid and lysine. Accordingly, it seemed possible that upon depletion of an essential amino acid, when no further cellular protein can be formed, synthesis of cell wall substance might continue, provided the depleted amino acid is not among those needed for that process. The formation of additional wall substance may result in "stronger" cells. This "strengthening" of the bacteria by formation of extra wall substance cannot occur if the depleted amino acid is a wall building block, in addition to being a protein building block, as in the case of lysine. It seemed further possible that during the early phase of growth when new cells are continuously formed by the process of half-hourly doubling, the objective of speedy reproduction may best be served by having the wall remain thin and fragile. When reproduction and wall synthesis stops, degradative proc- esses may prevail, or cell-wall-opening processes accompanying cell division may continue, with the result that the existing, tenuously protected cells fall apart. When further wall synthesis is possible, as in the case of valine or threonine depletion, disintegration is prevented by wall reinforcement.

The experimental data show that, when cells are allowed to grow to maximum density after depletion of valine (20 hours) or after depletion of threonine (40 hours), more than half the weight gain achieved is in both cases accounted for by new wall substance, while there is no significant change in the amount of protein present. These findings are in agreement with the notion that, upon depletion of individual amino acids which are essential components of protein but not of wall substance, net protein synthesis must stop but wall synthesis can continue, but they do *not* explain why the gain in substance following depletion of threonine is twice as large, and twice as protracted, as the gain which follows depletion of valine.

CELL MEMBRANE

Modern research has shown that bacterial cells have, in addition to the cell wall, another surrounding shell, the cytoplasmic membrane. Its site is inside the wall, and unlike the rigid and sieve-like structure of the wall, the membrane is flexible and delicate and its small pores control the entry and exit of substances to and from the cytoplasmic interior of the cell. For a fuller understanding of the nature of the different "depletion" cells, knowledge about the membrane seemed essential. Unlike the wall substance the membrane substance, because of its delicate structure, cannot easily be separated and weighed. When cells are broken by "beating" them with glass beads the membrane disintegrates into very minute fragments which resist centrifugation. However, it is possible to obtain specimens of the membrane substance by a milder technique. An enzyme named lysozyme which occurs in the saliva and other secretions of higher animals, has the power to decompose bacterial cell walls and thus to destroy the cells. The bacterial membrane substance, however, is not susceptible to the chemical attack of lysozyme. When bacteria are treated with lysozyme the wall is digested away and as a result of its removal the membrane ruptures and the liquid content of the cell spills out. By careful centrifugation and washing one can now obtain essentially pure membrane substance. The yield is low and variable because much of the membrane material disintegrates even in this mild procedure. It was known that bacterial membrane is relatively rich in phosphorus-containing fatty material (phospholipid), and further investigation showed that in the organism under study (*Streptococcus faecalis*) phospholipid occurs only in the membrane substance, while wall substance and cytoplasm are free of it. This finding made it possible to measure accurately how much membrane substance a bacterial culture contains.

DNA

It seemed important to know if existing cells are merely getting larger or if more cells are formed by division when cell mass increases by 45 and 90 per cent, respectively, after depletion of valine or threonine. Because of technical difficulties a direct answer to this question, by precise counts, has not yet been obtained. However, an indirect answer is available. The heart substance of all living matter is thought to be DNA (deoxyribonucleic acid). DNA is the chemical name for giant molecules, several million times as large as a hydrogen molecule, which, coded through the sequence and frequency of their component parts, contain all the information necessary to define the inherited properties of the species and their individual members.

DNA occurs in bacteria as a compact bundle of molecular threads. In view of these circumstances it is reasonable to postulate that in bacteria also individual cells contain identical DNA packages. A corollary of this postulate is that a cell may get larger without increase in DNA, but that an increase of DNA to twice the usual amount normally entails the division of a cell into two daughter cells. On that basis, then, one may conclude that, in a culture where bacterial substance increases but DNA does not increase, individual cells get larger, but that an increase in the amount of DNA present in a culture is an indication of cellular multiplication. Thus DNA is a substance which can give us information not only about cellular composition but also about cell size and number. It can be determined precisely by chemical methods.

DIFFERENT CELL TYPES

The determinations of DNA and of membrane substance both gave interesting and unexpected information about the nature of the three culture types under investigation. Table 2 summarizes the data. While the percentage of DNA is highest in the threonine depleted culture and lowest in the valine depleted culture, the opposite is true as regards membrane content. To evaluate these results further we will have to recall that bacterial dry weight increases by 45 per cent subsequent to valine depletion and by 90 per cent after the depletion of threonine. Accordingly, the 2.8 mg. of DNA present in rapidly dividing cells at the point of depletion will increase to 3.2 mg. ($= 2.2 \times 1.45$) after depletion of valine, and to 7.8 mg. ($= 4.1 \times 1.90$) after depletion of threonine. Similarly, the 18 mg. of membrane substance existing at the depletion point increase to 41 mg. after valine depletion and to 21 mg. after threonine depletion. The total amounts of wall substance which are present at the three stages of growth are (approximately) 19, 41 and 68 mg. The balance sheet resulting from these calculations is shown in Table 3.

Constancy of the amount of DNA per cell would mean that the cell number

TABLE 2

*Percentages of Deoxyribonucleic Acid and Membrane Substance
Found in Different Culture Types*

	DNA, %	Membrane substance, %
Rapidly dividing culture	2.8	18
Valine-depleted 20 hour culture	2.2	28
Threonine-depleted 40 hour culture	4.1	11

TABLE 3

Balance Sheet Showing Quantitative Changes Following
Depletion of Valine or Threonine

	Dry weight of culture mg	DNA mg	Membrane mg	Wall mg
Rapidly dividing culture at depletion point	100	2.8	18	19
Valine-depleted 20 hour culture	145	3.2	41	41
Threonine-depleted 40 hour culture	190	7.8	21	68

increases by about 14 per cent ($100 \times (3.2 - 2.8)/2.8$) after valine depletion, and by about 180 per cent ($100 \times (7.8 - 2.8/2.8)$) after threonine depletion. We can now draw some tentative conclusions in regard to what happens to cell number and cell weight in these experiments. Studies which involve measurements of turbidity, dry weight and cell number lead to an estimate of approximately 0.25 micromicrograms (trillionths of grams) for the average dry weight of an *S. faecalis* cell during the phase of rapid growth. Accordingly, the one hundred milligrams of bacteria present at the depletion point would consist of 400 billion cells. With the formation of the 20-hour post-valine-depletion cells, which involves an increase of weight to 145 milligrams, cell number would increase to 460 billions, and at the 40-hour post-threonine-depletion stage we would have 190 mg. dry substance and 1120 billion cells. Average cell weight therefore would increase in valine depletion from 0.25 micromicrograms to 0.32, and decrease in threonine depletion to 0.17, so that valine depletion cells would be about one-third larger and threonine depletion cells about one-third smaller than rapidly growing cells.

If, as suggested by DNA data, the volumes are in the ratio of 100:133:67 for the three cell types shown, one can estimate the thickness of the two coats. If one makes the simplifying assumption that the densities (specific gravities) of the different anatomical parts of the living cell do not differ, one obtains a value of 3.5 per cent of the cell diameter for the thickness of both wall and the membrane layer of rapidly growing cells. The calculated thickness increases by 60 and 110 per cent, for wall and membrane respectively, in the valine-depletion cells. It increases by 80 per cent for the wall, but decreases by 20 per cent for the membrane, in the threonine-depletion cells. As a first approximation, then, the data suggest that in the valine-depletion cells the thickness of both wall and membrane tends to double, while in the smaller threonine-depletion cells only the thickness of the wall undergoes such a change. Further research must show if these conclusions are valid. The physiological characteristics of these, and possibly other, cell variants induced by specific one-item nutritional deficiencies, must be studied.

Since net protein synthesis is impossible if one of the essential building stones is missing—as it is during the post-depletion stages of growth—it will also be necessary to elucidate the biochemical mechanisms by which incomplete amino acid complements function in giving rise to the observed changes in cellular composition. Amino acids, individually or in specific combinations, would seem to be capable of promoting such specific synthetic processes as underlie the formation of cell wall, membrane or DNA. One common channel of action of such metabolic control substances in advanced and primitive organisms may be that of derepressors of genes. Genes are the basic units of the "blueprint" assemblies which specify the sum total of heritable characteristics. Each body cell is thought to possess a complete set of the genes which define the whole organism, but it is assumed that in a given cell type only those genes are active which define its nature and function, while all others are inactive, possibly by virtue of their being combined with hypothetical repressor substances. These repressed genes, in turn, are supposed to be subject to activation by the intervention of equally hypothetical derepressor substances.

Whether it is that the severe logic of the laboratory calls for relief in flights of loose imagination, or whether the frigid facts unearthed by analysis tend to elicit a framework of fanciful embroidery, the description of an example of exploratory biochemical research would be misleading if the scientist's subservience to facts were to make him appear oblivious to the puzzles of their significance. Indeed, a wider appreciation of the esthetic appeal of both aspects of the scientific life—the facts and the fancies, or the certainties and the possibilities—may go far in bridging the much-discussed gap between the intellectual worlds of scientist and non-scientist.

THE NUTRITION OF ALGAE

In recent years, the development of means of rearing algae, protozoa, and smaller marine metazoa in pure culture has greatly increased our knowledge of algae and protozoa and has proved comparable in importance to the discovery of methods of rearing bacteria in pure culture. It now is possible to rear many marine and fresh-water algae and protozoa, and some crustacea, in the absence of contaminating organisms and thus to investigate their capacity to produce toxic products, their nutritional requirements, and their life histories under rigorous experimental conditions.

Shortly after the perfection of isolation and culture techniques for bacteria, biologists began to study the possibility of isolating unicellular green algae and protozoa in pure culture. P. Miquel published in 1890–1893 what is probably the earliest study of this kind; he described methods for rearing diatoms. An extensive literature developed, mostly on methods of isolating and culturing the commoner fresh-water algae. This literature was summarized by E. G. Pringsheim in 1946.

Most of the commoner unicellular algae and protozoa are large in comparison with bacteria. Both the marine and fresh-water forms are commonly found in water that is heavily contaminated with bacteria. Many of these algae and protozoa have a gelatinous or slimy outer coat in which bacteria flourish; hence the isolation of these algae and protozoa from their bacterial associates may be difficult. Isolation is often accomplished by the use of antibiotics, which kill the bacteria while leaving the algal or protozoan cells alive. However, since some species of algae or protozoa are sensitive to many of the antibiotics, prolonged washing in flowing sterile water may be the only possible method of getting rid of the unwanted bacterial contaminants.

Many protozoa and some algae are extremely exacting in their nutritional needs. Some require vitamin B_{12} (cobalamin), others require zinc, many will grow only in a soil extract, and some require a trace of iron. The maintenance of any marine organism in pure culture usually requires careful study of its nutritional requirements, especially its need for minute amounts of *trace nutrients* (vitamins B_2, B_6, and B_{12} and cholesterol or other sterols) or *trace minerals* (iron, zinc, etc.).

Our understanding of the fundamentals of human nutrition and of the role that trace nutrients play in the metabolism of plants and larger animals has profited immensely by studies of the nutritional requirements of the more fastidious microorganisms. Likewise, the study of the ecology of marine organisms has been furthered by the ability to rear these organisms on known species of algae, diatoms, and protozoa. Many of the marine flagellates are highly toxic, and the eating of fish or shellfish that have fed on poisonous dinoflagellates may result in severe or fatal illness. Marine dinoflagellates of the genus *Gonyaulax* cause the "red tide" disease that occasionally kills hundreds of thousands, or perhaps millions, of marine fish. In studies of poisoning by marine microorganisms, the suspected organisms generally must be raised in pure culture.

Other practical applications of our knowledge of the cultivation of unicellular microorganisms are appearing. Man is gradually acquiring a capacity to "farm" ponds, lakes, and even the ocean itself. Correct feeding of oyster sprat, shellfish, and fish species will require precise knowledge of the nutritional adequacy, and possible toxic effects, of each algal and protozoan species to which the fish or shellfish is exposed.

For reasons that will be explained in the paper reproduced next, the isolation and pure culture of marine microorganisms have proved much more difficult than the isolation and rearing of fresh-water algae. Dr. Provasoli and his colleagues have been leaders in the development of effectual methods for working with marine organisms. In addition to developing methods for culturing marine unicellular algae and protozoa, they have extended their studies to the rearing of multicellular green, red, and brown algae and of brine shrimp (*Artemia salina*) and smaller crustacea. Other workers have utilized these methods in rearing many species of worms, insects, and other invertebrates in the absence of bacterial or other microbial contaminants, i.e., in what has come to be called *axenic* culture.

Additional information can be found in the following sources:

E. G. Pringsheim, "Pure Cultures of Algae," Cambridge University Press, London, 1946.

Ellsworth C. Dougherty (ed.), Axenic Culture of Invertebrate Metazoa: A Goal, *Ann. N.Y. Acad. Sci.*, 77:25–406, 1959.

To a very great degree, we owe our knowledge of the isolation, the rearing, and the nutritional requirements of the algae and protozoa to the work of Dr. Provasoli and his colleagues in the Haskins Laboratories, New York City.

From *Ann. N.Y. Acad. Sci.,*
56:839–851, 1953.

ECOLOGICAL IMPLICATIONS
OF IN VITRO NUTRITIONAL REQUIREMENTS
OF ALGAL FLAGELLATES

BY LUIGI PROVASOLI AND IRMA J. PINTNER

INTRODUCTION

The productivity of fresh-water bodies and the ocean rests on the algal phototrophs* at the base of the food pyramid. To predict the fertility of natural waters it is obviously necessary to learn what governs the proliferation of these algae.

Lucas in 1947, reviewing the evidence supporting his broad concept of "non-predatory" relationships among organisms living in water, emphasized the importance of external metabolites produced by water organisms and pointed out that through these metabolites one kind of organism might affect the growth of others in several ways: (1) by producing necessary nutrients; (2) by removing inhibitory compounds; (3) by excreting inhibitory substances. The present paper describes the growth requirements of several algae in pure culture and, in so doing, documents some aspects of these "non-predatory" relationships.

Certain centric diatoms important in the pelagic phytoplankton were postulated by Harvey to need one or more growth factors. This heightens interest in the observation that the one strain of *Amphora perpusilla*, a neritic pennate diatom,** studied by us, requires cobalamin. When coupled with other similar findings detailed in this paper, it brings into sharper relief the problem of the relative incidence of auxotrophy in coastal and oceanic phytoplankton species.†

In the course of work with some fresh-water planktonic protists, a remarkable parallelism was observed between *in vitro* results on the effective concentration ranges of nutrients and the composition of natural waters established by chemical analysis, suggesting that the chemical data of the hydrobiologist are a

---

* Phototrophs are organisms growing in light, or in the upper layers of water illuminated by sunlight. *Editor.*

** Pennate diatoms are diatoms whose cells are elongate, often bilaterally symmetrical, but never radially symmetrical. *Editor.*

† Auxotrophs are strains incapable of growing on simple inorganic media. *Editor.*

reliable guide to pure culture studies. Conversely, nutritional studies, in revealing that many algae from a variety of environments require vitamins and trace elements, focus attention on these two classes of nutrients which have often been neglected in classical hydrobiological analyses. It would appear, accordingly, that coöperation between hydrobiologist and nutritionist should increase understanding of the factors underlying algal successions and blooms.

CULTURAL TECHNIQUES

General Methods.—These generally were the same as those described for *Ochromonas.* Distilled water was passed through a mixed-bed ion exchanger ("Deeminizer"); the purity being controlled by conductivity measurements. Volatile preservative was immediately added to the water, which was stored in polyethylene carboys. The culture vessels were screw-capped tubes with the liners of the caps removed. The cork liners retained objectionable quantities of the detergent used for cleaning, and so induced precipitates in the poorly buffered very dilute media needed for the more delicate fresh-water planktonts.

Technique of Isolation.—In attempting to isolate and cultivate an organism belonging to a group never previously grown aseptically *in vitro,* the main problem is to find a medium as complete as possible yet non-inhibitory. Motility is an excellent index of lack of inhibition. Loss of photosynthetic pigments serves as indicator of inhibition for non-motile forms. Before washing or plating (see Pringsheim [1946]), preliminary trials of the suitability of media are made by fishing 10 to 20 individuals from the natural waters and putting them into a variety of media and observing their behavior after 6 to 24 hours. For *Synura,* one of the most delicate forms, a peat-mineral medium was developed (TABLE 1) with the motility response as guide (the medium is basically a modified v. Wettstein medium). Other media which have proved useful for isolation of unicellular and colonial [green algae of the family] Chlorophyceae, for *Ochromonas, Cyanophora,* and for a fresh-water *Peridinium* are given in TABLE 2. These media are employed also as conservation media, either as such or slightly agarized (0.2 g per cent).

TABLE 1

Isolation Medium for Synura (mg. per cent)

Ca (as NO$_3$)	0.65	K$_2$HPO$_4$	0.4
MgSO$_4$ · 7H$_2$O	1.0	KCl	0.6
Ca (as Cl)	0.4	Fe (as SO$_4$)	0.06
CaSO$_4$ · 2H$_2$O	1.0	Peat extract*	13.0 ml./100 ml.

pH 5.0–5.5; determined with the glass electrode.

The Ca salts were prepared by dissolving CaCO$_3$ in HCl or HNO$_3$ and driving off excess acid. Since the chloride and nitrate are hygroscopic, the concentrations shown refer to the metal, not the salt, in the final medium.

* Prepared by autoclaving (118–121°C.) black peat with an equal weight of water and filtering, then diluting to the color of "light beer."

TABLE 2

Organic Media for Isolation and Conservation of Fresh-water Algae

A. Medium for *Chlorophyceae* and *Cyanophora* (mg. %)		B. Medium for *Peridinium* and *Ochromonas* (mg. %)	
Na_3 citrate $\cdot$ $2H_2O$	2.0	$Ca(NO_3)_2 \cdot 4H_2O$	10.0
$MgSO_4 \cdot 7H_2O$	2.0	$MgSO_4 \cdot 7H_2O$	2.0
K_2HPO_4	2.0	K_2HPO_4	2.0
Fe (as SO_4)	0.2	Glucose	50.0
Thiopeptone (Wilson)	60.0	Trypticase (B.B.L.)	50.0
Trypticase (B.B.L.)	16.0	pH 6.5	
Yeast extract (Difco)	5.0		
pH 6.5			

Rich media favor the growth of bacteria and molds and therefore have not been used for isolation of algae by the plating method. Mineral media have been used almost exclusively from Beijerinck on. Mineral media in effect selected for autotrophs and created the impression that algae, like most land plants, were completely autotrophic.

The designations of nutritional types employed here follow current usage. *Auxotrophs* require growth factors. *Autotrophs* derive all their carbon from CO_2. Van Niel [1943] pointed out that there is a continuous quantitative series between complete obligate autotrophs and heterotrophs,* and that the reliance on fixed carbon entailed by auxotrophy, while vital to the life of the organism, was only a slight quantitative impairment of autotrophy. To select an extreme example, a photo-autotroph, auxotrophic only in respect to cobalamin, has lost less than a billionth of its autotrophic capacity.

Rich media can be used in the washing technique since accompanying organisms are eliminated mechanically before the wanted organism is inoculated in the rich isolation medium. The advent of the washing technique permitted the discovery of auxotrophic algae. The restriction of the plating technique to mineral media can be partially lifted by adding appropriate antibiotics. As is to be expected, antibiotics proved to be more effective in combination. Mixtures of penicillin and chloramphenicol or streptomycin were useful. *Amphora perpusilla* and other diatoms, for example, were isolated from organic agar media containing penicillin 1,000 units/ml. + chloramphenicol 25 μg./ml. Streptomycin, however, is especially poisonous to blue-green algae (1 unit or less may be poisonous) and to a lesser degree to Chlorophyta (poisonous range 1–50 units/ml.). Certain *Euglenas* are not inhibited by high concentrations of streptomycin but may become permanently colorless.

Determination of Growth Requirements.—Once the organism is obtained in pure culture, much information can be gained in one step by inoculation of a

---

* Organisms which require one or more of their complex nutrients to be supplied in nutrient solution; incapable of synthesizing one or more of the organic compounds requisite for growth or reproduction. *Editor.*

variety of media ranging from mineral to increasingly complex, and at different dilutions. If complex media are needed (peptones, soil extract, yeast autolysate, *etc.*) the next step is to identify the active constituents. This is done by stepwise substitution of natural materials with a mixture of better-defined preparations (acid-hydrolyzed gelatin and casein; alkali-hydrolyzed yeast nucleic acid, *etc.*) and pure compounds in the form of a mixture of known vitamins and likely carbon sources. This screening procedure is illustrated in other papers from this laboratory.

One of the frequent difficulties encountered in applying screening procedures to planktonic organisms is that they tolerate very low overall concentrations of media. The ever-present problem is to supply materials in adequate yet nontoxic concentrations. Special care has to be exercised not to overlook mineral deficiencies induced in the process of replacing crude materials with pure compounds. To avoid precipitates of calcium, iron, and phosphates, it is helpful to add a solubilizing metal-complexer. Experiments are easier to interpret if the complex-former is unmetabolizable and does not penetrate the organism. In using such metal-buffering agents, essential trace elements ordinarily adequately supplied as impurities in the "chemically pure" minerals, become inadequate. The need then becomes strikingly evident, and the proper concentrations of these trace elements have to be determined. Occasionally, growth factors can be required which may be new to biochemistry.

Chemically-Defined Media.—Media developed for determination of the growth factor requirements of *Peridinium* sp., *Gyrodinium* sp., *Cyanophora paradoxa,* and *Synura* sp. are given in TABLE 3. The *Gyrodinium* is marine and therefore its medium is a substitute for enriched seawater. Its isolation medium consisted of seawater enriched with NO_3, PO_4, Fe, and soil extract.

The identification of requirements for growth factors and trace elements, and the recognition of optimal ratios and concentration boundaries for major inorganic and organic nutrients are treated here as separate topics for the sake of arriving at a general picture of nutritional specializations in algae. Obviously they are some of the interrelated factors to be considered in devising good artificial media. The identification of the nutritional requirements in all these categories for *Peridinium* and *Cyanophora* is advanced enough to allow reproducible macroscopic growth in a month. The other organisms are, as yet, unsatisfactorily known in one or more categories. It has not been determined whether the medium for *Synura* will support indefinitely subculturable growth.

GROWTH-FACTOR REQUIREMENTS

The findings to date for the flagellated and non-flagellated algae are summarized in TABLE 4. Many chlorophyceans, not included in this table, are maintained in algal collections on mineral agar. The great majority of these are probably non-auxotrophic, but a more rigorous avoidance of chemical con-

TABLE 3

Chemically Defined Media for Identification of Vitamins (mg. per cent)

	Cyanophora paradoxa	Peridinium sp.	Synura sp.	Gyrodinium sp.
Ethylenediamine tetraacetic acid (EDTA)		30.0	5.0	20.0
Citric acid · H_2O	30.0			
$NaNO_3$			2.0	
NH_4NO_3	3.0			
KNO_3		5.0		10.0
KH_2PO_4	10.0	2.0	1.4	2.0
$MgSO_4 \cdot 7H_2O$	5.0	10.0	2.0	30.0
*$MgCl_2 \cdot 6H_2O$				300.0
NaCl				2400.0
$CaCO_3$	10.0	10.0		
Ca (as Cl)		4.0	1.3	5.0
KCl			1.0	30.0
Fe (as NO_3 + Cl)	0.3	0.2	0.07	0.3
Zn (as Cl)	0.01	0.08	1.0	0.4
Mn (as Cl)	0.015	0.08	0.2	1.0
Mo (as Na salt)	0.01	0.05	0.001	0.05
Co (as Cl)	0.0004	0.001	0.003	0.003
Cu (as Cl)	0.0001	0.0001	0.0005	0.0003
†"Sr metals"				0.5 ml./100 ml.
Boron (as H_3BO_3)				0.2
Na H glutamate	15.0	100.0	10.0	2.0
Glycine		70.0		
DL-Alanine		70.0		
Na acetate · $3H_2O$	10.0		4.0	
Glucose		50.0		
DL-Lysine HCl				1.0
DL-Leucine				0.2
	pH 6.3	pH 6.2	pH 5.5	pH 7.5

* Concentration in stock solution standardized by chloride determination.
† "Sr metals": 1.0 ml. of the mixture contains the following metals: Sr (as Cl) 1.3 mg.; Al (as Cl) 0.05 mg.; Rb (as Cl) 0.02 mg.; Li (as Cl) 0.01 mg.; I (as KI) 0.005 mg.; also Br (as NaBr) 6.5 mg.

Vitamin concentrations needed for growth: Cobalamin is added for *Gyrodinium* and *Cyanophora* at the 0.1 µg.% level; for *Peridinium*, 0.06 µg. per cent; and for *Synura*, 0.15 µg. per cent. The need for other vitamins is under study.

Sources of metals. The Zn was prepared by dissolving Johnson-Matthey purified zinc rod in distilled HCl. The Co and Mn were Johnson-Matthey "spec-pure" solutions of the chlorides. The Fe solution was prepared by dissolving "spec-pure" metal in aqua regia compounded of distilled HCl and HNO_3; excess acid was then evaporated off.

taminations (thiamine, cobalamin, *etc.*) from agar, cotton, and distilled water might reveal auxotrophy in a few. Several *Euglenas* are omitted, since it is not clear whether or not a sufficiently rigorous technique was applied. It is not unlikely that all euglenids require cobalamin and thiamine.

Four general conclusions may be drawn from TABLE 4:

(1) Algae, like autotrophic bacteria, may be divided into auxotrophs and non-auxotrophs.

(2) Thiamine and cobalamin (vitamin B_{12}) are needed by the majority of the auxotrophs. The auxotrophic forms occur in all groups of algal flagellates and auxotrophy does not correlate with any particular environment: Most

TABLE 4

Incidence of Growth-factor Requirements in Algae

Species	Vitamins needed	Thiamine	Cobalamin	Other
CHLOROPHYTA				
Chlamydomonas agloëformis	o			
Chlamydomonas chlamydogama	+		+	Histidine
Chlamydomonas moewusii	o			
Chlamydomonas sp. ("marine")	o			
Chlorogonium elongatum	o			
Chlorogonium euchlorum	o			
Coelastrum (*morus* ?)	+	+		
Haematococcus pluvialis	o			
Lobomonas pyriformis	o			
Lobomonas rostrata	+		+	
Polytoma caudatum	+	+		
Polytoma obtusum	o			
Polytoma ocellatum	+	+		
Polytoma uvella	o			
Polytomella caeca	+	+		
Prototheca zopfii	+	+		
Selenastrum minutum (E. A. George strains)	o			
Selanastrum (*minutum* ?)	+	+		
CHRYSOPHYTA				
Amphora perpusilla	+		+	Uracil ?
Nitzschia closterium f. *minutissima*	o			
Nitzschia putrida	o			
Ochromonas malhamensis (3 strains)	+	+	+	Biotin + histidine
Poteriochromonas stipitata	+	+	+	Biotin + histidine
Synura sp.	+	?	+	?
Syracosphaera carterae	+	?	?	?
EUGLENOPHYTA				
Euglena gracilis vars. *typica, bacillaris, urophora*	+	+	+	
Astasia longa (= *klebsii* Von Dach)	+	+	+	
E. gracilis, streptomycin-bleached	+	+	+	
E. pisciformis	+	+	?	
E. viridis, E. stellata	+	+	+	
PYRROPHYTA				
Chilomonas paramoecium	+	+		
Cryptomonas ovata var. *palustris*	+	?	+	?
Cyanophora paradoxa	+		+	
Gymnodinium splendens	+		+	
Gyrodinium sp. (marine)	+	?	+	?
Peridinium sp.	+	+	+	?

TABLE 5

*Group Tendencies in Algal Flagellates**

	Tendency to loss of:		Tendency to phagotrophy
	chlorophyll	plastids	
Colonial Volvocales	none	none	none
Chlamydomonadaceae	pronounced	none	very rare
Polyblepharidaceae	pronounced	none	none
Euglenoids	pronounced	none	doubtful
Peranemids	total	widespread	total
Cryptomonads	rare	rare	very rare
Chrysomonads	widespread	widespread	widespread
Dinoflagellates	pronounced	pronounced	widespread

* Revised from Lwoff, [*Actualités Sci. et ind.* 970. Hermann et Cie, Paris, 1943. p. 216].

species of *Polytoma, Astasia,* and *Euglena* are found in environments rich in organic matter (polysaprobic) ; *Synura* and *Cryptomonas* live in waters poor in organic matter (oligosaprobic) ; *Gyrodinium, Nitzschia* (2 species, both non-auxotrophic, one, the colorless *N. putrida,* completely heterotrophic), and *Amphora* are marine. Considering the multiplicity of metabolites in nature, this pattern of dependency on cobalamin and thiamine is remarkably stereotyped and leads one to wonder whether this expresses a deep-seated evolutionary tendency in their physiology.

(3) Other vitamins may be needed besides the seemingly predominant thiamine and cobalamin; *e.g.,* biotin is required by *Ochromonas malhamensis* and *Poteriochromonas stipitata.* It might be expected that additional vitamins will be found to be required as the number of species of algae in pure culture increases.

(4) Auxotrophy is present in organisms having different degrees of heterotrophy. It may be the only heterotrophic requirement, as it appears to be in *Synura,* or it might be only one element of a many-sided heterotrophy: *e.g.*; *Euglena gracilis* utilizes various substrates, and *Ochromonas* and *Poteriochromonas* are photosynthetic phagotrophs exemplifying the coexistence of plant and animal nutrition, phagotrophy being the principal mode of heterotrophy in animals.*

Auxotrophy in algae was first detected by Lwoff and Dusi [1938] in several genera of colorless chlamydomonads, in a colorless cryptomonad, and in *Euglena pisciformis. . . .*

The question arises as to the extent to which auxotrophy is a sign of a heterotrophic tendency in algae. A better understanding may be obtained by reviewing the evolutionary trends in algae leading to the development of the animal forms, *i.e.,* the Protozoa. The new data on the physiology of *Euglena* and *Ochromonas* permit elaboration of the physiological implications that Lwoff attached to the morphological evolutionary tendencies recognized and systematized by Pascher and by Fritsch [1935]. These are outlined in TABLE 5. It will be noted that

* Phagotrophs are those organisms that feed by ingestion of particulate matter. *Editor.*

each algal group exhibits certain conspicuous morphological tendencies. These, in so far as they affect the photosynthetic apparatus, are bound to be reflected in a changed nutritional pattern. Obviously, when photosynthesis is lost, survival demands a compensatory heterotrophic ability. In different algal groups heterotrophy may assume either of two forms: In phytomonads, osmotrophy;* in euglenids and all other groups, osmotrophy and phagotrophy. The clearest index of an adequate heterotrophy is the ability to grow in darkness, as is shown by *Chlamydomonas agloëformis, Chlorogonium euchlorum, Euglena gracilis, Ochromonas malhamensis, Poteriochromonas stipitata, etc.* Many algae, however, utilize fixed carbon without being able to grow in darkness. Their heterotrophy is less efficient than is that of the dark-growing species. The existence of facultatively heterotrophic, photosynthetic organisms clearly indicates that facultative heterotrophy precedes loss of photosynthetic power and can be considered as a sign of an evolutionary tendency toward animal nutrition. In nature, organisms with dual capacities—phototrophy and heterotrophy—are abundant. Depending on external conditions, one or the other mode of nutrition may predominate. It does not necessarily follow that pigmented organisms with an efficient heterotrophy have a weakened photosynthesis. Cramer and Myers have shown that *Euglena gracilis* var. *bacillaris,* when provided with sufficient light and CO_2, photosynthesizes at least as vigorously as *Chlorella.* Furthermore, autotrophic growth under these conditions equals the best heterotrophic growth. The relative importance of autotrophy, osmotrophy, and phagotrophy in *Ochromonas* and *Poteriochromonas* remains to be determined. In view of the tendency already noted of all algal flagellates to lose photosynthetic pigments, the widespread occurrence of heterotrophy and auxotrophy in pigmented forms is not surprising. The minute heterotrophy represented by auxotrophy in algae is nevertheless all-important in determining which algae will multiply under a given set of circumstances. It is also tempting to look upon auxotrophy as one of the forerunners of a more pronounced heterotrophy.

Presence of Growth Factors in Natural Waters.—It is a reasonable assumption that if an organism requires a growth factor *in vitro,* then this metabolite or its physiological equivalent should be found in significant amount in the environment. Only the actual determination of the seasonal variation of these vitamins in nature will enable detection of the times when these vitamins actually become the limiting factors for growth. A promising start has been made. Robbins *et al.* [1950] charted the fluctuation of cobalamin content of a small pond which had shown *Euglena* blooms. The amounts of cobalamin found were high enough to satisfy the cobalamin requirement of *Euglena.* Hutchinson [1943] earlier showed that a thiamine cycle existed in a pond but did not attempt to correlate this with any particular organism.

The question arises as to the identity of the principal vitamin-producers in

---

* The capacity to feed by ingestion of nutrients in solution. *Editor.*

nature. Robbins *et al.* [1950] found that soil extract contains appreciable amounts of cobalamin and that 40 per cent of the bacteria from mud isolated at random excreted cobalamin. Since cycles of metabolites in soil parallel those in water, Lochhead and Thexton's [1951] demonstration is apropos that 70–84 per cent of the bacteria isolated at random from soil are cobalamin producers and that 14 per cent require soil extract. It is interesting to note that half the bacteria initially requiring soil extract were satisfied by cobalamin.

The data of TABLE 4 provide examples of the importance of external metabolites—of "non-predatory" relationships—existing in the water environment. Only a small part of the cobalamin cycle is known. The literature indicates that many other organisms participate in it. As with bacteria, algae include cobalamin-dependent organisms and cobalamin producers. Robbins *et al.* found that an extract of 7 fresh-water blue-green algae grown in mineral media contained relatively high amounts of cobalamin. The uninoculated medium showed no activity. Extracts of several red and brown algae contained cobalamin, especially *Ceramium rubrum*. Since the algae were obtained directly from the shore there is some doubt as to whether all the cobalamin was theirs. Oysters and clams were found by Robbins *et al.* [1951] to contain large amounts of cobalamin, suggesting that algal flagellates, an important item in their diet, are either producers or accumulators of cobalamin.

REQUIREMENTS FOR TRACE METALS

Requirements of Synura.—This organism, often abundant in unpolluted waters such as reservoirs, has long challenged the nutritionist as well as the hydrobiologist. It is selected here to exemplify the problems faced in culturing a planktont requiring very dilute media. It was cultured by Mainx [1929] in a highly diluted soil extract. Rodhe [1948] grew it in a very dilute mineral medium (his "medium VIII"; see TABLE 6) supplemented with an extract of soil or lake sediment. Ashed extracts were ineffective. Our medium (TABLE 3) was developed by replacing peat extract with a mixture of known vitamins. Since the medium is prone to precipitate, EDTA, an efficient solubilizing chelating agent, was added. This procedure revealed, as expected, deficiencies in trace metals which were satisfied by finding the suitable concentration of a series of different trace metal mixtures. Then, keeping constant the levels of trace elements, the major elements (Ca, Mg, K, NO_3, PO_4, and Fe) were adjusted to levels permitting better growth. Using, in turn, this information, the suitable concentration of each of the trace metals, previously added as a mixture, was determined. Inoculation of the experiments, at first, was from stock cultures maintained in the isolation medium, later from preceding experiments. Growth in defined media was better than in the original peat medium but decreased after repeated transfers. This indicated that the defined medium is still incomplete and that carry-over of factors from peat may play a role. In an attempt to identify other substances needed for growth, experiments are under way to identify the effective vitamins in the dilute vitamin mixture used. Cobalamin is required; but additional vitamins may be needed. The effect of exogenous carbon sources was also explored. In unagitated cultures, not supplied with extra CO_2, growth was unaffected by single additions of glutamate, acetate, fumarate, glucose, glycine, and alanine. It should be noted that Zn is required at a very high concentration as compared with Ca, Mg, and K, which are usually designated as major nutrients. *Euglena gracilis* var. *bacillaris,* supplied with a 10-fold higher concentration of EDTA, does not require for heavy growth more than 2.0 mg. per cent of Zn at pH 5.0.

Some acute problems are presented by dilute media; *e.g.,* adequate pH buffering is difficult to achieve because of the low tolerance to phosphate and osmotic pressure. Aconitic, trimesic, and succinic acids show promise as buffers in the acid region. Dilute media are especially difficult to reproduce, since environmental chemical contaminations from glassware, distilled water, and especially from "c. p." chemicals, may be of the same magnitude as the nutrients added intentionally. Media built around EDTA are an advance toward reproducibility. EDTA's metal-sequestering abilities make it, at the same time, a solubilizing agent preventing precipitation and a metal-buffering agent raising the threshold of metal availability and toxicity. Hit-or-miss dependence on "chemically pure" salts as a source of essential trace elements is thus minimized; now the trace elements have to be added as such.

Comparison of Artificial Media and Lake Waters.—Chu and Rodhe were the pioneers in devising artificial dilute media for many planktonts. Chu [1942] developed 16 different media of which "No. 10" permitted growth of several diatoms, a blue-green alga, a desmid, and *Botryococcus.* His other media were developed for the various single species. Rodhe's "No. VIII" served for cultivation of several Chlorococcales, Volvocales, Heterokontae, and desmids. Chu's and Rodhe's media were developed through determination of the concentration range for each constituent. The species cultivated by them are almost certainly complete autotrophs since growth factors were not supplied. As mentioned earlier in the discussion of growth factors, auxotrophy cannot be excluded until a rigorous technique is employed. However, Rodhe's failure to grow *Synura,* which requires cobalamin, indicates that his mineral media were not significantly contaminated with cobalamin, one of the most powerful and ubiquitous of growth factors. Our media, developed independently, ended by being as dilute as theirs. Our experiments with *Cryptomonas ovata* var. *palustris* indicate that, as a representative planktont, it has a very low osmotic tolerance. As little as 30 mg. per cent NaCl was inhibitory. These results also agreed with tolerances to neutral salts of organic acids.

TABLE 6 shows the striking similarity of the three mineral media and the similarity existing between them and Rodhe's standard mineral composition of lake waters having a similar content in total solids. This parallelism between

TABLE 6

Comparison of Lake Water of Standard Composition and Artificial Media
(Mg. per liter)

Elements	Rodhe's Standard Composition*	Chu No. 10	Rodhe No. VIII	Synura Medium†
N	0.5–0.6‡	7.0	10.2	3.3
P	0.03–0.05‡	1.8–9.0	0.89	3.1
Na	4.6	19.0	7.5	5.4
K	1.7	2.2–4.4	2.2	9.0
Mg	2.7	2.5	1.0	2.0
Ca	16.3	10.0	14.7	13.0
Fe	0.4–1.2‡	0.27	0.18	0.7
Mn	0.02–0.14‡		0.01	†
Total Solids	98.0	115–120	181	102–179**
Conductivity ($\psi.10^{-6}$)	120.0			

* Values from TABLE 2 of Rodhe, W., 1949. The ionic composition of lake waters. Proc. Intern. Assoc. Limnol. 10: 377–386.

† See TABLE 3 for concentrations of EDTA and minor elements; 0.2 ml/100 of a vitamin supplement was added (formula in Cowperthwaite et al. [1953]).

‡ Variation intervals, calculated from Rodhe's [1951] tables, for a conductivity of 120.

** In the higher value the sodium salts of glutamic and acetic acids are not included (Synura can grow without this addition).

In the lower value of glutamate, acetate, trace metals and EDTA are not included.

laboratory results and analyses of natural waters validates the idea that laboratory findings in respect to growth factors and mineral requirements are directly relevant to ecological problems. As already mentioned, use of a chelator reveals sharply the indispensability of trace elements. The finding of Chu that addition of trace elements was unnecessary implies that the impurities present in his major chemicals were adequate. Rodhe made an extensive study of the precipitation—i.e., unavailability—of Fe and found that addition of a Fe citrate-citric acid combination prevented precipitation. Although citric acid is only a moderately strong metal-binder and was used in very small amount, the need for Mn became evident. The use of chelators in the laboratory parallels the situation in natural waters where humic acids are among the most important, almost unmetabolizable, metal-buffering agents. Since planktonic organisms such as Synura, Peridinium, Cryptomonas, and Trachelomonas have been shown to require trace metals, more importance should be assigned to trace metals as ecological factors. A recent paper by Rodhe [1951] signalizes the increasing interest in the trace element content of natural waters.

Phosphate Requirements.—An in vitro result that cannot yet be correlated with ecological data is the requirement for phosphorus. In fact, the concentrations needed in synthetic media far exceed those normally present in nature. For instance, Chu and Rodhe [1948] found that Asterionella formosa is indifferent to 10–20 μg. P/liter. Maximal growth was obtained at about 1,000 μg. P/liter. Rodhe found that, in Lake Erken, where this organism is common, the P content scarcely attains 10 μg./liter. When his artificial inorganic basal medium was replaced by lake water (sterilized by filtration), maximum growth was obtained with the extremely small addition of 4–10 μg. P/liter. This striking discrepancy in utilization of P appears to support Rodhe's assumption that lake waters contain one or more factors facilitating the use by *Asterionella* of P at very low concentrations. A peculiarity in P utilization by *Cryptomonas ovata* may be relevant. In one experiment, different PO_4 optima were observed on varying the concentration of magnesium sulfate. For $MgSO_4 \cdot 7H_2O$ at 2.0 mg. per cent, the optimal level of KH_2PO_4 was 1.0 mg. per cent; while for $MgSO_4 \cdot 7H_2O$ 0.5 mg. per cent, the optimal level of KH_2PO_4 was 0.4 mg. per cent. If these preliminary results prove repeatable, it will be determined whether this varying response to KH_2PO_4 depends on the ratio of Mg to K. In any event, Rodhe's experiment should stimulate a search for factors in natural waters permitting growth at low P concentrations. P is undoubtedly one of the important natural limiting factors for most algae. Rodhe found, on the other hand, that blooms of *Dinobryon* and *Uroglena* appeared only when the P level was below 5 μg./liter and, experimentally, their growth was inhibited upon addition of 5–10 μg. P/liter. Our results with *Peridinium, Gyrodinium, Synura, Cryptomonas,* and *Trachelomonas* further document the well-established fact that the need for PO_4 varies among algae, and indicate, moreover, that some plankton organisms have a surprisingly narrow optimal PO_4 range. This last point may be important in ecology.

DISCUSSION

The water environment is the one in which metabolites are interchanged most efficiently. It is to be expected that the interdependent growth of the different groups of water organisms should sensitively reflect the excretion and consumption of metabolites. Undaunted by new intricacies, we should envisage all the possibilities in these relationships, and not hesitate to follow Lucas's lead in constructing theoretical frameworks upon which to hang data. In the present paper, only a few aspects of the nutrition of photosynthetic forms are considered. It is possible, nevertheless, to state more definitely some of the interdependencies based upon "external metabolites": (1) the interchange of growth factors; (2) the lowering of inhibitory concentrations of several major mineral nutrients, especially PO_4; and (3) the preferential utilization of minerals, including trace metals, may condition waters, bringing their concentrations into the optimal zones for succeeding forms. The practical aim—to predict algal successions and blooms—may be achieved through a comprehensive knowledge of vitamin cycles as well as mineral cycles. An immediate problem is to trace the thiamine and cobalamin cycles. In fresh-waters, these can be worked out by applying techniques such as those used by Hutchinson and by Robbins *et al.*, but tracing these vitamins in the ocean requires the exploitation of new assay organisms and concentration techniques.

The role of other organic materials as ecological factors remains problematic at the moment. It is likely that, in waters high in organic content, such as sewage, organic compounds may serve as substrates for photosynthetic organisms endowed with heterotrophic abilities. A familiar example of this utilization of substrates is presented by the algae which form blooms in sewage lagoons and similar polysaprobic environments. The algae, *e.g., Euglena gracilis* and *Chlorella,* isolated from these habitats are well endowed with heterotrophic abilities.

The coastal waters of well-vegetated, well-populated land masses should be comparatively rich in organic matter. Many phytoplanktonts appear to be coastal rather than pelagic—an indication that the land may be a significant source of essential metabolites. . . .

Bacterial cells exposed to sufficiently strong doses of ultraviolet and subsequently kept in darkness will be "killed," that is, rendered incapable of multiplying and forming colonies when seeded in appropriate media; but if they are later exposed to visible light, many of the cells will "recover." This apparent reversal of death, called *photoreactivation,* was first noted in 1936 by a Czech investigator, Sylvester Prat. Its significance was not grasped, however, until the phenomenon was rediscovered by Kelner in 1948.

In the 15 years that have elapsed since Kelner's paper was published, a substantial literature on photoreactivation has appeared. It is now known that the phenomenon of photoreactivation is not confined to bacteria: it is quite general throughout microorganisms and has been observed in plant and animal cells. However, a few species of bacteria, as well as sperm cells and the bacteriophage virus, have never been successfully photoreactivated.

The mechanism of photoreactivation is still obscure. It is not certain that the nongerminable bacterial cells present in irradiated suspensions are in fact dead: it is possible that they are alive but incapable of dividing (though apparently they never revive unless exposed to visible light). Drs. A. Novick and Leo Szilard, then at the University of Chicago, conjectured that the irradiation of bacteria with ultraviolet light results in the production of a poisonous substance that is present in two forms, one of which breaks down upon exposure to visible light. It is also possible that the apparent death of irradiated cells may be caused by depolymerization of either or perhaps both of the nucleic acids present in the cell. This conjecture is supported by the observation that when cells are killed by monochromatic ultraviolet of various wavelengths, ultraviolet of approximately 2650 A is the most effective; this is also the wavelength that is most effective in depolymerizing the nucleic acids. The ultraviolet frequency curve of photoreactive "killing" of bacterial cells is apparently identical with the curve of absorption of ultraviolet by nucleic acids.

The wavelength characteristics of the light that photoreactivates killed bacterial and fungal cells differ somewhat from species to species; usually peak photoreactivating efficiency lies in the violet region of the spectrum (3000–4550 A). Light of this wavelength is absorbed by a variety of pigments, but not appreciably by the nucleic acids.

It is now known that in the deoxyribonucleic acid helices of cells that have been exposed to ultraviolet light, two adjacent thymine residues may be chemically bonded to each other to form a larger unit, or doublet, known as a *thymine dimer*. Many such dimers can form in a single strand of DNA. Thymine dimers block DNA synthesis, and this blockage is sufficient to account for much, possibly all, of the lethal effects of ultraviolet on cells. Thymine dimers are split by light in the presence of extract of yeast cells. The formation of thymine dimers may therefore be the primary lethal effect of ultraviolet on cells, and the splitting of such dimers by light may be the true explanation of the photoreactivation process.

For additional information see the following:

A. Novick and Leo Szilard, Experiments on Light-reactivation of Ultraviolet Inactivated Bacteria, *Proc. Nat. Acad. Sci.*, 35:591–600, 1949.

John Jagger, Photoreactivation, *Radiation Res. Supp.*, 2:75–90, 1960.

R. B. Setlow and W. L. Carrier, The Disappearance of Thymine Dimers from DNA: An Error-correcting Mechanism, *Proc. Nat. Acad. Sci.*, 51:226–231, 1964.

Dr. Kelner carried out his early researches on photoreactivation at the Long Island Biological Laboratory (now the Long Island Laboratory of Quantitative Biology), Cold Spring Harbor, Long Island, New York. He is presently at the Department of Biology, Brandeis University.

From *Proc. Nat. Acad. Sci.,*
35:73–79, 1949.

EFFECT OF VISIBLE LIGHT ON THE RECOVERY
OF STREPTOMYCES GRISEUS CONIDIA
FROM ULTRA-VIOLET IRRADIATION INJURY

BY ALBERT KELNER

It is well known that cells rendered non-viable by ultra-violet or x-irradiation may at times regain their viability if stored under suitable conditions after irradiation. In the case of microorganisms the criterion for viability is usually the ability to form a colony on a solid medium. By recovery is meant the restoration of the ability of an irradiated microorganism to grow and form a colony.

Little is known about the mechanism of the recovery phenomenon; experimental results reported in the literature have been extremely variable. Moreover, at best only a small percentage of the cells rendered non-viable in an irradiated population recover their viability—that is, the over-all recovery is usually relatively slight.

During a study of antibiotically active mutants in actinomycetes we observed that the per cent survival of ultra-violet irradiated *Streptomyces griseus* ATC3326 (a non-streptomycin producer) conidia increased about 10-fold when irradiated suspensions were stored one or two days following irradiation. So little was known about the recovery phenomenon, with which our observation was obviously connected, and the implications of this phenomenon to genetics, medicine, and cellular physiology seemed so important to us, that an intensive study of recovery from irradiation was initiated.

Since observers have found recovery to take place when irradiated cells are stored in the cold, and since our own first observations were made on suspensions which had been stored in the ice box, the first study was one on effect of temperature. It was soon clear that recovery was not dependent on storage in the cold. However, results were extremely variable even in duplicate experiments; for example, one suspension of ultra-violet irradiated spores showed no recovery upon storage at 35°C., while another suspension prepared from the same lot of spores and irradiated in exactly the same way, showed a 100,000-fold recovery. Some variable factor seemed present in our experiments which overshadowed in importance the effect of temperature *per se* on recovery. Careful consideration was made of variable factors which might have accounted for such tremendous variation. We were using a glass-fronted water bath placed on a table near a window, in which were suspended transparent bottles containing the irradiated spores. The fact that some of the bottles were more directly exposed to light than others suggested that light might be a factor. Moreover, the greatest and most consistent recovery in our preliminary experiments had taken place in suspensions stored in transparent bottles at room temperature on an open shelf exposed to diffuse light from a window. Experiment showed that exposure of ultra-violet irradiated suspensions to light resulted in an increase in survival rate or a recovery of 100,000- to 400,000-fold. Controls kept in the dark (experiments were made between 15°C. to 37°C. only) showed no recovery at all.

The magnitude of the light effect can hardly be overemphasized. The recovery was so much more complete than any previously observed, that we felt we were dealing here with a key factor in the mechanism causing inactivation and recovery from ultra-violet irradiation.

Methods.—The ultra-violet source was a General Electric 15-watt germicidal lamp, 80 per cent of whose ultra-violet radiation was at 2537 Å. The spores of *S. griseus* ATC3326 were suspended in saline or distilled water and irradiated in a thin layer in an open petri dish placed under the ultra-violet source. The suspension was shaken gently during irradiation. Preparation of spores, irradiation, and assay for viable count were otherwise similar to those described previously. Following ultra-violet irradiation, the spore suspensions were placed in glass bottles or test tubes and suspended in a thermostatically controlled glass-fronted water bath. Visible light illumination from various sources as described under individual experiments was directed against the suspension. The light passed through two glass thicknesses, and about $1/2$ cm. of water, before reaching the ultra-violet irradiated cells. Filters were used in later experiments as described below. Counts were made of the viable cells in a suspension by plating on nutrient agar and incubating 3 days at 28°C. Ultra-violet treated cells which were to be kept in the dark were placed in a covered can suspended in the water bath.

Effect of Dosage of Ultra-violet Light on Recovery.—Conidial suspensions were irradiated with ultra-violet at 60 cm. distance from the lamp (intensity about 960 ergs $\times$ min.$^{-1}$ $\times$ mm.$^{-2}$) for periods [of 4, 5, 6, 7, 8, and 9 minutes]. Immediately after irradiation the suspension was divided into two portions, one of which was kept as a dark control, and the other exposed to light from a window about 2 feet away. In this early experiment the visible light source was not controlled, the suspensions being in the dark at night, and subject to variation in light intensity during the day. However, this experiment [showed] well the consistent recovery which occurred only in the light. Non-ultra-violet treated controls were little affected by visible light, there being if anything a decrease in the count in the light-exposed tubes. In no case did the tubes of ultra-violet treated cells kept in the dark show significant recovery, while in all cases the light-exposed tubes showed recovery varying from 14- to over 72,000-fold according to ultra-violet dosage in this experiment. If the decrease in count of the non-ultra-violet irradiated suspension exposed to light is taken into account it is seen that in the 4-minute experiment the recovery is complete by the fifth day, the count in the ultra-violet irradiated suspension (1.8×10^5) equaling that of the non-ultra-violet irradiated suspension (1.7×10^5).

Effect of Intensity and Duration of Visible Light Illumination.—A conidial suspension was irradiated with ultra-violet for $1\frac{1}{2}$ minutes at 20 cm. distance from the mercury lamp. Immediately after irradiation it was placed in a 28°C. water bath and exposed to as high an intensity of artificial light as was conveniently possible to obtain in our laboratory (two photoflood lamps and light from a projection lantern, all placed about 30 cm. from the cells). [The table given below] shows the extent of recovery after various time periods. The temperature of the cell suspension did not rise more than 2 degrees during the illumination. Recovery is proportional to duration of illumination, within limits.

In another experiment (with different light source) a 3-fold recovery was observed after as little as 2 minutes of illumination, and 810-fold after 4 minutes. An experiment in which the duration of illumination was constant, but the intensity varied, showed that the rapidity of recovery was proportional to intensity, within limits.

Temperature.—[The effect of temperature on the rate of recovery was studied in experiments in which a constant light source and a constant illumination period were employed, the irradiated conidia being held at constant temperatures ranging from 20°C to 60°C. In one experiment a suspension of 800,000 conidia per milliliter was irradiated for 90 seconds at 2 cm distance from the ultraviolet lamp. Germination studies begun immediately after irradiation showed less than 10 viable conidia per milliliter. When exposed for 10

Effect of Duration of Visible Light Illumination on Recovery

Illumination time, min.	Viable cells per ml. of suspension	Relative increase in survival rate
0	2.5*	—
10	2.5×10^3	1,000-fold
20	9.2×10^3	3,700-fold
30	1.3×10^5	52,000-fold
40	1.6×10^5	64,000-fold
50	2.0×10^5	80,000-fold
60	5.3×10^5	210,000-fold
145	5.5×10^5	220,000-fold
173	7.7×10^5	310,000-fold
240	8.0×10^5	320,000-fold

* The count of the non-ultra-violet irradiated suspension was 4.2×10^6, so that the survival rate at time zero was 6.0×10^{-7}.

minutes to uniform light from a 500-watt Mazda projection bulb (the outer lens of the lamp being placed about 5 cm from the cells, in order to obtain as intense an illumination as possible), the numbers of viable conidia per milliliter of suspension were found to be 9600, 39,000, 36,000, 100,000, and 110,000 respectively for suspensions held at 20°, 25°, 30°, 35°, and 40°C. In a second experiment, in which less than 10 viable cells per milliliter were found in tests begun immediately after irradiation, counts of viable cells were 230,000 per milliliter in suspensions held at 40°C, 240,000 at 40°, 330,000 at 50°, 290,000 at 55°, and 220,000 per milliliter in suspensions insulated at 60°C.] An independent ultra-violet irradiation was made for each temperature determination; this may partially account for some of the variability in the results. It is seen that the rate of recovery increases with rise in temperature up to about 50°C.

Ultra-violet irradiated suspensions could be kept at 5°C in the dark for up to 4 hours without interfering with subsequent recovery when illuminated.

The knowledge furnished by the experiments just described enabled us to induce over 100,000-fold recovery with a high degree of reproducibility, by illuminating ultra-violet irradiated suspensions with a light source as described for 20 to 30 minutes at 37°C.

The light source used by us emitted infra-red as well as visible light. Since considerable work has been done on the effect on mutation and chromosomal rearrangements of pre- and posttreatment of x- or ultra-violet irradiated cells with near infra-red, it was of importance to determine the comparative effect on recovery of the infra-red and visible components of our light source. Suspensions illuminated with light in which the infra-red had been eliminated by a filter consisting of a 3.2-cm. deep cell containing 0.5 N $CuCl_2$ aqueous solution, recovered almost as much as controls with no filter. This filter absorbs some of the visible red, as well as the infra-red. On the other hand, interposition of a filter consisting of a 3.2-cm. deep cell containing a saturated solution of I_2 in CCl_4, which eliminates most of the visible light and passes the infra-red, resulted in no recovery at all. There was moderate recovery when an I_2-CCl_4 filter 1 cm. deep was used, but use of this filter was not a critical test, for a considerable portion of the visible light passed through this filter. These simple experiments do not of course exclude the possibility that infra-red illumination of sufficient intensity will not induce recovery; they do show that the most active component of our light source was the visible light. One of the main features of the infra-red-ultra-violet, or -x-ray studies, is that pretreatment with infra-red has a marked effect on the behavior of cells to subsequent irradiation with ultra-violet or x-rays. We therefore illuminated conidial suspensions of S. griseus with visible light before irradiating with ultra-violet. There was no increase whatever in the survival rate on subsequent irradiation with ultra-violet.

The magnitude of the recovery phenomenon made it imperative to make sure that it was not due to some experimental artifact, such as declumping of clumped cells; and to ascertain whether the effect of visible light was on the menstruum rather than on the cells themselves.

Elimination of clumping and declumping as a factor was shown by experiments where ultra-violet and subsequent visible light irradiation was done on cells which had first been smeared on the surface of nutrient agar plates. Light-induced recovery occurred as usual.

That recovery was not due to a stimulation of germination in cells which had a long lag phase due to ultra-violet irradiation, was shown by the fact that prolonged incubation of plates which had been seeded with irradiated cells never disclosed the presence of slow-growing colonies. The maximum number of colonies was always reached after 3 days of incubation.

There was a possibility that the killing effect of ultra-violet light on *S. griseus* was due chiefly to ozone dissolved in the menstruum from the air, or to peroxides or other compounds formed in the menstruum by the ultra-violet light. If these toxic compounds rendered cells non-viable, then their elimination by decomposition by visible light, might allow cells to germinate and form colonies —i.e., recover.

Numerous experiments were made to detect a possible unusual sensitivity of *S. griseus* to the ultra-violet irradiated menstruum, with negative results. Air from the vicinity of the mercury lamp was bubbled for one hour through a suspension of cells, with no sign of toxicity. Sterile nutrient agar plates were irradiated for one hour, then inoculated with spores with no sign of more than a negligibly lower count than controls. Non-irradiated spores were added to suspensions of irradiated spores to see whether substances given off by irradiated cells might be toxic to non-irradiated cells with negative results. Any toxicity that was observed in these experiments never resulted in more than about 20 per cent killing, whereas ultra-violet irradiated cells under the conditions of our recovery experiments had usually a survival of the order of 1×10^{-6}.

Discussion.—The evidence presented suggests that in visible light we have a factor which uniformly, reproduceably causes the recovery of many of the cells which had been rendered non-viable by ultra-violet irradiation. The action is probably directly on the cells rather than on the menstruum, and there was no evidence of any experimental artifacts being involved. The magnitude of the effect makes it likely that a key factor in the lethal effect of ultra-violet light is being affected by the visible light. Whether or not light-induced recovery bears a relation to other types of recovery previously recorded is difficult to say. All such studies, as well as studies on ultra-violet induced mutation must be evaluated on the basis of whether light-induced recovery has played a part. There can be no doubt that the latter is at least partly responsible in some cases for the notorious variability of ultra-violet-mutation studies.

That the phenomena described here are not confined to actinomycetes only is suggested by observations in the older literature (summarized in the review by Prat) of the antagonism to ultra-violet light of radiations of other wave lengths. These observations were usually made on cells or tissues irradiated by a mixture of wave lengths as compared to monochromatic irradiations, but consistently showed that the biological effect of ultra-violet light was diminished by simultaneous irradiation with visible or infra-red light. Since such effects were usually slight, these older experiments are hard to evaluate. They, as well as other chemical and physical evidence of antagonism of ultra-violet and other light (also summarized by Prat), suggest the phenomenon may be a general one.

While it is premature to do more than speculate on the mechanism involved in light-induced recovery, the following is suggested as a working hypothesis. Much of the killing effect of ultra-violet light is due to a light-labile alteration of some constituent in the cell. Exposure to visible light restores this altered constituent to its former state.

The powerful action of light on the resuscitation of the ultra-violet treated cell leads us to hope that further study of this phenomenon may yield clues leading to the discovery of factors causing similar recovery from x-irradiation of irradiation from radioactive materials. There is thus the possibility of at least a partial physiotherapy of radiation injury.

Of great importance is the relation of recovery to the mutagenic action of ultra-violet light. Work is in progress on light-induced recovery in the various microbial groups, such as bacteria, yeasts, fungi, and bacteriophage, and on the genetic aspects of light-induced recovery in microorganisms. . . .

DEFENSES AGAINST INFECTION

PHAGOCYTOSIS

White blood cells of several kinds take part in phagocytosis. The most numerous, and the most important (at least in the early stages of most bacterial infections), are the polymorphonuclear leucocytes. These are somewhat larger than the erythrocytes, or red blood cells. Addition of a small quantity of a hemolytic substance, such as saponin, to a drop of blood disrupts the membranes of the red blood cells, allowing the hemoglobin to escape; destruction of the red blood cells allows the various kinds of colorless cells (leucocytes) present in the blood to be seen, more distinctly if stained by such a substance as hematoxylin dye. Polymorphonuclear leucocytes have a densely granular cytoplasm and a nucleus that is bent or horseshoe-shaped in young cells and that consists of three or four densely stained lobes in older cells.

Polymorphonuclear leucocytes, sometimes called granulocytes, are an important component of the body's defense against invading bacteria. They are actively motile; and on the microscope slide they may be seen migrating toward clumps of bacteria present in the field, a process known as *chemotaxis*. Their cell surfaces are sticky, and they tend to adhere to the surfaces of solid particles. They possess amoeboid movement and are capable of squirming between the endothelial cells that make up the lining of capillaries.

Granulocytes actively ingest bacteria or other foreign particles with which they come in contact. Most kinds of bacteria, once ingested, are killed and dissolved. The dissolution and perhaps the killing of the bacteria appear to be associated with enzymes present in the cytoplasm of the granulocytes. It is very possible, in fact, that the granules present are actually solid, or inactive, storage forms of the cells' digestive enzymes, which are rendered soluble as soon as a bacterium or group of bacteria are ingested.

The blood contains another type of phagocyte, the *macrophage,* also called the *mononuclear leucocyte* or *monocyte*. These are as a rule much less numerous than the polymorphonuclears, are larger, and possess an oval or spherical nucleus and an abundance of clear, non-granular cytoplasm. Similar, perhaps identical, cells are present outside the blood vessels, lying quietly or migrating among the cells of the body tissues. These are known as *histiocytes*. Monocytes mobilize in an abscess or infected sites in great numbers, usually a few days after the polymorphonuclear leucocytes have been mobilized; they ingest and destroy bacteria and also senile leucocytes and damaged body cells, thus playing the role of a scavenger in preparing the infected or injured site for repair.

A great deal of research has been done on the process of phago-cytosis. Careful, detailed microscopical studies have been made of the ingestion and disappearance of bacteria and other particles during phagocytosis. Biochemical studies on the composition of leucocytes have been carried out, and their enzymes have been investigated in great detail. Work of this kind has been performed in nearly all the principal medical schools throughout the world. The Rockefeller Institute for Medical Research in New York City is prominent in this research, and its *Journal of Experimental Medicine* contains scores of excellent papers on phagocytosis, by Rockefeller Institute scientists and others. Dr. James G. Hirsch, a member of the Rockefeller Institute staff, is one of the world's most eminent students of phagocytosis. The paper presented below is quite typical of recent studies of phagocytosis.

From *J. Exp. Med.*,
116:827–847, 1962.

CINEMICROPHOTOGRAPHIC OBSERVATIONS ON GRANULE LYSIS IN POLYMORPHONUCLEAR LEUCOCYTES DURING PHAGOCYTOSIS

BY JAMES G. HIRSCH

In a previous study, techniques were described for isolating in a reasonable state of purity the cytoplasmic granules of rabbit polymorphonuclear leucocytes. Several hydrolytic enzymes and the bactericidal agent phagocytin were found to be localized in these structures. Exposure *in vitro* of leucocyte granules to a pH below 5.0, or to certain surface-active substances resulted in lysis with liberation of their enzymes in a soluble form. Cytoplasmic granules in polymorphonuclear leucocytes thus resemble closely the structures called lysosomes by deDuve and coworkers [1959].

Disappearance of cytoplasmic granules following ingestion of bacteria was first observed by Robineaux and Frederic in phase contrast motion pictures of guinea pig leucocytes [1955]. Degranulation and release of granule-associated enzymes into soluble cell fractions have also been demonstrated during phagocytosis of microorganisms by rabbit polymorphonuclear leucocytes. Two possible mechanisms were proposed for granule rupture associated with particle ingestion: (*a*) acid lysis, with the fall in intracellular pH resulting from the increased lactic acid production known to occur during phagocytosis, and (*b*) fusion of the granule membrane with the invaginated cell membrane surrounding the engulfed material, in which event granule contents would be discharged directly into the phagocytic vacuole. This communication presents the findings on direct microscopic observation and motion picture recording of granule rupture accompanying phagocytosis of microorganisms by human, rabbit, and chicken polymorphonuclear leucocytes.

METHODS

Leucocytes were prepared from heparinized human blood by the dextran sedimentation technique, from rabbit peritoneal exudates induced by glycogen, and from buffy coats of heparinized chicken blood. White cells were suspended in homologous plasma or serum.

Microorganisms to be engulfed were *Bacillus megaterium* and zymosan (yeast cell walls), selected because of their large size and susceptibility to phagocytosis. *B. megaterium* was cultured overnight at 38°C in penassay broth, collected and washed in saline on the centrifuge, and finally suspended in saline. Zymosan (Standard Brands, Inc., New York) was boiled in saline for 10 minutes, followed by repeated washing and suspension in saline. Concentrations of leucocytes and of organisms to be ingested were adjusted to yield satisfactory densities on the slide preparations.

Thin preparations of the mixture of phagocytes and organisms were essential for adequate visualization of intracellular events. Standard microscope slides and 20 × 40 mm coverslips were washed in non-ionic detergent and rinsed thoroughly. At the time of use these were polished with a lint-free cloth and all dust was removed with the aid of a camel's hair brush. Approximately 0.02 ml drops of the cell and particle suspensions were mixed on one end of the slide, after which 0.003 ml of the mixture was transferred to the coverslip by means of a platinum loop. On inversion of the coverslip a rapid and uniform spread of the suspension indicated adequate cleanliness. The coverslips were sealed with petroleum jelly and placed in a microscope stage incubator at 38°C (human cells) or 40°C (rabbit and chicken cells). On microscopic examination three zones were apparent in these slide preparations: (*a*) a large central area too thick to permit adequate definition of intracellular structures, (*b*) a peripheral very thin zone in which cells were ruptured or so confined as to interfere with locomotion, and (*c*) a narrow strip between the above two, showing well spread cells exhibiting normal movements.

Cinemicrophotography under phase contrast was accomplished using a Zeiss ultraphot II with neofluar phase 100 × oil immersion objective, a monocular tube with a Zeiss kpl 10 × ocular, and an arriflex 16 mm motor-driven camera without lenses. Motion pictures were recorded under tungsten illumination on kodak tri X negative film at a speed of 10 frames per second.

Illustrations shown in this communication were enlarged in the ultraphot from single frames of the motion pictures. An adapter to accommodate 16 mm film was constructed to replace the microscope stage. Enlargements were made employing a 1 × objective with no condenser. Kodabromide F-4 paper was placed in the 4 × 5 inch film cassettes. Final magnification could not be calculated with precision, but ranged from 1000 to 2000.

RESULTS

Under the conditions employed polymorphonuclear leucocytes spread out and began to move almost immediately. Direction of locomotion was random, usually in a zigzag pattern, until the granulocyte came within 10 to 20 microns of a zymosan particle or *Bacillus megaterium,* at which time chemotaxis became evident with directed straight line movement towards the microorganism. Phago- cytosis was accomplished readily. On contact the leucocyte and particle appeared to become firmly adherent; the cell cytoplasm then flowed around the particles until the process of ingestion was completed by fusion of cell membranes. At all stages cell membrane was seen to be in close apposition to the material being ingested; no visible extracellular fluid was taken in along with the particle, and no vacuoles were seen surrounding the engulfed material until the degranulation reaction began (see below). Completion of phagocytosis usually required 30 seconds to 2 minutes, depending on rate of locomotion of the cell and size of the objects to be ingested.

During ingestion of zymosan or of *B. megaterium* by human neutrophilic leucocytes, cytoplasmic granules seemed to become adherent to the surface of the engulfed particle. Disappearance of granules was readily noted during the over-all process, but the small dimensions of human leucocytic granules ren- dered it impossible to observe directly individual granule lysis or to establish with certainty the site of granule rupture. Clear zones formed slowly about both types of particles and frequently it appeared that granule lysis preceded and was associated with vacuole formation.

Rabbit polymorphonuclear leucocyte granules also adhered to the surface of the engulfed microorganisms, and their size was sufficiently large to allow ob- servations on individual granule disruption. Granule lysis characteristically began early in the course of engulfment; as soon as firm attachment between phagocyte and particle had been made and the enveloping process had begun, granules in contact with the invaginating cell membrane began to rupture. As ingestion proceeded additional granules which encountered the zymosan or *B. megaterium* lysed. Upon completion of engulfment most of the granules had disappeared except for those located in other parts of the cell. With passage of time and shift in intracellular position of the engulfed organism, additional granules contacting it frequently ruptured. In healthy cells granule lysis was never seen spontaneously (*i.e.* in the absence of phagocytosis), nor did granules rupture in cytoplasmic sites removed from the engulfed particle. Rabbit leucocytic de- granulation consisted of rapid, almost explosive disappearance of the phase- dense granules, leaving in their place bright empty-appearing spaces which themselves soon vanished. The over-all effect was one of flashes of light re- placing the dark granules. In many instances vacuoles were seen to form about the engulfed organisms as soon as granule lysis began; these vacuoles enlarged with continuing granule rupture, giving the impression that granule contents were discharged into the space between the microorganisms and the invaginated cell membrane surrounding it.

Studies on chicken polymorphonuclear leucocytes made possible observations on detailed morphologic aspects of granule lysis. Cytoplasmic granules in these cells are oblong bodies much larger than those of rabbit white cells. Those granules adjacent to the particle being ingested began to lyse early in the course of phagocytosis. Approximately 0.1 second prior to rupture they commonly rounded up. Rupture was usually completed in 0.1 to 0.2 second, leaving in place of the phase-dense granule a bright clear space with a tiny round phase-dense body in its center. Concurrent with bursting of the granule a rim of darkening was visible on the adjacent surface of the particle being ingested. Lysis of chicken leucocyte granules appeared to be a violent process, accompanied by recoil of adjacent granules. The instantaneous rupture was followed by rapid (usually several seconds in duration) disappearance of all residuals; first the tiny dark remnant in the clear zone faded, then the phase-dense area on the surface of the adjacent engulfed particle lightened, and the clear zone began to shrink towards the organism, finally to disappear completely. On occasions granule rupture spread contiguously; *i.e.,* following initial lysis an adjacent granule or granules ruptured into the remaining clear zone. Spreading lysis of this type occasionally led to formation of a clear zone occupying up to one-fourth of the cell cytoplasm. As was the case with individual ruptured granules, these large clear zones gradually contracted towards the engulfed particle and eventually disappeared.

DISCUSSION

The observation of Robineaux and Frederic [1955] that cytoplasmic granules disappeared in guinea pig polymorphonuclear leucocytes which had engulfed microbes has been confirmed by Sbarra *et al.* [1961]. Our previous studies [1960] and the present work establish that degranulation also follows phagocytosis in human, rabbit, and chicken leucocytes.

Robineaux and Frederic suspected that granule disruption occurred principally in sites adjacent to the engulfed particles, but their techniques were not adequate to provide a clear picture of detailed aspects of granule lysis. Two technical factors employed in the present work made it possible to visualize these detailed aspects: (*a*) Use of the chicken polymorphonuclear leucocyte was advantageous because of the large size of its cytoplasmic granules; and (*b*) motion pictures were taken at a "fast motion" speed of 10 frames per second, rather than employing a time lapse system. The degranulation reaction proceeds with such rapidity that much of the process would be missed under conditions of time lapse exposure.

Possible mechanisms proposed for degranulation during phagocytosis were: (*a*) fusion between granule membrane and the leucocyte membrane overlying the engulfed particle, with discharge of granule contents into the phagocytic vacuole, and (*b*) rupture of the granule membrane by acidity developed during the ingestion process, with discharge of granule contents into the cytoplasm. Results of the present investigation may now be discussed in relation to these two working hypotheses. Five points may be considered:

1. Lysis occurred only in those granules situated adjacent to the engulfed organism (or, more precisely, the invaginated cell membrane surrounding it), or in apposition to clear zones remaining from prior granule rupture. Obviously this finding fits well with the membrane fusion concept. If, on the other hand, degranulation were due to acidity or other physicochemical changes in the cytoplasm, then it becomes necessary to explain why these conditions develop only in the immediate vicinity of the engulfed material.

2. Visible vacuoles commonly began to form about the ingested organisms shortly after initial granule rupture, and these vacuoles grew larger as degranulation progressed. This observation also supports the notion of membrane fusion, with discharge of granule contents into the "extracellular" space surrounding the microorganism leading to the formation of a visible vacuole. Conceivably, however, degranulation and vacuole formation could be correlated in time but not be directly related one to the other.

3. Rupture of an individual granule in the chicken polymorphonuclear leucocyte was rapid and violent, with recoil of adjacent structures and creation of a sharply demarcated clear zone somewhat larger than the original granule, thus suggesting that granule contents were under tension. At first thought these findings seem to favor rupture of granules free in the cytoplasm. However, if a rigid granule membrane were to fuse with a cell membrane having distensible properties, a similar picture might result. Firm attachment between leucocytic cell surface and the engulfed particle could impair immediate spread of granule contents in the phagocytic vacuole; such spread when it did occur could then account for contraction of the clear zone towards the ingested organism as observed.

4. Associated with lysis of chicken leucocytic granules was a rim of darkening on the adjacent surface of the particle being engulfed. One possible explanation of this phenomenon is that some granule contents combine with and alter the phase properties of the surface of the organism (if membrane fusion occurs) or the cell membrane surrounding the organism (if free lysis takes place). Alternatively, the rim of darkening might be an optical "artifact," the phase density in this case being merely a consequence of change in the adjacent medium; *i.e.*, replacement of adjacent cytoplasm by a clear zone.

5. A small, phase-dense, round body was often seen in the clear zone resulting from lysis of chicken white cell granules. The possibility that this body is contracted granule membrane comes to mind, a concept which does not fit with the membrane fusion hypothesis. The perfectly round nature and very rapid disappearance of this structure speak somewhat against its being granule membrane. Perhaps this dense body is contained within the granules, to be liberated and then dissolved following their rupture.

The membrane fusion hypothesis cannot in any event be established firmly by observations made with the light microscope. Further evidence may be obtained by electron microscopy; specimens for this purpose would need to be fixed early in the ingestion process and would probably require considerable searching, since lysis proceeds so rapidly (0.1 second or less) that the likelihood of catching a granule in the act of discharging would be small.

Why does lysis not occur in granules situated near the membrane of the normal cell which has not engulfed foreign material? In ameboid cells a clear zone, the hyaloplasm, lies immediately beneath the cell membrane and might well prevent contact between cytoplasmic organelles and the inner membrane surface; it is thus necessary to suppose that the hyaloplasm disappears from invaginated cell membranes overlying engulfed particles. In addition, change in charge or other physicochemical properties of cell membrane to which a microorganism has become attached might lead to development of an attractive force or a lytic system for granular membrane.

Markedly degranulated leucocytes survived for periods up to 1 hour as evidenced by continuing cell locomotion. Since the mature polymorphonuclear leucocyte has a short life span *in vitro* (less than 24 hours), no observations could be made on the possibility of regeneration of granules. These highly specialized cells are incapable of reproduction and deficient in endoplasmic reticulum; it seems on these grounds highly unlikely that regeneration of granules can occur.

Metchnikoff originally coined the name phagocyte (eating cell) to signify their similarity to free-living motile cells whose nutrition was dependent on ingestion of food particles from the environment. He also pointed out that phagocytes were richly endowed with a variety of ferments to enable them efficiently to perform their task. We may now add to these early concepts of Metchnikoff the fact that, in mammalian polymorphonuclear leucocytes, digestive enzymes and some antibacterial substances are sequestered within cytoplasmic granules (lysosomes), to be discharged at time of need directly into or about the "stomach" or digestive vacuole surrounding engulfed foreign matter. It remains to be determined whether or not similar mechanisms operate in other types of phagocytic cells such as macrophages and free-living amebae. . . .

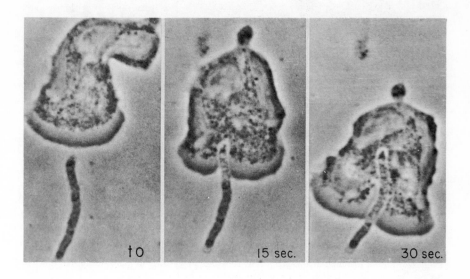

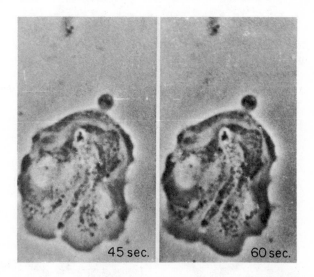

FIGURE 1

Phagocytosis of *Bacillus megaterium* by a human polymorphonuclear leucocyte. Note the over-all reduction in content of cytoplasmic granulations by the time ingestion has been completed. Approximately × 2000.

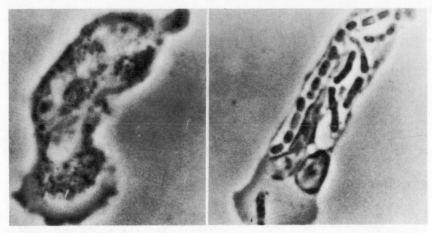

FIGURE 2

Comparison of a normal human polymorphonuclear leucocyte (left), and a granulocyte which has engulfed large numbers of *Bacillus megaterium* (right). Large vacuoles have formed about the bacteria; in the living cell the microorganisms floated freely in these clear zones. The cell at right also shows nearly complete disappearance of cytoplasmic granules and increased phase contrast definition of nuclear structures. This degranulated leucocyte exhibited normal locomotion and phagocytic function, proceeding to ingest in normal fashion the bacillus seen at the bottom of the picture. Approximately × 2000.

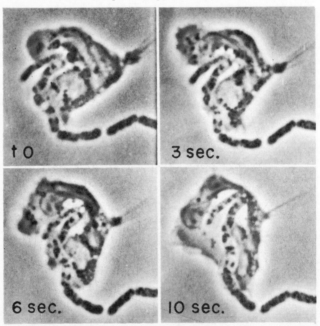

FIGURE 3

Phagocytosis of *Bacillus megaterium* by a rabbit polymorphonuclear leucocyte. Note the disappearance of cytoplasmic granules, and the formation of a visible vacuole about the microorganism following granule lysis. Approximately × 1000.

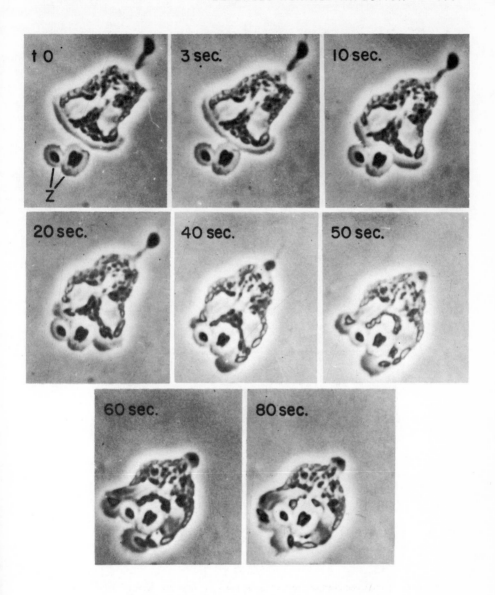

FIGURE 4

Phagocytosis of zymosan bodies by a chicken polymorphonuclear leucocyte. The phase contrast appearance of the zymosan particles (Z) is seen in the t o picture; they are composed of a central phase-dense nucleoid structure and a surrounding layer of cell wall which appears lighter.

The sequence of prints demonstrates over-all aspects of the phagocytic process. Note the close apposition of leucocytic membrane to the zymosan. Clear zones seen in the cytoplasm in 50 and 60 second prints are the result of granule lysis, demonstrated more clearly in following illustrations. Note the reduction in content of granules in the leading half of the leucocyte; *i.e.,* that part of the cell containing the zymosan particles. Approximately × 1000.

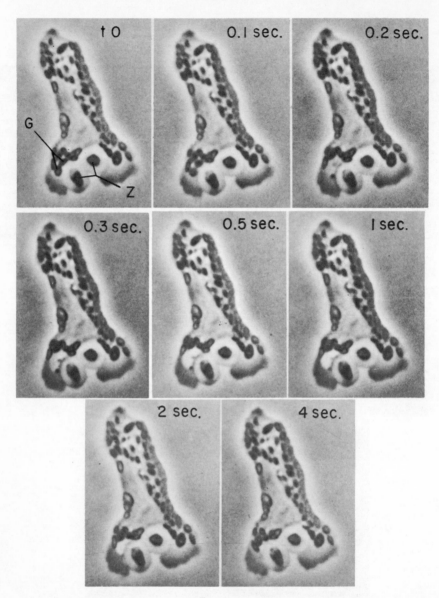

FIGURE 5

Sequence of enlargements at short time intervals to illustrate detailed aspects of chicken leucocyte granule rupture during phagocytosis of zymosan. Both the phase-dense oval bodies (Z) and the surrounding large transparent zones are parts of the zymosan. Phagocytosis of the two zymosan particles is at this stage not yet completed. Two cytoplasmic granules (G) which lie adjacent to one of the zymosan bodies are seen to round up (o.1 second), then disappear with formation of a clear zone in the cytoplasm (o.2 second and o.3 second). Note at this stage also the two small phase-dense bodies within the clear zone, and the appearance of a phase-dense layer on the surface of the zymosan adjacent to the clear zone. During the following 4 seconds the small dense bodies disappear, the phase-dense appearance of the adjacent surface of the zymosan fades, and the clear zone gradually contracts towards the engulfed particles. Approximately × [1850].

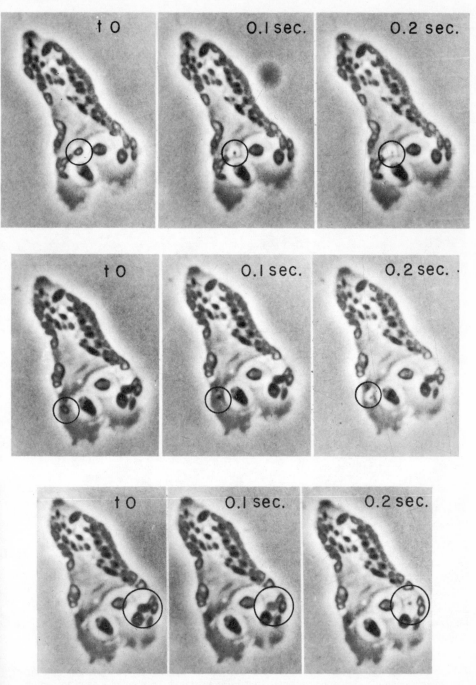

FIGURE 6

The same cell as in Fig. 5 at a slightly later stage of phagocytosis showing, in the circled areas, lysis of individual cytoplasmic granules. The rapidity and morphologic features of the lytic process are illustrated. Approximately × 2000.

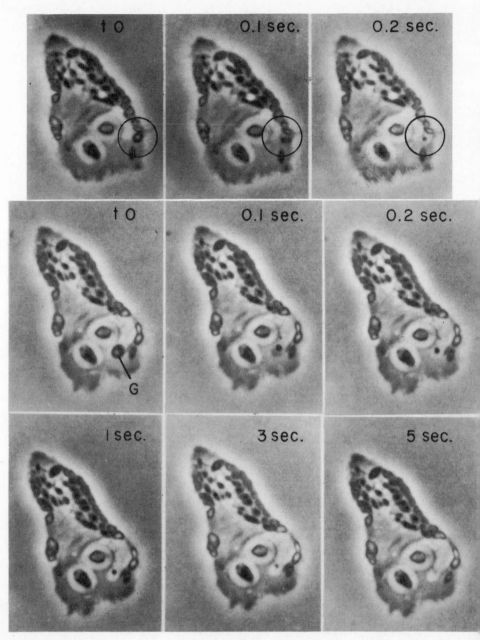

FIGURE 7

The same cell as that in Figs. 5 and 6, showing in the upper sequence a granule rupturing in apposition to a clear zone remaining from previous granule lysis, rather than in apposition to the engulfed particle. The lower sequence illustrates the lysis of a particularly large cytoplasmic granule (*G*) which results in formation of an unusually large dense body. This dense body gradually fades from view over the course of 5 seconds. Approximately × 2000.

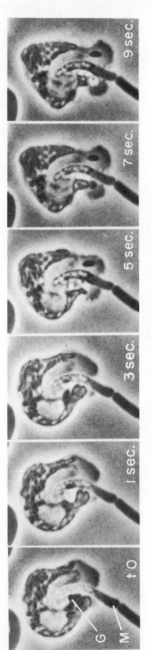

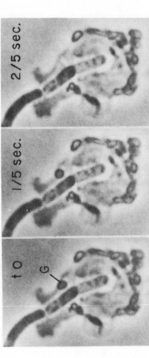

FIGURE 8

Lysis of chicken polymorphonuclear leucocyte granules (*G*) during ingestion of *Bacillus megaterium* (*M*). The upper sequence shows particularly well the change in phase contrast appearance of the bacterial surface following granule rupture. At 1 second a phase-dense area is seen on the bacterial surface adjacent to the clear zone resulting from lysis of several granules (*G*) seen in the *t* o print. At 3 seconds this dense area is less prominent, but now the entire surface of the engulfed bacillus appears darker. With continuing granule lysis the edges of the bacterium appear to darken further. Approximately × [800].

The lower sequence illustrates lysis of an individual large granule (*G*) in a chicken leucocyte engulfing *Bacillus megaterium*. The granule becomes somewhat rounded (1/5 second) and disappears from view (2/5 second). At this time no dense body or sharp clear zone is seen; rather there is seen on careful examination of the 2/5-second print a "ghost" of the granule, that is a fine membrane, oval in shape and appearing to be firmly attached to the surface of the bacterial cell, or to the invisible invaginated cell membrane overlying it. Approximately × [1200].

Knowledge of antibody reactions began with Pasteur's studies on immunity to disease. Late in the nineteenth century, antibodies were identified as complex compounds existing in the blood and to some extent in other body fluids and secretions. Any substance which, when injected into or fed to a vertebrate, elicits antibody formation was designated as an *antigen*. Proteins, many carbohydrates, and bacterial cells will usually elicit antibody formation if injected into man or one of the experimental animals. The bacteriological literature of the nineteenth century seemed to regard the whole cells of pathogenic bacteria as the antigens which elicited the antibodies that made humans and experimental animals resistant or immune to infection by these pathogens. Each species of bacterium and each strain within many of the bacterial species could elicit immunity specific to itself.

A sharper definition of the meaning of *antigen* arose through the discovery that in certain bacteria possessing flagella, at least two antigens could be distinguished: a flagellar antigen and a somatic or bacterial-wall antigen.

As knowledge of bacterial metabolism increased, it became evident that bacterial cells and their capsules are composed of a large variety of proteins, carbohydrates, and mucopolysaccharides and that many of these, when isolated, are antigens. It gradually became apparent that the antigenic response of humans and experimental animals to invading bacterial cells is in fact the sum of many antigenic responses to a great variety of chemical compounds (antigens) derived from the bacterial cells. Some of these are compounds released from the bacterial cytoplasm by the rupture or dissolution of the bacterial cell walls; others are antigenic compounds loosely held on the periphery of the bacterial cell wall or are substances diffusing outward through the cytoplasmic membrane and the cell wall. Thus the number of distinct antigenic compounds present in the blood or body fluids, derived from a single species of bacterial pathogen, may be quite large. Some of these compounds may be feebly antigenic, and others may be potent antigens. Some may elicit an antibody response that is important in eliminating the pathogen and in protecting the host from subsequent infection, whereas others may be of little or no importance.

The analysis of bacterial cells into their components is one of the major efforts of contemporary microbiology. Immunochemical techniques have proved valuable in identifying the antigens and in giving an indication of their purity and their importance.

The immunochemical techniques employed are based upon the precipitin reaction. Under certain conditions, a soluble antibody molecule may combine chemically with one or more antigen molecules which are in solution or in clear suspension, resulting in the formation of a precipitate. In water or other liquids, turbidity may develop, and the precipitate may eventually settle to the bottom. When homologous antibody and antigen are put in separate holes, or "wells," in a gel (gelatin or agar), each diffuses radially; the invisible diffusion halos of antigen and antibody eventually meet, laying down a cloudy precipitate along the line of contact. The sole functions of the gel are to retard diffusion and hold the precipitate in place. A perfectly clear, transparent agar is an ideal gel for this purpose.

Several devices have been designed for conveniently exhibiting the lines of precipitate where antigens and antibodies meet. In the method described in the paper below, clear agar is poured into a petri dish and allowed to solidify. A circular well is punched out of the center of the agar sheet, and five or six similar wells are punched out surrounding it. A suspension of antiserum may be placed in the center well, and various preparations containing known or suspected antigens are put in the wells around the periphery. As indicated above, both antigen and antibody molecules diffuse through the agar; the several lines of precipitates formed may serve as an indication of how many antigen-antibody pairs, capable of forming precipitate at the given temperatures and concentrations, are present. If a single antigen is present in the fluid in two neighboring peripheral wells, the diffusion rates may be so nearly identical that a single, continuous line of precipitate results. This is called a *reaction of identity*.

Imaginative, carefully planned application of these techniques (e.g., the article by Halbert and Keatinge on pages 197 to 209 in this volume) has opened new avenues of investigation, giving promise of fresh and important insights into the nature and number of the antigenic substances produced by pathogenic bacteria and into the several defenses the host organism is capable of developing to cope with these substances.

The following article is one of the classics of modern microbiology. Its author, Dr. Ouchterlony, is Professor of Bacteriology at Göteborg University, Göteborg, Sweden.

From *Acta Pathol. Microbiol. Scand.,*
26:507–515, 1949.

ANTIGEN-ANTIBODY REACTIONS IN GELS

BY ÖRJAN OUCHTERLONY

If an antigen and the corresponding precipitating or flocculating antibody diffuse towards each other in an indifferent gel of suitable consistency, e.g. gelatin or agar, there will appear, under certain circumstances, a streak- or bandlike precipitation in the gel between the two diffusing components. The reaction is probably of the same nature as that between an antigen and an antibody. The position of this band of precipitation in relation to the two diffusion centres depends inter alia upon the initial concentration and the diffusion velocity of the two reacting substances. A similar reaction is obtained if antigens are allowed to diffuse in gels with a suitable constant proportion of antibodies or vice versa. In these cases the reaction appears at varying distances from the diffusion centre, depending partly on the concentration, the diffusion velocity and the time elapsed before the reaction becomes visible.

The fact that antigens and antibodies diffusing in gel react in this way was observed many years ago. In 1905 Bechhold describes a reaction of this kind in 1% gelatin between goat serum and anti-goat-serum obtained from rabbit. A similar observation is made by Nicolle, Cesari and Debains in 1920 for diphtheria toxin and antitoxin from horse. Diphtheria immune serum as surface layer in a tube was allowed to react with toxin mixed with an equal part of 10% gelatin. They then observed a disc-like precipitation of toxin-antitoxin character. In 1932–34 Petrie, Sia and Chung and Kirkbride and Cohen described specific and non-specific "halo" phenomena around bacteria colonies growing on substrates containing immune serum. Their investigations concern meningococci, pneumococci and Shiga dysentery bacilli. The method was later worked out for the serological typing of meningo- and pneumococci. In 1948 diphtheria toxin-antitoxin reactions of similar character were described by the author.

The object of this paper is to describe, by means of some model experiments, toxin-antitoxin reactions in solid and semisolid agar media.

EXPERIMENTAL

Most experiments were carried out with diphtheria toxin and antitoxin. The former was culture filtrate of the strain PW 8, cultivated on Philippe Loiseau's medium. The latter was serum from a horse, immunized with toxin and toxoid, from such a culture filtrate. Growing bacteria of the same strain were used in some of the tests instead of the toxin already produced in the filtrate.

The experiments were made in Petri dishes (about 10 cm. in diameter) where both or one of the reacting substances were allowed to diffuse in an agar medium of varying composition. A thin layer of 2% washed agar was poured into each dish in order to obtain an even layer for the diffusion medium.

Test 1.—On a surface layer of serum agar (agar 1%, serum 50%) two so-called penicillin cups were placed at a distance of about 3 cm. from each other. One of the cups was filled with toxin (27 FIU/ml) and the other with antitoxin (45 FIU/ml). The plate was then incubated at 37°C. After 48 hours a thin line, which gradually spread laterally, could be seen between the two cups. Fig. 1 shows a reaction of this kind.

Test 2.—On a surface layer of serum agar to which antitoxin had been added (5 FIU/ml medium), a cup was placed and filled with toxin (25 FIU/ml). The plate was incubated at 37°C and after 48 hours a "halo"-like, sharply defined, bandlike precipitation was observed around the diffusion centre. The precipitation grew more and more distinct during the following days. Figs. 2 and 3 show the appearance of this kind of reaction.

Test 3.—The initial conditions were the same in this experiment as in test 2, but the cup was refilled at the same rate as toxin diffused into the medium. The time of observation was extended and under these conditions the "halo"

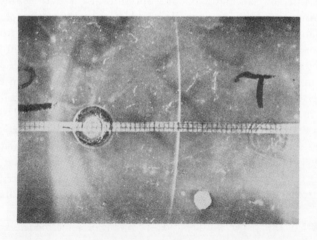

FIGURE 1

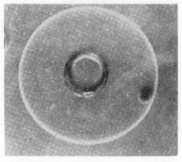

FIGURE 2   FIGURE 3

was found to move slowly out from the diffusion centre. After two refillings the "halo" was 18 mm in diameter on the second day. After seven further refillings and nine days, the same "halo" was 20.5 mm in diameter.

Test 4.—The initial conditions were the same as in test 2, but there was a higher concentration of antitoxin in the plate. More or less sharply defined, multiple, concentrical "halo" formations were observed by extending the observation time. The first, and most distinct "halo" corresponded to that described in the previous experiment. Multiple "halo" reactions of this kind are shown in fig. 4.

Test 5.—In the same way as in test 2, a series of immune serum plates were poured with media of decreasing antitoxin concentration 10 — 5 — 2.5 — 1.25 FIU/ml. A cup with diphtheria toxin 25 FIU/ml was placed on each plate. The plates were then incubated at 37°C. "Halo" formations appeared around the diffusion centre in the immune serum agar. The lower the content of immune serum the larger the diameter of the most distinct "halo" on each plate. The precipitation appeared first in the plate with the highest concentration of immune serum.

Test 6.—On an immune serum agar plate, prepared as in test 2, the strain PW 8 was spread. The plate was incubated at 37°. After 24 hours a "halo"

FIGURE 4

FIGURE 5

formation appeared around the growing strain. This became more intense during the following days. Fig. 5 shows such a "halo" formation.

Test 7.—A diphtheria strain which had given varying results in toxicity tests in vivo was spread on a plate prepared as in test 2. The inoculum was taken from a culture which had given positive results in toxicity tests on guinea pigs. The plate was incubated at 37°. "Halo" phenomena could be observed after a few days around some of the growing colonies whereas others showed no such reactions even after continued observation. Positive results were obtained in toxicity tests on guinea pigs from colonies showing "halo" formations. Those without "halo" formations gave negative results.

Test 8.—On a serum agar plate as in test 1 two basins (2 × 5 cm. in size), placed at right angles to each other, were cut out from the surface layer. One was filled with toxin 25 FIU/ml and the other with antitoxin 25 FIU/ml. The plate was then incubated at 37°. After 48 hours a streak was observed between the two basins. Several streaks appeared later. These streaks grew peripherally, later forming constant angles to the toxin and antitoxin basins. The most distinct

FIGURE 6

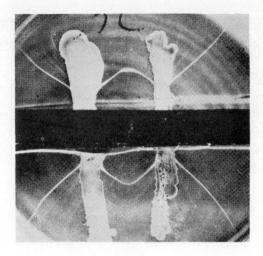

FIGURE 7

streak formed an angle of 39° with the edge of the immune serum basin. Fig. 6 shows such an experiment.

Test 9.—A bottom layer of ordinary agar was poured into a Petri dish with high edges. When it had congealed a mixture of horse serum and ordinary meat infusion agar in equal parts was poured over it in a thin layer. After refrigeration, a two cm. strip was removed from the surface layer and replaced by serum agar to which diphtheria immune serum (200 FIU/ml substrate) had been added. The plate was then inoculated with the strain PW 8 in two parallel streaks at right angles to the "trench" and incubated at 37°. After 24 hours raylike precipitates were observed extending from the streaks of bacteria. Gradually these precipitates grew out peripherally and on meeting similar precipitates from adjacent strains, turned away from their original direction to confluate with them. Such precipitates interfering with each other are shown in fig. 7.

Test 10.—The same initial conditions were used as in the previous experiment. On this plate, PW 8, one atoxic and three toxic diphtheria strains, tested on guinea pigs, were inoculated side by side. After incubation for a couple of days, precipitates were extending from all of the five strains, those from PW 8 and from the toxic strains interfering with each other, whereas those proceeding from the atoxic strain crossed the toxin-antitoxin streaks of the toxinproducing strains without being affected. They did, however, interfere with a weaker streak, proceeding from PW 8. Interference and crossing phenomena of this kind are shown in fig. 8.

DISCUSSION

The reactions described above show a definite resemblance to flocculation reactions between toxins and antitoxins observed during experiments in tubes

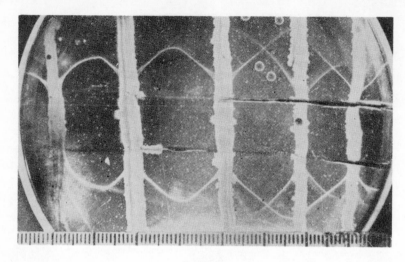

FIGURE 8

with liquid media. A certain time after mixing of the reacting substances the antigen-antibody compound precipitates, first in tubes, where the components react in optimal proportions. Around this flocculation optimum, a weaker and slower flocculation appears within a limited zone. By further addition of either of the reacting substances it is possible to dissolve floccules already formed. If, in tube tests, several antigen-antibody systems are simultaneously present, they react independently with regard to flocculation time, optimal proportions of the different systems etc. and do not interfere with one another. With diphtheria toxin and immune serum two different flocculation optima are sometimes observed. One of the flocculation reactions is a true toxin-antitoxin reaction and the other a so-called false flocculation, with a possible participation of a bacterial antigen and a corresponding antibody. . . .

In diffusion tests in agar gels with diphtheria toxins and antitoxins, the distinct streaklike precipitation appears to be of toxin-antitoxin character, since it does not appear, if the toxin has been destroyed before the experiment, e.g. by heating. The position of the toxin-antitoxin streak in the diffusion medium is probably influenced by such factors as where optimal proportions between antigens and antibodies appear, the time necessary for the formation of a visible precipitate and the concentration—threshold value—of the reaction. In immune serum which contains several kinds of antibodies beside antitoxin multiple precipitates appear, somewhat less distinct however, than the toxin-antitoxin reaction. In the diphtheria immune sera examined, up to four antibody components beside antitoxin could be detected. By absorption of immune serum with appropriate antigens selective disappearance of the corresponding streaks of the precipitation spectrum was achieved.

The toxin-antitoxin precipitate in the agar seems to be soluble in excess of one of the reacting substances, as is the case with the floccules in liquid media. This phenomenon may possibly explain the results in test 3, where by a further addition of toxin, the radius of the "halo" increased considerably during the course of the experiment.

Tests 9 and 10 show that adjacent reactions between reacting substances of the same kind affect each other in such a way that the streaklike precipitations interfere with one another. That is not the case in antigen-antibody reactions of different kinds, where so-called crossphenomena appear instead. It is possible with the help of these interference- and crossreactions, to demonstrate serological difference or identity between different precipitating or flocculating substances.

When antigens and antibodies diffuse at right angles to each other . . . there were only moderate variations in the angle formed by the precipitation streak with the directions of diffusion. For approximately equivalent quantities of toxin and antitoxin, as in test 8, the angle to the diffusion direction of the toxin was $38°–39°$. In multiple reactions it was observed that the angle for other precipitations differed in certain cases from that of the toxin-antitoxin reaction. Most often the origin of the precipitation streak also varied. The size of the angle and the situation of its vertex seemed to depend on such factors as the concentration, the diffusion velocity of the reacting substances and the proportions in which they combine.

As regards the sensitivity of the precipitation reaction in agar between diphtheria toxin and antitoxin it may be mentioned that visible, clearly defined streaks appeared in concentrations down to one FIU/ml.

The quantitative conditions of the reaction are demonstrated schematically in fig. 9. Toxin of a strength of T_4 and T_5 diffuse in media with a varying anti-

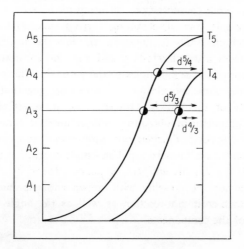

FIGURE 9

toxin content A_1 to A_5. The reaction is presumed to appear at determined optimal concentrations of T and A. Optimal concentration in this method does not necessarily mean the same as optimal ratio in tube flocculation. The example given demonstrates the following.

Toxin with a lower strength than T_5 does not give any visible reaction in the medium with the content of antitoxin A_5, lower than T_4 none in A_4 and so on, down to the sensitivity limit of the reaction which is about one FIU/ml.

With an antitoxin content of A_3 toxin strength T_5 gives a reaction farther away from the diffusion centre than with an antitoxin content of A_4. Toxin of the same strength in media with successively lower content of antitoxin gives a precipitation more and more peripherally situated.

With an antitoxin content of A_3, toxin of strength T_5 gives a more peripheral reaction than toxin of strength T_4. With a constant content of antitoxin, the stronger the toxin tested, the more peripheral the reaction.

The examples illustrate that the concentration of the reacting substances are of decisive importance for whether and where the reaction will appear. Furthermore if the concentration of one of the substances is known, it is even possible, under certain conditions, to estimate the other substance quantitatively.

The application of the diffusion method thus also affords a possibility of making a quantitative comparison between the toxinproducing capacity of different diphtheria strains. The more strongly toxinproducing the tested strain is, in the higher concentration of immune serum does it give a positive reaction.

According to the facts stated above it is important to choose suitable concentrations of immune serum in the diffusion medium to obtain visible reactions. Since in practice there is often very little or nothing known about the toxinproducing capacity of the strains to be tested, it may be difficult to choose the adequate immune serum concentrations on using media with a constant content of antitoxin. A simple way of obtaining varying concentrations in the same medium within definite limits is, however, to allow the antibody to diffuse in a substrate, e.g. from a trench (tests 9 and 10) and to arrange the diffusion direction of the antigen at right angles to the antibody. This method does not, it is true, give the same possibility of estimating quantitatively the toxinproducing capacity of the growing bacteria, but it nevertheless offers other advantages. The simplicity of obtaining suitable immune serum concentrations has already been discussed. Furthermore, interference and crossreactions with known antigens contribute to more rapid and more conclusive results. The most convenient way to register the antigen components found by this method is to note their interference and crossing with known antigens and the position in relation to the toxin-antitoxin reaction as well as the angle to the diffusion direction of one of the components. . . .

Bacterial disease is generally caused by chemical substances—toxins or antigens—synthesized by pathogenic bacteria present in the blood or tissues or within the mouth, intestine, or other body cavities. These substances are considered to be *toxins* if they produce symptoms of illness or of poisoning when administered in small amounts; they are considered to be *antigens* if, on administration to man or to one of the experimental animal species, they cause specific *antibodies* to appear in blood or in tissue fluids. Toxins are often antigenic. The specific antibodies produced in response to the presence of a bacterial product combine with and often destroy that product, thus forming an important part of man's defense against bacterial disease.

Over a period of many years, microbiologists have been attempting to identify the bacterial toxins that cause disease. The identification of the diphtheria toxin and of the tetanus toxin were two of the early triumphs in this effort.

It has been known for several years that a variety of human diseases are associated with, and apparently caused by, streptococcal infections: septic sore throat, scarlet fever, rheumatic fever, and rheumatic heart disease are some of these. The streptococci are, of course, a large group of species or strains, difficult to classify. The *erythrogenic toxin,* an antigen produced by some of these strains, is the substance that causes the skin rash and reddening associated with scarlet fever. A few years ago, there were indications that *streptolysin O,* a product of other streptococcus strains, causes the heart damage in rheumatic heart disease.

When streptococci are grown in liquid nutrient medium and are then removed by centrifugation or filtration, a variety of bacterial products are found to be present in the medium. Many of these substances are proteins, and some are enzymes. Some of these may be formed within the bacterial cell and diffuse through the cell membrane into the surrounding culture medium; others may be formed at the cell membrane as part of the bacterial wall. The precise site of formation of these substances is not known. Those that are antigens can often be detected by the methods reported in the paper that follows.

Dr. Seymour Halbert, the author of the paper here presented, attempted to find out how many substances are produced by the pathogenic streptococci in liquid culture media and in the blood and tissue fluids of infected humans. Over a period of several years he has been carrying out extensive experiments to determine the validity of the sup-position that streptolysin O is the real cause of rheumatic heart disease.

Dense suspensions of streptococcal cells were grown, often in 200-gallon containers; the living and dead bacterial cells were removed by filtration; and the culture medium was concentrated, dried, and sub-jected to a great variety of chemical fractionation and purification procedures.

Ouchterlony immunodiffusion techniques (see preceding paper) were used in the beginning to determine how many antigens were present in a given batch. Later, a still more sensitive detection test known as immunoelectrophoresis also was employed. It may reason-ably be assumed that most humans have at some time in their lives been infected by streptococci and carry in their blood antibodies against a number of the substances produced by streptococcal cells. The Ouchter-lony tests (which were reported in detail in earlier papers by Dr. Hal-bert) involved the placement of pooled human serum in the center well of an Ouchterlony plate and of various fractions of streptococcal cul-ture filtrates in the peripheral wells. At least 16 antigens were identified by formation of line precipitates with antibodies present in the pooled human serum.

It turns out that streptolysin O is indeed implicated in the causation of rheumatic heart disease. Several of the other antigens present in the filtered culture medium have been identified. A few of them are well-known enzymes.

The work here reported was carried out in the Departments of Microbiology and Ophthalmology, College of Physicians and Surgeons, Columbia University. Dr. Halbert is now Professor of Microbiology at the University of Miami, Florida, and is continuing his studies of rheumatic heart disease. Miss Keatinge is continuing her graduate study at Columbia University.

From *J. Exp. Med.*,
113:1013–1028, 1961.

THE ANALYSIS OF STREPTOCOCCAL INFECTIONS

*Immunoelectrophoretic Observations on Extracellular
Antigens Detectable with Human Antibodies*

BY SEYMOUR P. HALBERT AND SUZANNE L. KEATINGE

A complete understanding of any human infection requires knowledge of the toxins or antigens that the organisms release *in vivo* during the disease process. Until recently, discovery of these substances has tended to be on a chance basis. Demonstration of the resolution and sensitivity of antigen-antibody reactions in agar gels has opened the way to a rational analysis of the total number of antibody responses occurring after a given infection, and thereby the total number of antigens or toxins released by the organisms during its residence in the tissues. These immunological tools also furnish the means for following the purification of each of the antigens thus shown to be released *in vivo* when human convalescent serum, or its equivalent, is used as the source of detecting antibodies.

Studies of this sort with human streptococcal infections have been carried out during recent years in this laboratory. It has been found that sera from patients with rheumatic fever are very rich in precipitating antibodies to *extracellular* streptococcal products, but contain few if any to *cellular* extracts prepared from the same strain. These observations have since been confirmed. It appears from these data that non–type-specific cellular antigens often do not reach antibody forming sites in significant amounts during human disease, while extracellular ones do so in great numbers. It was found that a high proportion of sera from non-rheumatic patients without recent histories of upper respiratory infections also contained antibodies to some of the streptococcal extracellular products, although many fewer than were seen with sera from rheumatic fever subjects. For this reason, normal pooled human gamma globulin, such as is used for the prophylaxis of measles or poliomyelitis, was also tested against streptococcal products. A number of different globulin samples were shown to be extraordinarily rich in antibodies against the extracellular secretions and to be poor in antibodies against cellular components. On Ouchterlony plates, several normal human gamma globulin specimens revealed at least 8 or 9 distinct antistreptococcal antibodies. When large scale purifications of crude culture supernates containing these antigens were carried out by means of continuous flow electrophoresis combined with column chromatography on calcium phosphate gels, it was then found that the systems were even more complex. At least sixteen extracellular antigens were detected for which humans had spontaneously developed antibodies.

Because of the possibility that this number still failed to account for all of the extracellular antigens which the streptococcus might secrete *in vivo* during human infections, immunoelectrophoretic observations have now been made. It was also the aim of this study to explore the potential usefulness of this technique for the analysis of individual sera from rheumatic fever patients during the course of infection.

MATERIALS AND METHODS

Most of these present observations have been made with culture supernate concentrates or fractions derived from the C203S strain of Group A hemolytic streptococci. The preparation of the crude culture concentrates and the various assay procedures have been described previously. . . . The immunoelectrophoretic technique of Grabar and Williams [1953] as modified by Scheidegger [1955] was used principally. Early difficulties had been encountered in these studies because of the need to use highly concentrated gamma globulin (16 per cent) solutions which were precipitated by the low ionic strength buffer used in the agar. These difficulties have been adequately overcome by the following procedure. Bacto-agar (Difco) in 0.8 per cent solution was dissolved in veronal-acetate buffer pH 8.2 μ0.05 containing 1:10,000 merthiolate, 4.0 ml. of agar being poured per slide (1 × 4 inches). The antigen wells were usually 2.0 mm. in diameter, and the serum trench was 4.0 mm. wide. The distance between the edges of the two was 6.4 mm. in most instances. A potential difference of 6 to 7 volts/cm. was employed, usually for 2½ hours when the small slides were used. When longer migration paths were required, 1 × 6, or 2 × 10 inch slides were prepared with a proportionate volume of agar and increase in the well dimensions, as well as longer exposure to the electrical field. The electrophoreses were carried out at 4°C. without a cover, but precipitin development was allowed to take place at room temperature. This helped alleviate non-specific precipitation of the gamma globulin due to the low ionic strength of the system.

Comparative tests were carried out with four horse antisera. These had been prepared by hyperimmunization with different Group A streptococcal filtrates. The Richards strain of streptococcus was the source of the antigens for the lyophilized serum from the Wellcome Laboratories, Beckenham, England. It was reconstituted to contain 2,000 Todd antistreptolysin units/ml. The NY 5 strain of streptococcus, and a mixture of filtrates from 8 different streptococcal types respectively, furnished the antigens for two other horse sera kindly supplied by

Dr. L. Hanson of Göteborg, Sweden. The gamma globulin fractions of the latter two had been separated and concentrated roughly tenfold. The fourth horse antiserum was obtained from Lederle Laboratories, New York, as therapeutic scarlet fever antitoxin, lot 1570. It was prepared by injection of filtrates of the NY 5 strain plus filtrates of two other strains. The globulin fraction was concentrated about sixfold.

In addition, samples of sera from rheumatic fever patients were obtained from the Irvington House Hospital, Irvington, New York, and similarly tested. These represented samples obtained at varying times during an acute episode of the illness. Control sera from 22 non-rheumatic patients were obtained from the diagnostic laboratory of the Presbyterian Hospital, New York. The *Haemophilus influenzae* cell extract was obtained by sodium desoxycholate lysis of type b cells as described elsewhere.

RESULTS

When tested at a concentration of 47 or 74 mg. protein/ml. against pooled normal human gamma globulin, the crude concentrate used as a standard reference system (H461-A3) revealed a total of at least twenty distinct antigen-antibody systems. These were often best visualized when longer migration paths were used, but the reproducibility of the patterns was excellent. Composite results of numerous tests are diagrammatically represented in Fig. 1, in which the electrophoretically separated streptococcal antigens are revealed with human antibodies. The complexity of the systems, and the possibility that even larger numbers exist was suggested by the prolonged development of some of the slides for 4 to 7 days. Under these circumstances, either several new bands appeared, *or* artifactual splitting occurred of some of the arcs. These possible new systems usually developed in the region of arcs 4, 6, and 10. In addition, fuzzy precipitates at the level of the antigen well were frequently seen on either side of it. The latter may represent still other systems in which the relative concentrations of the antigens were too low to produce clear precipitin lines.

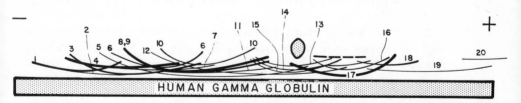

FIGURE 1

Diagrammatic representation of Group A streptococcal extracellular antigens detectable with naturally occurring human antibodies in normal pooled gamma globulin, as seen by immunoelectrophoresis. The crude streptococcal concentrate (H461A3) was prepared from the C203S strain of streptococcus, and showed these results at 47 or 74 mg. protein/ml. The human gamma globulin was a 16 per cent solution, as used for the prophylaxis of measles or poliomyelitis.

Other crude concentrates prepared from the same strain of organisms showed surprising variability in relation to the reference system. Several batches revealed significantly fewer precipitin arcs at equivalent protein concentrations, while one showed two heavy arcs where only one was present in the reference system. The differences found between the reference system and this latter crude concentrate is shown in Fig. 2 a. It may be seen that H414-6 showed two large heavy arcs in the region of No. 17 of the standard system, in contrast to the latter. It is possible that this represents an increased concentration of the components forming arcs 13 or 15. In addition, the crude H414-6 reveals a suggestion of at least one other component not seen in the standard. This is indicated by the arrow below arc 4. The No. 2 arc is only occasionally seen in the reference system, but may be barely detected in the photograph with crude H414-6, indicated by the arrow below arc 1. Although other systems may be present, these were not visualized often enough for certainty. Those which are noted in Fig. 1 possessed sufficiently different mobilities from each other to almost certainly represent distinct components. It may be pointed out that the large scale cultures (25 liters) yielding these supernate concentrates were all grown in the same dialyzable medium under presumably identical conditions. The inoculum for each batch was taken from a fresh vial of lyophilized organisms drawn from a large supply prepared at one time and stored *in vacuo* at 4°C. It therefore seems that intensity of production of some of these antigens depends on presently intangible factors. In Fig. 2 b the reproducibility of the reference pattern may be noted, as well as the occurrence of 8 or 9 systems with a Group C streptococcal culture filtrate concentrate.

When crude concentrates differing in their apparent immunoelectrophoretic composition were placed in adjacent wells on Ouchterlony plates, no instances were observed of "non-identity" reactions. This at first suggested that the differences between the C203S crude concentrates were quantitative, not qualitative. However, recent absorption studies with the standard reference system (H461A3) and other crude preparations indicate that the crude H414-6 may actually contain a component not present in the other concentrates (see inner arrow, Fig. 2 a).

In previous studies, a number of components had been separated in varying states of immunological purity. Attempts have now been made to identify the arcs seen with the reference crude concentrate and gamma globulin. Examples of these tests are shown in Fig. 3, with proteinase precursor, desoxyribonuclease B (DNase B), streptolysin O . . . and the "antigen excess" components. The arcs were tentatively identified on the basis of the correlation of the electrophoretic mobilities in the crude concentrates and the separated fractions, as well as by the appearance of the precipitin lines. The data thus far obtained are summarized in Table 1. In all of these instances electrophoretic mobility coincided quite well with arcs seen in the crude concentrate, except in the case of DNase B. The arc of this purified fraction was often displaced

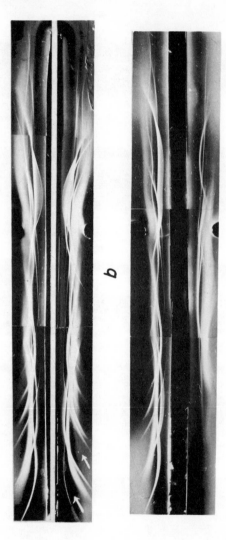

a

b

FIGURE 2

Streptococcal extracellular antigens detectable with naturally occurring human antibodies in normal pooled human gamma globulin. Slides 2 × 10 inches were used, and 6 volts/cm. were applied for 4½ hours. Photographed after 3 days of development at room temperature. Gamma globulin, Squibb, lot 321-1, was placed in the trenches. Anode on the right.

(*a*) Upper antigen well: standard reference crude concentrate (H461A3) of group A strain C203S, 74 mg./ml.
   Lower antigen well: crude concentrate H414-6 of the same strain, 56 mg./ml.

(*b*) Upper antigen well: standard reference crude concentrate H461A3, 74 mg./ml.
   Lower antigen well: crude concentrate of a group C streptococcal strain, 40 mg./ml.

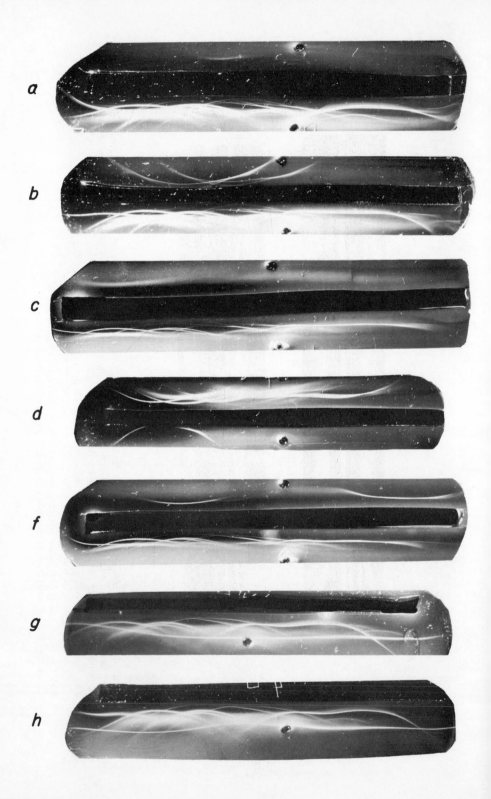

TABLE I

Tentative Identification of Group A Streptococcal Extracellular Antigens Involved in Precipitin Arcs Seen with the Reference Crude Concentrate H461A3 and Normal Pooled Gamma Globulin

Arc	Tentative identification
I	Proteinase precursor
4	C carbohydrate-protein (complex ?)
5, 12	"Antigen excess" components, No. 5 possibly related to erythrogenic toxin
10	Streptolysin O
17	Desoxyribonuclease B
19	Far left component

toward the anode (see Fig. 3 *f*). Identification of these arcs has also been made by a method recently described, using a second trench as antigen source, and the results confirm the above data. Examples of the latter tests with proteinase precursor and streptolysin O are shown in Figs. 3 *g* and 3 *h*. . . .

In addition, six individual *whole* sera from rheumatic fever patients were tested as antibody source, using the reference crude streptococcal concentrate as antigen. Examples of the types of results with the [three] strongest sera are shown in Fig. 4. It may be seen that they were remarkably potent, and the one tested in Fig. 4 *a* revealed at least 14 distinct precipitin systems. The results in Fig. 4 *d* [omitted here] were recorded at 24 hours, a development time which experience had shown to be inadequate for detecting faint systems. In spite of this, *at least* 12 arcs could be readily seen on the original photograph. The two other sera tested, but not shown in Fig. 4, showed fewer and less intense streptococcal precipitin systems, 9–10 in one case, and 6–7 in the other. In contrast to these findings, *whole* sera from 22 control non-rheumatic patients were found to contain considerably fewer and fainter precipitin arcs. . . . The number of systems found with the control sera varied from 0 to 8, as can be seen in

FIGURE 3

Tests of previously isolated streptococcal extracellular fractions by immunoelectrophoresis with normal pooled human gamma globulin as antibody source, on 1- × 4-inch slides. In all instances, the anode was at the right. In *a, b, c,* and *f*, the reference crude concentrate (H461A3) was in the lower well, while in *d* . . . it was in the upper. All of the fractions were dissolved from the lyophilized state at 1 mg./ml. in veronal acetate buffer. In *c* and *f*, the development period was short, somewhat less than 1 day, while the others were developed for 2 to 3 days. In *g* and *h*, the reference crude (H461A3) was separated by electrophoresis, and gamma globulin was placed in the upper trench. The isolated antigen was placed in the lower thin trench. The separated components tested were:

(*a*) Streptolysin O
(*b*) "Antigen excess" components
(*c*) C-carbohydrate-protein (complex?)
(*d*) Crystalline proteinase precursor, rechromatographed and crystallized 3 times
(*e*) "Far left" antigen [omitted here]
(*f*) Desoxyribonuclease B, contaminated with "antigen excess" components
(*g*) Proteinase precursor, as in *d*
(*h*) Streptolysin O, as in *a*

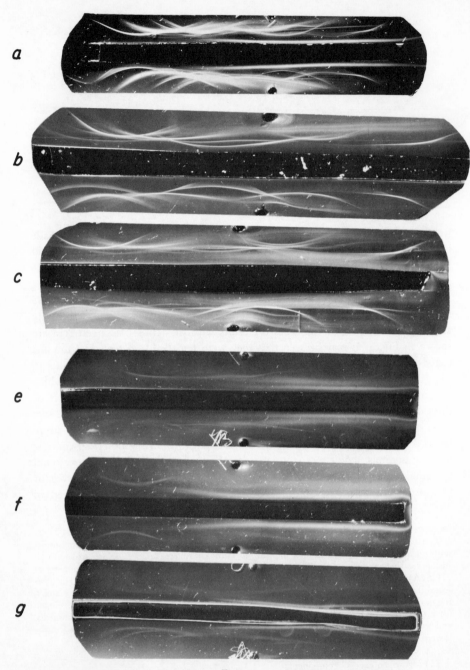

FIGURE 4

Immunoelectrophoretic analysis of streptococcal extracellular antigens as revealed by antibodies in *whole* sera from [three] rheumatic (a, b, c) and three control patients, (e, f, g) on 1- × 4-inch slides. In all instances, the upper wells contained the reference crude concentrate (H461A3) at 74 mg./ml., while the lower contained crude concentrate (H414–6) at 57 mg./ml. The anode was placed on the right. Development time 2 days. . . [Fig. 4 *d* is omitted here.]

TABLE 2

No. of Precipitin Arcs Seen with Sera from Non-rheumatic Patients with a Variety of Illnesses

The single patient showing 8 systems was suffering from an acute attack of streptococcal pharyngitis and pneumonia, and had an antistreptolysin titer of 1250 units/ml.

No. of arcs	No. of sera
0	1
1	1
2	7
3	3
4	4
5	2
6	1
7	2
8	1

Table 2. The patients from whom the control sera were obtained suffered from a variety of disturbances such as ulcerative colitis, goiter, hypertensive heart disease, malignancy, etc., and were mostly in the age group from 30 to 60. The only patient whose serum revealed 8 precipitin arcs was an 18 year old boy suffering from an acute streptococcal pharyngitis and bronchopneumonia. His antistreptolysin titer was 1250 units/ml., but no history or evidence of rheumatic fever was found. Three other patients of this control group were found to have had a mild upper respiratory infection just prior to the blood sampling. The differences between the observed precipitins in the control and rheumatic group is similar in general to that found in previous studies using the more poorly resolving Ouchterlony technic.

Because of the possibility that the rheumatic patients possessed antibodies against streptococcal products that were not present in the normal gamma globulin, a few tests were carried out with such sera and gamma globulin being placed in adjacent wells in Ouchterlony plates, and tested against a crude streptococcal concentrate. In no instances were any antigen-antibody systems found with the sera from rheumatic patients, which were not represented with normal gamma globulin. The relative concentrations of these antibodies might be somewhat different in the individual sera, however, as evidenced by the position and intensity of several of the bands. Examples of these data are shown in Fig. 5.

As a check on the validity of the observations made with pooled human gamma globulin, a few sera from rheumatic patients were tested against several of the isolated streptococcal components described earlier. The purpose of these tests was to see if individual patients' whole sera contained antibodies not present in the normal gamma globulin. Such was not the case, and when a single band was found between a given fraction and the gamma globulin, not more than one band was seen with an individual rheumatic serum. Typical results are shown in Fig. 6 with one serum sample. In this case, desoxyribonuclease B,

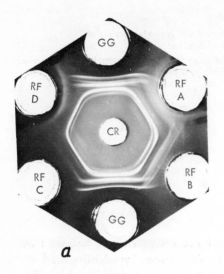 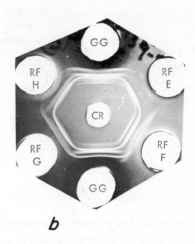

FIGURE 5

Comparative tests of human normal pooled gamma globulin and whole sera from rheumatic fever patients. The sera in *a* were also examined by immunoelectrophoresis, but those in *b* were not.

CR   —crude concentrate H461A3 at 10 mg./ml.
GG   —gamma globulin
RF-A, RF-B, etc.—different rheumatic fever sera

diphosphopyridinenucleotidase, and streptolysin O showed single bands such as were found earlier with gamma globulin. The "antigen excess" fraction showed two components also similar to the reactions seen with gamma globulin, as did the proteinase precursor containing 105II. The *Haemophilus influenzae* extract failed to show any precipitin bands with this serum while gamma globulin revealed 2 to 3 systems.

DISCUSSION

The data presented amply confirm the complexity of the immune response to streptococcal extracellular products in humans. It is clear that at least 20 such substances are secreted or released by the organisms in the tissues during the course of human infections. Suggestions were obtained that perhaps even more are involved. It may be stressed that almost all of the observations made here were with materials derived from a single Group A hemolytic streptococcal strain (C203S) isolated from a patient with scarlet fever about 25 years ago. It is possible that a detailed examination of different streptococcal strains may reveal still other substances not secreted by the C203S strain. However, it may be advisable to grow the organisms in a completely defined medium when comparing different strains, in view of the variability shown above with a number

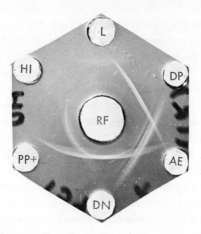

FIGURE 6

Reactions of whole serum from a rheumatic fever patient with several isolated streptococcal antigens. The serum is in the central well.

L   —streptolysin O, Group C, 0.4 mg./ml.
DP —diphosphopyridine nucleotidase, 0.1 mg./ml.
AE —"antigen excess" components, 0.1 mg./ml.
DN —desoxyribonuclease B, 0.1 mg./ml.
PP+—proteinase precursor containing fraction 105 II
HI —*Haemophilus influenzae* bacterial cell extract

of crude concentrates produced by the C203S organisms under presumably identical conditions in a dialysate medium.

Should this variability of antigen production be resolved, it would be of
importance to examine the potential capacity of streptococcal strains isolated
from patients with distinct clinical syndromes, with respect to the synthesis of
these extracellular antigens. Different streptococcal types and groups could also
be examined in this way. The clarity and complexity of the reactions found
above with individual rheumatic fever serums, indicate that a re-investigation
of the "total" antibody responses in patients with various post-streptococcal
states might also be most informative. Such a study is planned.

Although emphasis has been placed on *non–type-specific* components in this
series of studies, the possibility that *type-specific* antigens may also be detected
and explored with such methods is worthy of consideration. It would only be
necessary to employ serum from individual convalescent patients and to use the
streptococcal strain causing their illness as antigen source. In searching for
cellular type-specific antigens, sonic-vibrated cell extracts could be used as
antigen, and absorption of the sera could be carried out with other streptococcal strains in order to remove *non–type-specific cellular* antibodies. In view
of the relative paucity of the latter seen in our laboratory, it seems likely that
this problem would be considerably less difficult than in the case of the extracellular antigens.

Although substantial progress has already been made in identifying the arcs of precipitate in the reference system, it is clear that much more effort will be required to complete the identification. The method of using a second trench as antigen source as shown in Figs. 3 *g* and 3 *h* will be of much help in this respect. It should be possible to sort out the components in the numerous and often rather complex chromatographic fractions isolated previously.

It has long been known that patients with rheumatic fever tend to develop significantly higher average antibody responses to a number of streptococcal extracellular antigens, than do patients with uncomplicated streptococcal infections. For example, this has been shown to be true for antistreptolysin "O," anti-streptokinase, anti-hyaluronidase, anti-streptococcal proteinase and anti-desoxyribonuclease. Total gamma globulin levels in the sera of rheumatic patients also tend to be higher than those found in patients with uncomplicated streptococcal infections. It is therefore worth stressing the anti-streptococcal potency of human gamma globulin, and individual rheumatic sera found here, in comparison to antibody concentrates prepared from hyperimmunized horses. The latter had received numerous injections of other streptococcal filtrates over long periods of time. The abundance of the human antibodies suggests that the antigenic stimuli with these substances in man must be rather intense, and probably frequently repetitive. This finding tends to support the working hypothesis developed earlier implicating antigen-antibody complexes of streptolysin "O" in the pathogenesis of rheumatic fever.

It is also important to point out that the horses were immunized with filtratés of a number of streptococcal strains other than the C203S strain. In spite of this, they responded with antibodies of apparently the same specificities as those seen in human gamma globulin which were reactive with C203S products. These findings imply that the other streptococcal strains secrete many similar or identical extracellular substances.

In some instances, prolonged development of the slides resulted in possible splitting of a few of the arcs of precipitate. Some of these cases might have been artifact, since the site and appearance of the extra arcs seemed to coincide. In a few instances, however, the extra arcs were somewhat different in appearance from the arc which appeared first. It is possible that the arrangement used here produces a relative excess of some antibody concentrations, unlike the numerous tests carried out with these systems in Ouchterlony plates. In the latter instances, no clear cut suggestion of antibody excess artifacts were encountered, although antigen excess effects, such as precipitin band abolition, or splitting, were seen. However, the large amount of accumulated data indicate that the *early* developing precipitin bands or arcs undoubtedly represent distinct streptococcal antigen-antibody systems. In addition, the twenty precipitin arcs seen in immunoelectrophoresis almost certainly are valid because of the different electrophoretic mobilities represented by the arcs.

Finally, it may be pointed out that the distribution of antigens seen here by immunoelectrophoresis appeared to be slightly different from that found by paper-supported continuous flow electrophoresis of crude concentrates. In those separations, however, acetate buffer at pH 6.0 was used as compared to veronal acetate at pH 8.2 in the present experiments. In addition, differences in adsorption properties of the two supporting media could contribute to the observed differences in the patterns. . . .

In recent years, a major preoccupation of microbiologists and immunologists has been the study of the chemical composition and structure of antibodies, of the manner of their formation, and of the way in which they exert their protective effect. A formidable body of research literature has been written. It would be premature to say that we fully understand the nature and functioning of antibodies, but a great deal has been learned.

By 1896 it had been shown that antibodies are proteins present in the globulin portion of the blood serum, i.e., in the portion that is insoluble in pure water but soluble in salt solution. The theory that the serum globulin is a complex mixture of chemical species was confirmed about 30 years later, when methods of separating blood proteins according to their migration rate in an electric field were worked out. This method of protein analysis, called *electrophoresis,* was significantly improved and successfully applied to the separation of blood proteins by a distinguished Swedish physical chemist, Arne Tiselius, in 1933. (Tiselius was awarded a Nobel Prize for this discovery.) The protein that moved most slowly during electrophoresis of serum at alkaline pH, termed *gamma globulin,* was found to contain nearly all the antibodies in the blood.

By a variety of methods it was possible to estimate the size and shape of gamma globulin molecules. By 1949 it seemed likely that gamma globulin is a fairly homogeneous suspension of ellipsoid molecules, about five times as long as broad, with a molecular weight of at least 156,000.

Electrophoresis sorts out particles that are identical or nearly identical in charge, or more precisely, in charge-to-bulk ratio. Centrifugation, on the other hand, sorts out particles essentially according to their density. In the 1940s and 1950s ultracentrifuges were developed as precision instruments for separation of large-molecular compounds. Dr. H. G. Kunkel and his colleagues at the Rockefeller Institute were pioneers in the study of antibody molecules by ultracentrifugation. In extensive studies in 1956–1957 they proved that gamma globulin is far from being a simple homogeneous substance; there are at least two forms: a normal form, designated as 7 S, with a molecular weight probably around 150,000 or less, and a larger, heavier component designated as 19 S.

According to current views, *gamma globulin* designates a hetero-geneous collection of proteins similar in solubility relations and electric charge. The three main components of human gamma globulin are the 7 S gamma globulin, comprising perhaps 75 to 80 per cent of the total, with a molecular weight of 150,000 to 190,000; a gamma$_2$ A globulin, comprising around 10 per cent of the whole and consisting of mole-cules the same size as the 7 S fraction but containing carbohydrate; and macroglobulin, or the 19 S gamma globulin, comprising 5 to 10 per cent of the whole. At least the first and the third fractions have antibody activity.

Antibody combines chemically with antigen. Specifically, *epitopes,* certain determinants, groups, or sites on the surface of the antigen, combine chemically with *paratopes,* complementary chemical groups, or sites, on the surface of the antibody molecule. The chemical bonds between an epitope and a paratope are apparently comparatively weak, such as those involved in London–Van der Waals forces or hydrogen bonds, rather than strong covalent bonds.

Dr. Cebra used silk fibroin, a fairly simple fibrous protein, in his attempts to determine the size and the amino acid composition of the epitopes on a protein antigen, and the binding forces between such an epitope and the corresponding paratope on its specific antibody. Silk fibroin provided more revealing information than could be obtained when a more complex globular tissue protein was employed. When raw silk was dissolved and injected into rabbits, it caused the produc-tion of an antifibroin antibody. Reaction of this antibody with fibroin could be blocked by the presence of small fragments of the large fibroin molecule, which presumably combined with the paratope of the anti-fibroin antibody. The composition of the small fibroin fragments that were able to accomplish this blockage was studied as a basis for an understanding of the chemical union between the antigen, the fibroin, and its antibody.

The foundations of immunology date from Edward Jenner's studies on the prevention of smallpox by inoculation, in the latter part of the eighteenth century. Steady advancement was made after Louis Pasteur's work on the immunization of chickens against fowl cholera (1880) and of other domestic animals against anthrax (1881). Karl Land-steiner's classic treatise "The Specificity of Serological Reactions" (1945) may be regarded as the beginning of the science of immuno-chemistry. In recent years, progress toward a clear understanding of the antibody defense mechanism has been especially rapid. The paper repro-duced below is one of the more important of recent contributions. Additional information may be found in the following:

Philip D. McMaster, Antibody Formation, *The Cell,* edited by

Jean Brachet and Alfred E. Mirsky, vol. V, part 2, 1961, pp. 323–404.

H. Metzger and S. J. Singer, Binding Capacity of Reductively Fragmented Antibodies to the 2,4-Dinitro-phenol Group Gamma Globulin, *Science,* 142:674–676, 1963.

Robert Cruikshank (ed.), "Modern Trends in Immunology," vol. 1, Butterworths, Washington, D.C., 1963, 263 pp.

From *J. Immunol.*,
86:190–214, 1961.

STUDIES ON THE COMBINING SITES
OF THE PROTEIN ANTIGEN SILK FIBROIN

BY JOHN J. CEBRA

I

Characterization of the Fibroin–Rabbit Antifibroin System

The size and chemical structures of the regions of any protein which react specifically with antibody are not yet known. Present evidence indicates that protein antigens are multivalent and that each "combining site" is a limited region of the whole molecule. Attempts to reveal the chemical structures which impart immunologic specificity to a protein have taken three main forms: a) chemical alteration of the antigen, b) use of synthetic polypeptides and poly α-amino acids as determinant groupings, and c) partial degradation of a protein antigen. The latter approach, first used by Landsteiner and Chase in 1933, involves isolation of fragments which retain serologic activity with respect to antibody specific for the intact antigen.

Using the analytic approach, Landsteiner, in 1942, isolated fractions from partial acid hydrolysates of the antigen silk fibroin. These fractions did not precipitate with antifibroin sera, but some were able to inhibit the precipitin reaction occurring between fibroin and antifibroin. The active preparations had an approximate average chain length of 7–12 amino acid residues. Hara in 1956 obtained similar results with another structural protein, eye lens crystallin.

Attempts to obtain small peptide fragments of native globular protein antigens that retain reactivity with antibody prepared to the intact protein have not been successful. Products of the enzymic hydrolysis of ribonuclease and ovalbumin had no inhibitory effect in the corresponding precipitin systems. Porter, however, was able to isolate an active fragment from chymotryptic hydrolysates of bovine serum albumin (BSA). This apparently homogeneous fragment had a molecular weight of about 12,000 and when present in the low molar ratio to whole BSA of 1.8 sufficed to give complete inhibition.

A number of other protein antigens such as human serum albumin, diphtheria toxin, rabbit gamma-globulin, and human gamma-globulin have yielded fragments on enzymic hydrolysis that were capable of precipitating with antibody stimulated by the intact antigen. All of these fragments appear to represent relatively large segments of the whole antigen.

The lack of success in obtaining small active peptides from globular proteins in contrast to the results reported for the fibrous proteins silk fibroin and lens crystallin may reflect the importance of secondary-tertiary structure in maintaining intact the combining sites of globular proteins. The loss of immunologic activity of the BSA fragment upon reduction of disulfide links and of ribonuclease upon oxidation or reduction of the disulfide bonds or alkaline denaturation support this suggestion.

To avoid the complexities inherent in the folded structure of globular proteins the fibrous protein silk fibroin was selected for this present study of the immunologic determinant grouping of a protein antigen. This antigen was also recommended by the simplicity of its amino acid composition—glycine, alanine, serine and tyrosine together account for 90% of the total nitrogen—and the possibility of repeating sequences in the molecule. In this paper the immunologic and chemical characteristics of several fibroin-rabbit antifibroin systems are reported and the inhibitory effect of fragments of fibroin produced by a rather specific enzymic cleavage is studied quantitatively. In the following papers the isolation of single peptides and their interaction with specific antibody are reported.

MATERIALS AND METHODS

Raw silk (13/15 denier) of *Bombyx mori* was degummed in a 1% sodium oleate solution maintained at 97–100°C for 1 hr as described by Lucas *et al.* [1957]. The washed and dried fibroin was dissolved in concentrated LiBr solution. Ordinarily 20 g of fibroin was dispersed in 500 ml of 10 N LiBr by maintaining the suspension at 37°C for 3 hr. The viscous solution, after passage through Schleicher and Schull No. 1450½ paper, was dialyzed against 12 L of precooled distilled water at 4.5°C. After six daily changes of outer fluid the last dialysate gave a negative test for Br⁻. Aqueous solutions of fibroin were stored at 4.5°C and they remained fluid for between 10 and 30 days, after which they set spontaneously to a stiff gel. Treatment of the highly viscous fibroin solution in any way which results in exposure to interfaces leads to formation of insoluble strands and films of fibroin. Soluble fibroin is polydisperse but it probably consists of a spectrum of chain lengths all containing like sequences, as does dextran for example.

Fibroin prepared as described was shown to contain 17.55% nitrogen corrected for ash and moisture and had an average molecular weight of 50,000–60,000 determined by a modification of the dinitrophenyl method with use of the method of hydrolysis (37°C, 27 days) suggested by Lucas *et al.* [1957] for minimal degradation of dinitrophenyl-glycine. The breakdown of dinitrophenyl-glycine under the conditions of hydrolysis was 20%. This value represents a maximal correction factor since it has been shown that glycine, serine and alanine occur as amino-terminal residues and the dinitrophenyl derivatives of the latter two amino acids are considerably more stable to acid hydrolysis. The molecular weight calculated on the basis of 17.55% nitrogen in fibroin and the presence of only a single peptide chain per molecule was 60,000 (no correction) or 48,600 (maximum correction).

Rabbit antisera were obtained by intraperitoneal injections of fibroin absorbed to blood charcoal; intravenous injection of fluid antigen was not effective in eliciting a useful antibody response. A 17-ml aliquot of fibroin containing 340 mg of protein was added with gentle stirring to a suspension of 5.0 g of acid washed blood charcoal in 73 ml of saline. After 30 min 100 ml of saline and 10 ml of 5% phenol were added and the suspension was kept at 4.5°C. Rabbits were given six intraperitoneal injections (15 ml each) of this suspension containing approximately 25 mg of fibroin and 275 mg charcoal. Injections were repeated every 6–7 days. Two of the sera (4386 and 4260) chosen for the studies reported in this and the following papers were prepared by the late Karl Landsteiner in 1939 to 1941, and stored in fluid form without preservative. The fibroin used to prepare these latter sera was solubilized by brief exposure to concentrated hydrochloric acid. . . .

Hydrolysis of fibroin was carried out on a preparative scale. Twelve hundred milliliters of a 1.3% solution of fibroin was brought rapidly to 37°C, placed in a 37°C constant temperature room, and stirred magnetically with an egg-shaped, polyethylene coated bar chosen to avoid the formation of insoluble strands of fibroin. The pH was adjusted to 7.8 with 1 N NaOH and α-chymotrypsin (Worthington) was added as a solution in the proportion 1:80 (W/W) to substrate. The pH was maintained at 7.8 by intermittent additions of 1 N NaOH. The progress of the reaction was followed readily by pipetting 1.0-ml portions of the reaction mixture into tubes containing 1.0 ml methyl cellosolve and 0.5 ml 0.2 M, pH 5.0 citrate buffer. Insolubles were removed by centrifugation of the methyl cellosolve solution, and the supernatants were assayed by the ninhydrin method of Cocking and Yemm [1954]. After 4 hr, 100 mg fresh enzyme was added to the main reaction mixture, but no further increase in soluble amino nitrogen resulted. At the end of 6 hr, the reaction mixture was centrifuged, the characteristic precipitate was washed with N/50 acetic acid, and the pooled supernatant and washings were first reduced to a small volume by "flash evaporation" at 30°C and then lyophilized. The final product, referred to as "soluble peptides," designedly had a very low salt content, since hydrolysis was carried out in unbuffered solution. In agreement with other workers, the characteristic insoluble "core" fraction arising upon chymotryptic hydrolysis was found to comprise 61.1% of the total nitrogen. The balance of the nitrogen (38.9%) was contained in the soluble peptide fraction. These peptides had an average chain length of 15.5 amino acid residues as determined by the dinitrophenyl technique (correction for breakdown of dinitrophenyl-glycine taken as 20%). The calculated average chain length of the soluble peptide fraction is 9.3, cleavage being assumed at every tyrosine and phenyl alanine residue; hence, the soluble fraction represents a partial and not a complete enzymic hydrolysate of fibroin.

Before the immunologic activity of the soluble peptide fraction was tested, the chymotrypsin was inactivated by heating a solution of the peptides at pH 7 for 3 min in a boiling water bath. Alternately, chymotrypsin was removed by passing a solution of the peptides in pH 4.5, 0.01 M ammonium acetate buffer through a carboxymethyl cellulose column equilibrated with the same buffer. The chymotrypsin was retained by the ion-exchange column whereas 94% of the peptides were recovered in the first 3.5 column volumes of effluent.

The quantitative inhibition assay was a slight modification of that used by Pauling et al. [1942] and Kabat [1954]. The test was carried out in saline at pH 7.2, antisera were preincubated with inhibitor for 30 min at room temperature and the complete reaction mixture was allowed to stand 3 hr at room temperature and 21 hr at 4.5°C before centrifugation.

Total soluble hydrolysate was subjected to rocking dialysis as a 2.4% solution in $18_{32}''$ diameter Visking tubing. Three changes of an outer volume that was twice that of the sample were made over a 36-hr period. Over 72% of the material was recovered in the dialysate and lyophilized.

RESULTS AND DISCUSSION

The five sera chosen for the study of fibroin-combining sites are characterized in Table 1. The molar ratio of antibody to antigen at equivalence was calculated on the basis of molecular weights of 60,000 and 160,000 for fibroin and antibody respectively. For four of the sera, molar ratios ranging from 1.3 to 1.6 were found, whereas serum 202 gave a value of 3.2. It will be noted that the two sera prepared with acid dissolved silk—4260, 4386—are similar to (but

TABLE I

Characterization of Antifibroin Sera

Serum	γAb N/ml	γAg N Reacting with 1.0 ml Serum at Equivalence	γAb N /γAg N at Equivalence	M Ab/ M Ag at Equivalence	Band Positions Preer Double Diffusion Test (% Penetration)	
					3 days	7 days
199	114	33.8	3.4	1.3	43 d—	43 d (71 e)
201	137	33.8	4.1	1.5	42 d—	41 d 50 c— 66 e
202	233	27.3	8.5	3.2	56 b	58 b+ (48?)
4260	56	16.4	3.4	1.3		67 d—
4386	73	16.4	4.4	1.6	68 d	67 b—

have a lesser concentration of antibody than) sera 199 and 201 prepared with silk dissolved in LiBr. If divalency of the antibodies and a molecular weight for antibody of 160,000 are accepted, these ratios represent 2.6–3.2 combining sites of fibroin occupied at equivalence per 60,000 molecular weight for four of the sera, whereas a higher number of sites, 6.4, is indicated in the case of serum 202. Aside from the latter case, the "valency" of fibroin is only about half as great as that found for other protein antigens, if comparisons are made on an equal molecular weight basis.

An analysis of the five systems was made by the Preer gel diffusion method using an antigen concentration of 500 μg/ml. The readings given in Table 1 were made after 3 and 7 days. Each system is seen to be characterized by a single major band. A few secondary bands of precipitation occur in several cases, signifying some immunologic heterogeneity of the fibroin preparation. The contribution of these minor components to the over-all precipitin reaction would appear to be very small. Since Fell has shown sericin (gum) and

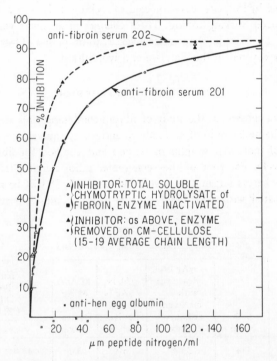

FIGURE 1

Inhibition of the fibroin-anti-fibroin precipitin reaction with soluble chymotryptic hydrolysate of fibroin. Systems contain: 201, 54.7 μg Ab N and 13.1 μg Ag N; 202, 69.9 μg Ab N and 8.3 μg Ag N; anti-HEA (hen egg albumin), 73.3 μg Ab N and 8.3 μg Ag N, all reactants in final volume of 1.0 ml.

fibroin to be antigenically distinct, the minor bands may represent a small sericin contamination.

Attempts to fractionate soluble fibroin by several methods (ammonium sulfate precipitation, ion-exchange chromatography on cellulose, electrophoresis in agar) were largely unsuccessful owing to the properties of irreversible insolubility and interfacial denaturation mentioned above. Thus the fibroin antigen was used without further purification although it was to a slight extent immunologically heterogeneous.

Figure 1 presents the inhibition secured in systems 201 and 202, by the addition of varying amounts of unfractionated soluble hydrolysate. Inhibition is expressed as 100 minus the ratio of nitrogen in the precipitates formed in the presence and absence of inhibitor, multiplied by 100. Almost complete inhibition of both systems can be produced by 130–160 μm soluble peptide nitrogen/ ml. Thus, with respect to these two systems, it appears that no essential structure in the combining sites is entirely destroyed by chymotryptic hydrolysis and that the discarded insoluble core fraction does not contain sequences of unique immunologic specificity.

Concentrations of fibroin hydrolysate comparable to those used to inhibit the fibroin system are without effect on a hen ovalbumin-rabbit antiovalbumin system of comparable antibody concentration. These results are also plotted in Figure 1 and attest to the specificity of inhibition.

An alternate explanation of the results might be considered: one might imagine that chymotrypsin, protected from heat inactivation by the high concentration of hydrolysis products, is able to split the highly susceptible fibroin when the latter is added to the mixture of immune serum-plus-inhibitor and so produce an apparent specific inhibition in the fibroin system. Native ovalbumin might be resistant to residual chymotrypsin and serve falsely as a "control." To rule out such an explanation, total hydrolysate was passed through a carboxymethyl cellulose column under conditions such that chymotrypsin was completely retained by the ion-exchanger. Figure 1 indicates that there is no change in activity of soluble peptides after this treatment.

In Table 2 the activity of the rapidly dialyzable fraction of the soluble hydrolysate acting in seven different antifibroin systems is shown. The results are presented in terms of the qualitative inhibition test introduced by Landsteiner. In agreement with the finding by Landsteiner for acid hydrolysates of fibroin, the dialyzable fraction is active in all of the serum systems, hence the inhibitory activity of the unfractionated soluble hydrolysate cannot be ascribed solely to the presence of small amounts of high molecular weight material.

The dialyzable peptides possess differential activity as was demonstrated by testing crude fractions obtained by partition column chromatography. Figure 2 shows the effluent diagram obtained by partitioning the dialyzable peptides on a column of ethyl esterified cellulose with use of a butanol solvent system as the moving phase. Pools "A" through "E" were made of the resulting fractions.

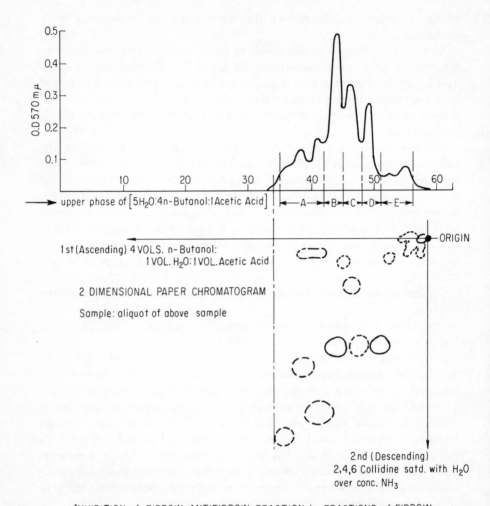

INHIBITION of FIBROIN–ANTIFIBROIN REACTION by FRACTIONS of FIBROIN

	≈1200 & each fraction						
	Sample 500 γ	A	B	C	D	E	Saline
Serum 4386	0	+ ±	+	+	ftr	0?	+ ±

0.2 ml 150 γ/ml fibroin + 0.05 ml inhibitor, then 2 drops serum

FIGURE 2

Inhibitory activity of crude fractions of a mixture of dialyzable peptides derived from chymotryptic hydrolysate of fibroin. Thirty-milligram sample applied to column of ethyl esterified cellulose 100 cm x 1.3 cm (i.d.).

TABLE 2

Inhibition of the Fibroin-Antifibroin Reaction* by Dialyzable Peptides in Chymotryptic Hydrolysate of Fibroin

Rabbit Antifibroin Sera	1 Hour†		Overnight	
	Saline	Inhibitor	Saline	Inhibitor
199	+str	tr	++	±str
201	+str	tr—	++	±str
202	++	±str	+++	±w
4386	+	o	++	ftr
3324	ftr	o	±str	fftr
4260	±	o	+±w	o
4782	±w	o	tr or str tr	o

* Reaction mixture: 0.2 ml 150 µg/ml fibroin, 0.05 ml (1000 µg) inhibitor, then two drops of immune serum.

† Visual turbidity readings: f = faint, str = strong, tr = trace, w = weak.

The lower portion of Figure 2 shows the results of testing equal weights of the various fractions for inhibitory activity. The best inhibitors appear to be present in the fractions that are more retarded in issuing from the column. A two-dimensional paper chromatograph of an aliquot of the same sample of dialyzable peptides fractionated on the column provides some idea of the complexity of each fraction. Such a chromatograph is presented in Figure 2 and it can be matched as shown with the elution diagram of the partition system since one of the solvent systems used to develop the paper chromatograph was similar to that employed for the column fractionation. The matching was made by chromatographing the individual column fractions separately on paper.

The paper chromatograph indicates that some of the active fractions are relatively simple mixtures. Therefore, we undertook to isolate single active peptides from the mixture in order to better understand the fibroin-rabbit-antifibroin interaction. These results are presented in paper II of this series. . . .

II

Isolation and Characterization of Peptides from Chymotryptic Hydrolysate of Silk Fibroin (Bombyx mori)

The preceding paper in this series reported on the inhibition of the fibroin—rabbit antifibroin precipitin reaction by means of a soluble chymotryptic hydrolysate of fibroin. Since certain fractions of the hydrolysate, found to be serologically active, appeared to be relatively simple mixtures, the individual peptides that comprise part of the fibroin molecule were investigated.

The limited data concerning the primary structure of silk fibroin has been reviewed several times. Study of the di- and tripeptides in acid hydrolysates of fibroin has indicated the abundance of Gly.Ala,* Ala.Gly, and Ser.Gly bonds in fibroin and that the sequence of amino acids is not random. A few workers have secured a number of larger peptides from fibroin; however, no general procedures are available for isolating homogeneous peptides of a size which Landsteiner [1942] found to be serologically active (*i.e.,* containing 7–15 residues). In the present study a series of peptides in the appropriate size range has been isolated from chymotryptic hydrolysates of fibroin.

Enzymic digestion of solubilized silk fibroin using chymotrypsin results in an insoluble "core" which accounts for 60% of the total nitrogen and contains only glycine, alanine, serine, and tyrosine. This core fraction has been analyzed and one group presents strong evidence that it is largely comprised of the repeating hexapeptide Ser.Gly.Ala.Gly.Ala.Gly.

The balance of the nitrogen in chymotryptic hydrolysates of fibroin (40%) is present in the form of soluble peptides. Because this mixture of peptides contains all of the rarely occurring amino acids present in fibroin and, as reported in the preceding paper, is almost completely able to inhibit the fibroin-antifibroin precipitin reaction, it was used as the source of all peptides isolated and characterized below. Most of the peptides present in this mixture appear to have similar amino acid compositions, contain in part identical amino acid sequences, and lack acidic or basic amino acids. The interpretation of the immunologic data derived from studies with peptides isolated from soluble hydrolysate rests on the evidence for homogeneity and composition of these peptides as reported in this paper.

MATERIALS AND METHODS

The soluble fraction of chymotryptic hydrolysate of fibroin was prepared as described in the preceding paper.

Soluble chymotryptic hydrolysate was fractionated on Dowex 50X-2 columns. The resin was wet-sieved through U. S. No. 120 mesh copper screen before use. Ammonium acetate buffers were removed from the fractions by repeated freeze-drying *in vacuo.* Nonvolatile buffer salts were removed on a short Dowex 50X-2 column (5 cm × 1.3 cm i.d.) in the H + form that had been washed with water until effluent was neutral. After application of the sample and passage of 10 column volumes of water, peptides were eluted from the column with 0.05 M NH_4OH and immediately evaporated to dryness *in vacuo* several times and lyophilized.

Ethyl esterified cellulose powder (LKB Produkter) was equilibrated over the

---

* Fibroin is a linear polymer consisting of six amino acids—alanine (Ala), aspartic acid (Asp), glycine (Gly), serine (Ser), tyrosine (Tyr) and valine (Val). When fibroin is split enzymically into fragments, the fragments differ in the amino acids present, and in their proportion and sequence. *Editor.*

lower phase of a water-*n*-butanol-acetic acid (5:4:1) mixture in a desiccator. Partition columns were poured by using a slurry of this cellulose powder in upper phase and enough upper phase was passed through the column to ensure equilibration. Columns were 100 × 1.3 cm i.d. and were used at 4.5°C.

Column electrophoresis was carried out by the method of Porath [1956], using jacketed columns of ethyl esterified cellulose 50 cm × 2.0 cm i.d. at 4.5°C.

The quantitative amino acid composition of the peptides was determined by the method of Moore *et al.* [1958] using Amberlite IR-120 resin and the ninhydrin assay procedure of Moore and Stein [1954]. The peptides were hydrolyzed with constant boiling hydrochloric acid in sealed evacuated ignition tubes at 110°C for 20 hr.

Molecular sieving was carried out using Sephadex G-25 (Pharmacia, Uppsala, Sweden) columns. Distilled water was employed as solvent and all columns were used at 4.5°C.

The homogeneity of peptides was checked by paper electrophoresis in a pyridine-acetic acid buffer system at pH 3.5 and by paper chromatography on Whatman No. 1 filter paper with the following systems: a) *n*-butanol-acetic acid-water 4:1:1, V/V; b) 2,4,6-collidine saturated with pH 12 buffer; c) *n*-propanol-pyridine-water, 6:1:1; sec-butanol-88% aqueous formic acid-water 15:3:2. The phenol system of McFarren, buffered at pH 12, was used to analyze for the presence of serine in the hydrolyzed peptides.

The amino terminal residues of the peptides were identified by the dinitrophenyl method of Sanger [1949, 1953] with the addition of trimethylamine to the required pH and by allowing hydrolysis to occur at 37°C for 20 days in sealed, evacuated tubes. After removal of dinitrophenol on silica gel columns, the dinitrophenyl-amino acids could be unequivocally identified by the use of the toluene system of Levy [1954] alone. Amino acid and dinitrophenyl-amino acid standards were obtained from Mann Research Laboratories.

The carboxyl-terminal residues of the peptides were identified by use of carboxypeptidase (Worthington) present in the proportion of 1 mg to 4.5 μm of peptide in a final volume of 3.1 ml, and acting at 37°C for varying periods of time.

Recovery of peptides was determined quantitatively by nitrogen analysis and occasionally—if containing tyrosine—by the colorimetric method of Ceriotti and Spandrio [1957]. This latter method was found to yield quantitative results for the tyrosine content of the octapeptides without requiring preliminary hydrolysis. The extinction coefficient ($E_{1cm}^{1\%}$) at 510 mμ, calculated from the color yield of peptides containing 10–50 μg tyrosine was constant and equal to the value of 308 secured for free tyrosine.

RESULTS

Peptides Containing a Single Tyrosine Residue.—The resolution of soluble hydrolysate obtained by use of Dowex 50X-2 and an ammonium acetate buffer

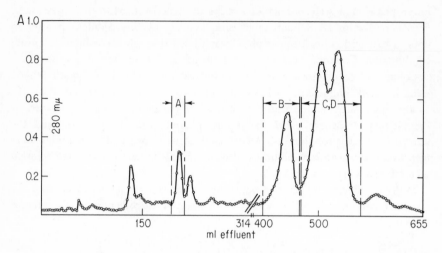

FIGURE 1

Dowex 50X-2 chromatography of soluble peptides in chymotryptic hydrolysate of silk fibroin. Typical load was 25–30 mg of nitrogen on a column of Dowex 50X-2 125 cm x 1.3 cm internal diameter (i.d.). Approximately 200 mg of lyophilized hydrolysate was dissolved in 2.0 ml pH 3.5 buffer and applied to column. A gradient elution system was used employing a 250-ml mixing chamber initially filled with pH 4 ammonium acetate-acetic buffer 0.07 M in NH_4^+. A pH 5.5 buffer 0.45 M in NH_4^+ replaced the fluid in the mixing chamber; 2.85-ml fractions were collected at a rate of 11 ml/hr.

system at 4.5°C is shown in Figure 1. Up to 1.0 g hydrolysate could be fractionated usefully on the column described. The fractions shown in Figure 1 account for about 24% of the nitrogen applied to the column. Peaks B, C and D alone account for 18.8 ± 0.6% of the applied nitrogen (average of five experiments, three of which utilized a Na^+ system; each charge was derived from a different preparative enzymic hydrolysis). Ninhydrin assay of an aliquot of each fraction obtained with the Na^+ system indicated that no detectable peak was overlooked when one used absorption at 280 mμ for detection of peptides. Buffer concentrations up to 2.5 M did not result in any significant further recovery of peptides from the column.

The major component of fraction A was resolved by column electrophoresis as shown in Figure 2. A phosphate buffer system at pH 6.8, $\mu = 0.05$ was used. The current was 35 ma and the potential across the apparatus was 940 volts during a 16¾-hr run.

Fraction B can be resolved into two components by partition column chromatography. Figure 3 represents the elution diagram of such an experiment when the method of Ceriotti and Spandrio [1957] is used to assay the fractions. Amounts of fraction B up to 100 mg can be completely resolved on such a partition column.

Fractions C and D could be resolved fairly well on a Dowex column under

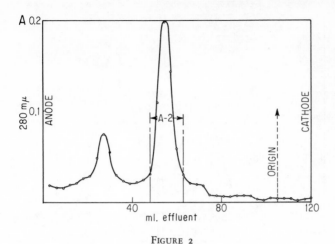

FIGURE 2

Column electrophoresis at pH 6.8 of peak A.

the same molarity and pH conditions of the primary separation excepting that Na^+ instead of NH_4^+ buffers were used (Fig. 4). Alternatively and usually, complete resolution of mixed C and D peptides (100-mg amounts) was obtained by partition column chromatography using a *n*-butanol-acetic acid-water solvent system as described for fractionation of peak B.

After the homogeneity of the resulting fractions (A-2, B-1, B-2, C, D) had been verified by paper chromatography in four solvent systems, and also by paper electrophoresis at pH 3.5, they were subjected to quantitative amino acid analysis. The amino acid composition of these five peptides is given in Table 1.

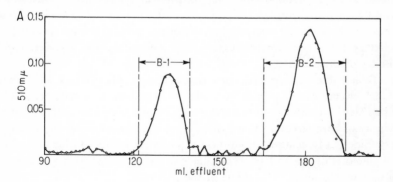

FIGURE 3

Partition column chromatography of peak B. Peptide tyrosine (1050 μg) was applied to column in 1.5 ml of lower phase. Upper phase was passed through column at a rate of 3.0 ml/hr and 1.5-ml fractions were collected. Assays for tyrosine were done on aliquots of each fraction and on the pools shown. Tyrosine (300 μg and 637 μg) were recovered in peaks B-1 and B-2 respectively. These two peaks account for 89.5% of the tyrosine applied.

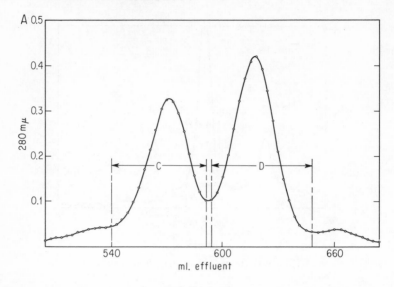

FIGURE 4

Dowex 50X-2 chromatography of peaks C and D in a Na+ system. Nitrogen (2200 μg) was applied to the column and gradient elution beginning with pH 4.0 sodium acetate-acetic acid, 0.07 M in Na+, in a 250-ml mixing chamber was employed. Replacement fluid was pH 5.5 buffer, 0.35 M in Na+; 3.0-ml fractions were collected at a rate of 13.5 ml/hr. Peaks C and D contained 905 μg and 1067 μg of nitrogen respectively and accounted for 89.5% of the nitrogen applied.

The tyrosine figures shown have not been corrected for degradation during hydrolysis. An independent check of the tyrosine content of the peptides was obtained from the ratio of the total nitrogen to tyrosine determined colorimetrically on the unhydrolyzed peptide. This ratio is recorded in the last column of Table 1. The simplest interpretation is that one peptide is a hexapeptide, two are tetrapeptides, and two are octapeptides. Alternately, the peptides may be multiples of these units.

In Table 2 the peptides are characterized further. All peptides have amino-terminal glycine except peptide A-2 which has alanine as a terminal residue. All peptides have carboxyl-terminal tyrosine, a result consistent with the known specificity of chymotrypsin. By use of carboxypeptidase it can be shown that all the tyrosine can be removed from these peptides before appreciable amounts of other amino acids are liberated. Thus, these peptides are indeed hexa, tetra, and octapeptides and not some multiple of these units.

The R_F values are expressed as the means ± standard error (N = 10) and are given only for the butanol system since this parameter is highly variable in the collidine system. Two peptides, Gly(Gly,Ala)Tyr and Gly(Gly₃,Ala₂,Val) Tyr, which could not be resolved in the n-butanol system, could easily be separated in the collidine system where the latter peptide runs about twice as fast as the former.

TABLE 1

Quantitative Amino Acid Composition of Peptides from Fibroin

Peptide	Gly	Ala	Val	Tyr	Asp	Nitrogen Recovery	Moles N/ Moles Tyr
						%	
A-2	1.98	1.09	1.03	0.80	1.08	100	6.15
B-1	2.02		1.09	0.91		94	3.82
B-2	2.05	1.10		0.85		103	4.15
C	4.06	2.08	0.97	0.89		105	8.17
D	4.10	3.07		0.85		104	8.17

Peptides of Higher Molecular Weight in the Hydrolysate.—Since only 24% of the nitrogen in samples of soluble chymotryptic hydrolysate could be recovered from Dowex 50 columns under the conditions used to obtain the elution pattern shown in Figure 1, attempts were directed to secure a further yield. Peptides bound so tightly as not to be removed from Dowex 50 by 2.5 M ammonium acetate at 4.5°C were assumed to be characterized by one or more of the following: rich in basic amino acids, of high molecular weight, or tyrosine rich.

To get an estimate of the amount of higher molecular weight material in the hydrolysate and to obtain any resolution that molecular sieving would permit, columns of Sephadex were employed. Figure 5 shows the fractionation of 1 g of hydrolysate on a 108-cm × 2.2-cm i.d. column of Sephadex G-25 at 4.5°C. About 94% of the applied nitrogen could be recovered from such a column. The first and largest peak in the elution diagram represents peptides which pass directly through the column and emerge at the "exclusion" volume. Since Sephadex G-25 has been found by the manufacturer to exclude dextrans of molecular weight 2000–3000 and larger it appears that the fibroin hydrolysate contains a considerable proportion of higher molecular weight peptides. The

TABLE 2

Characteristics of Peptides Isolated from Hydrolysates of Fibroin

Peptide	R_F for *n*-Butanol: H_2O: Acetic Acid (4:1:1)	N-Terminal Amino Acid	C-Terminal Amino Acid	Nitrogen Recovery Soluble hydrolysate	Nitrogen Recovery Total fibroin
				%	%
A-2	0.22 ± 0.02	Ala	Tyr	0.58	0.23
B-1	0.43 ± 0.03	Gly	Tyr	0.70	0.27
B-2	0.26 ± 0.03	Gly	Tyr	1.48	0.58
C	0.28 ± 0.04	Gly	Tyr	6.13	2.38
D	0.17 ± 0.03	Gly	Tyr	7.22	2.81

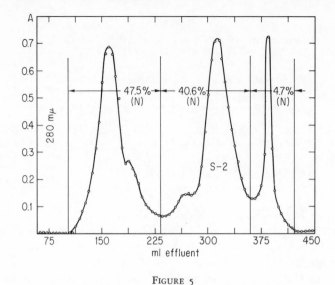

FIGURE 5

Fractionation of soluble peptides in chymotryptic hydrolysates of fibroin on Sephadex G-25.

sum of nitrogen recoveries in the second and third peak is 45.3%. The third peak in the elution diagram consists almost solely of the two tetrapeptides characterized in Table 1.

The material represented by the second and third peaks in Figure 5 was pooled and tested for inhibitory activity in antiserum system 201. At least 75% inhibition of the fibroin-antifibroin precipitin reaction could be obtained using an inhibitor concentration of 160 μm N/ml. From quantitative inhibition studies it was known that 18 μm/ml (144 μm N/ml) of the most active peptide listed in Table 1, Gly(Gly$_3$,Ala$_3$)Tyr, produced only 40% inhibition in system 201. The middle fraction (S-2) from Sephadex G-25, accounting for about 40% of the nitrogen in soluble hydrolysate, was then refractionated on Dowex 50X-2 in an attempt to isolate a component that would be more active than the octa-peptide which it also contained. The conditions for this refractionation are shown on the elution diagram of Figure 6. Over 90% of the 280 mμ absorbing material was recovered. The first peak (hexapeptide) and the following most prominent peak (containing both the octapeptides) are followed by several other peaks.

The first large peak to emerge from the Dowex column after the temperature was raised to 50°C yielded upon hydrolysis only glycine, alanine, valine and tyrosine. The molar ratio of nitrogen to tyrosine was found to be approximately 6.5. Since this fraction contains no basic amino acids a possible explanation for its retardation on Dowex compared with the peptides of similar quantitative composition would be the presence of more than a single tyrosine residue per molecule. Upon hydrolysis with one-fourth part by weight of chymotrypsin this fraction was cleaved and approximately equimolar amounts of octa- and tetra-peptides were formed.

The upper elution diagram of Figure 7 shows the result of passing the last mentioned hydrolysis mixture through a column of Sephadex G-25, 100 cm × 1.3 cm i.d. The initial peak represents chymotrypsin emerging at the exclusion volume, after which the two large peaks emerge at the positions of known octa- and tetrapeptides respectively.

It cannot be decided from this experiment in which chymotrypsin was used how many of the two types of units are present in a single molecule. To resolve this question, a 3.3-mg amount of the fraction was incubated with 1 mg of carboxypeptidase at pH 9 and 35°C for 10 hr. A hydrolysis time of 3 hr under these conditions is sufficient for removal of all carboxyl-terminal tyrosine from an octapeptide. The lower plot in Figure 7 shows that approximately equimolar amounts of peptide-bound tyrosine and free tyrosine are found in the hydrolysate (280 mμ absorption plot). Basic hydrolysis did not increase the ninhydrin color yield of the material represented by the second prominent peak, signifying that it was a simple amino acid; identification as tyrosine was made by paper chromatography.

Due to the low color yield of all of the unhydrolyzed peptides containing amino-terminal glycine, the increase in ninhydrin color value on basic hydrolysis did not give an accurate estimate of the chain length of the first prominent peak in the lower plot of Figure 7. However, the ratio of ninhydrin color after basic hydrolysis to the absorption at 280 mμ when measured on the fraction before the action of carboxypeptidase was slightly less than half this same ratio meas-

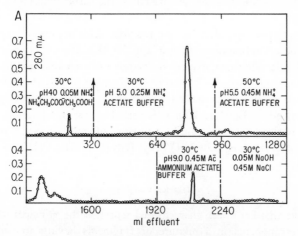

FIGURE 6

Dowex 50X-2 chromatography of Sephadex G-25 fraction S-2. Jacketed columns 150 cm × 1.3 cm internal diameter were used to resolve 300–500 mg of sample. Stepwise elution was employed.

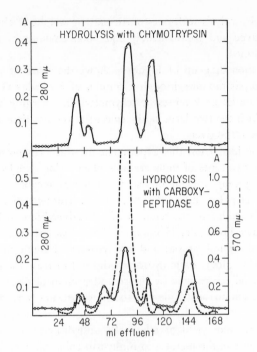

FIGURE 7

Analysis of "dodecapeptide" fraction.

ured on the first peak from the enzymic hydrolysate. This finding signifies that one-half of the tyrosine residues are present at the carboxyl-terminal end of the intact fraction.

Since chymotryptic hydrolysis of the fraction yields approximately equimolar amounts of octa- and tetrapeptides it appears that this fraction contains 12 residues/molecule. However, paper chromatographic analysis of the tetra- and octapeptide units produced by chymotryptic cleavage reveals that they are mixtures composed of the same two tetra- and octapeptides respectively that have been characterized in Table 1. Thus it is probable that this fraction, containing two tyrosine residues per molecule, is a mixture of dodecapeptides of the type: [Gly(Gly₃,Ala₃)Tyr] [Gly(Gly,Val)Tyr], [Gly(Gly₃,Ala₂,Val)Tyr] [Gly(Gly, Ala)Tyr], etc.

DISCUSSION

The peptides that have been characterized represent the principal lower molecular weight components in a mixture of fragments having an average chain length of 15.5. In selecting only the soluble fraction of the chymotryptic hydrolysate of fibroin, 60% of the total nitrogen present in the core fraction has been excluded from these studies. If Lucas *et al.* [1957] are correct regarding the repeating unit of "core," then almost all of the serine residues should occur in this insoluble fraction, thereby explaining the conspicuous absence of serine from the soluble peptides isolated.

Levy and Slobodian [1952], using the extremely sensitive isotope derivative carrier technique, found essentially no glycyl-glycine in partial acid hydrolysates of fibroin and proposed a repeating structure for fibroin characterized by glycine residues alternating with other amino acids. In all of the peptides isolated, excepting Ala(Gly$_2$,Val,Asp)Tyr, the amino acid glycine accounts for half of the residues, hence it is possible that glycine alternates with the other residues in these peptides. It should be pointed out that the designation of an octapeptide as Gly(Gly$_3$,Ala$_3$)Tyr does not imply the existence of glycyl-glycyl bonds but only signifies that the exact sequence of the amino acids enclosed by brackets is not known.

Peptides similar to one of the tetrapeptides and the hexapeptide in Table 1 have previously been mentioned in the literature. Fischer and Abderhalden, in 1907, proposed the structure Gly.Ala.Gly.Tyr for a peptide isolated from acid hydrolysates of whole fibroin and Ziegler and Spoor, in 1959, secured the hexapeptide Val.Ala.Gly.Asp.Gly.Tyr by high voltage electrophoresis of soluble chymotryptic hydrolysates. This latter peptide has the same quantitative amino acid composition as the hexapeptide listed in Table 1 but the two differ in the assigned amino terminal residues.

By use of the preparative methods outlined in this paper up to 500 mg of single peptides could be secured. These peptides are completely soluble in saline or distilled water at pH 7. In the following paper, their inhibitory activity in the fibroin-antifibroin precipitin system is reported. . . .

III

Inhibition of the Silk Fibroin–Antifibroin System by Peptides Derived from the Antigen

Landsteiner and van der Scheer first demonstrated the specific interaction of peptides of known structure with antibody. These workers synthesized peptides of glycine and D,L-leucine ranging up to a length of five residues and found that these peptides would function as determinant groupings when attached to protein carriers. Inhibition tests indicated that some antibodies stimulated by the peptide-protein conjugates were specific for the whole of the attached pentapeptide sequence. Presumably naturally occurring protein antigens also contain more or less well defined configurations of amino acid residues which function as determinant groupings.

TABLE I

Peptides Isolated from Silk Fibroin

Size	Peptide
4	Gly [Gly, Ala] Tyr
4	Gly [Gly, Val] Tyr
8	Gly [Gly$_3$, Ala$_2$, Val] Tyr
8	Gly [Gly$_3$, Ala$_3$] Tyr
6	Ala [Gly$_2$, Val, Asp] Tyr
12	(Gly[Gly, Val]Tyr) (Gly[Gly$_3$, Ala$_3$]Tyr) and (Gly[Gly, Ala]Tyr) (Gly[Gly$_3$, Ala$_2$, Val]Tyr) etc.

This paper reports a comparison of the inhibitory activities of a series of peptides derived from silk fibroin, a naturally occurring protein antigen. The structures of these peptides are shown in Table I. The results obtained permit some conclusions regarding the chemical structure and size of the combining sites of fibroin, the heterogeneity of antifibroin antibodies, and the role of tyrosine in protein antigen-antibody interaction.

MATERIALS AND METHODS

Methods for the isolation and characterization of the peptides listed in Table I were given in the preceding paper. All peptides other than the dodecapeptide fraction appeared to be homogeneous.

Each of the sera used in these studies derives from a single bleeding of a single rabbit. The sera are characterized in the first paper of this series. The soluble fibroin antigen was prepared as a 2% solution 48 hr prior to use. Dialysis to remove the LiBr was conducted against 1000 volumes of prechilled distilled water at 4.5°C with stirring for 15 hr. The concentration of a stock solution of antigen was determined by Kjeldahl nitrogen analysis.

The concentrations of antigen and antiserum in any given test system were always constant and at the ratio for equivalence. The concentrations of antibody and antigen in the final reaction mixtures containing inhibitor were, for the respective immune sera: 201, 54.7 μg Ab N and 13.1 μg Ag N per ml; 202, 69.9 μg Ab N and 8.3 μg Ag N per ml; 4386, 58.4 μg Ab N and 13.1 μg Ag N per 2.0 ml; 4260, 56.1 μg Ab N and 16.4 μg Ag N per 2.2 ml; and 199, 57.1 μg Ab N and 16.4 μg Ag N per 1.0 ml.

Stock solutions of the peptide inhibitors were prepared either by dissolving the lyophilized product directly in the required amount of saline or, in the event that a solution of high concentration (30–40 μm/ml) was required, by dissolving it in excess distilled water, evaporating some of the solvent *in vacuo,* and adding the required amount of sodium chloride as a 10% solution. Inhibitor concentration of the stock solutions was determined spectrophotometrically by the method of Goodwin and Morton [1946] or from nitrogen content. Agreement was within 1–3% when both methods were used to assay a single sample.

The peptide inhibitors remained soluble in the presence of the other components of the reaction mixture at the concentrations used. Neither the peptide inhibitors nor the fibroin, alone or in mixture, showed precipitation or opalescence with normal rabbit serum within the 24-hr period allowed for the precipitin reaction to occur. None of the peptides precipitated directly with anti-fibroin sera. The synthetic dipeptides Gly-L-Ala and Gly-L-Tyr were obtained from Mann Research Laboratories.

The quantitative inhibition assay involved a slight modification from those used by Pauling et al. [1942] and Kabat [1954] with respect to pH and time. The precipitin reaction was carried out at pH 7.2 in saline and after 3 hr incubation of the reaction mixture at room temperature and 21 hr at 4.5°C, the precipitate nitrogen was determined by micro-Kjeldahl analysis.

Carboxyl-terminal tyrosine was removed from octapeptides with carboxy-peptidase (Worthington). A 40-mg amount of peptide dissolved in 2.0 ml of water was brought to pH 9.2 with a few drops of 1 N NaOH. A 0.05-ml aliquot of a suspension of carboxypeptidase containing about 5 mg of enzyme was added to 0.45 ml of a 10% solution of LiBr. When the enzyme had dissolved, this solution was added to the peptide and the reaction mixture was placed at 37°C for 5 hr. Thereupon, the entire reaction mixture was applied to a Sephadex G-25 column (2.2 cm i.d. × 95 cm) at 4.5°C and distilled water was passed through the column. Yield of peptide with tyrosine removed was about 78% in three experiments.

RESULTS

The inhibitory effect of $Gly(Gly_3,Ala_3)Tyr$ in five soluble fibroin-antifibroin systems is shown in Figure 1. Percentage of inhibition is plotted vs μM of peptide/ml. The extent of inhibition appears to be directly proportional to the concentration of inhibitor—at least at low concentrations of the latter. If inhibition is specific, it will reflect competition between inhibitor and intact antigen for combining sites on the antibody. Therefore, the values for the slopes of these plots of inhibition values would be expected to depend partly on dissociation constants of antibody-inhibitor complexes. However, the relative affinities of a single inhibitor for the antibodies present in different sera cannot be deduced accurately from such plots. Put in another way, one cannot say that the octa-peptide combines more strongly with antibodies in serum 199 than with anti-bodies in serum 201 even though these two systems are being compared at equal inhibitor and antibody concentrations. Other factors—such as the dissociation constants of the antigen-antibody complexes, solubility of these complexes, and heterogeneity of antibodies with respect to binding of inhibitor—will affect the slopes of inhibition plots, and these factors can differ from serum to serum.

In general, the effectiveness of the octapeptide acting in the five serum systems does not vary greatly; however, differences in the shapes of the individual

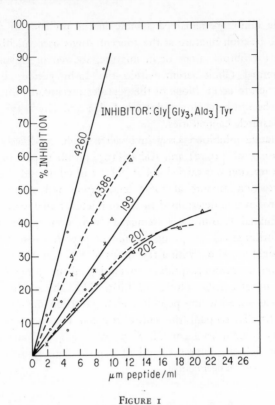

FIGURE I

Inhibitory effect of Gly (Gly₃, Ala₃) Tyr on the
reaction of fibroin with five antifibroin sera.

inhibition plots are apparent. Sera 4260 (26 μg Ab N/ml) and 4386 (29 μg
Ab N/ml), and sera 199 (57 μg Ab N/ml) and 201 (55 μg Ab N/ml)
represent two pairs of antigen-antibody systems, each compared at nearly equal
antibody and inhibitor concentrations. It has been found that variation of degree
of inhibition with either antibody or inhibitor concentration (the concentration
of antigen being varied with that of the AB so as to preserve equivalence) is of
the same order of magnitude; hence, the plots do not indicate that the octapeptide is more active in the first pair (4260, 4386) of systems since antibody
concentration is only about one-half that used for the second pair of systems
(199, 201).

Some of the plots in Figures 1–3 show a tendency to depart from linearity
at higher concentrations of inhibitor. This effect can be ascribable to several
causes. The total nitrogen of the antibody-antigen precipitates, rather than antibody nitrogen alone, is measured and the former values were plotted *vs* inhibitor
concentration. Antigen nitrogen comprises 10–22% of the total nitrogen precipitated in the five systems in the absence of inhibitor. If the ratio of antibody

to antigen nitrogen should decrease with increasing inhibition, then the apparent inhibition of antibody precipitation would be less than the actual inhibition. Such an effect would be relatively small and would be apparent only at high degrees of inhibition. Inhibitor, combined to antibody in the precipitate, is also a source of nonantibody nitrogen. However, the washing of the precipitate and the low molecular weight of the peptide inhibitors would make this a small contribution only.

Departure from linearity of plots of inhibition *vs* inhibitor concentration, apparent at high inhibitor concentration, have also been noted in systems containing nitrogen-free antigens and inhibitors. Pauling *et al.* [1944] ascribe this deviation from nonlinearity to heterogeneity of antibodies with respect to affinity for a given inhibitor. This concept will be considered in the discussion section in greater detail but it will be used now in a qualitative, descriptive sense. Thus, a plot extending linearly from the origin up to total inhibition would suggest that all antibodies present in a given serum had nearly equal affinities for the inhibitor. Serum 4260 would be an example of such a serum. If the sparse data available for systems 201 and 202 at high concentrations of inhibitor can be taken to suggest a departure from linearity, starting at around 40% inhibition, then a substantial part of the antibodies in these sera may have low affinities for the octapeptide.

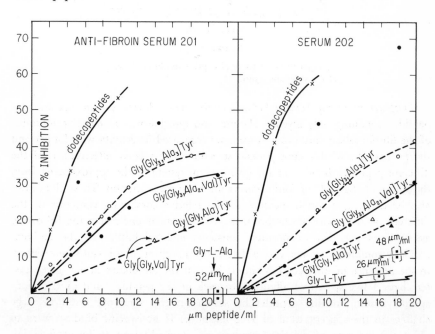

FIGURE 2

Comparison of activity of peptide inhibitors in serum systems 201 and 202.

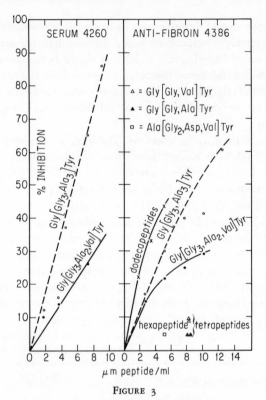

FIGURE 3

Comparison of activity of peptide inhibitors in serum
systems 4260 and 4386.

Comparisons of the Several Peptide Inhibitors.—Having shown that an octapeptide containing only glycine, alanine, and tyrosine was an effective inhibitor
of the fibroin-rabbit antifibroin system, we compared its activity with longer and
shorter peptides of this same general structure. The relative effectiveness of the
different peptide inhibitors in any given serum system can be approximated from
the slopes of the plots of inhibition *vs* inhibitor concentration. These slopes can
also be taken as a rough measure of the relative combining constants of the
different peptides with antibodies in a given serum if one makes the following
assumptions: a) that dissociation constants and solubilities of the antigen-
antibody complexes are not very different for any given fibroin-antiserum system
in the presence of different inhibitors; b) that the antibodies in any given system have a like spread of affinities for each of the peptides; and c) that non-
specific binding of the peptides by serum proteins does not result in large
changes in the concentration of free inhibitor. If nonspecific binding were to
affect the outcome of relative comparisons, it would have to be preferential.
Since most of the peptides differ only slightly in over-all structure and since
their molar concentrations are large compared with molar concentrations of

serum proteins, nonspecific binding probably does not affect relative comparisons. Referring to Figures 2 and 3, the following general observations can, therefore, be made:

1. In all five systems the octapeptide $Gly(Gly_3,Ala_3)Tyr$ was superior to $Gly(Gly_3,Ala_2,Val)Tyr$ when tested for activity on an equimolar basis. The difference in activity between these two octapeptides is considerable in systems 4260, 4386 and 202, and less in system 201 and also, although not shown in the plot, system 199. The peptide of lesser activity differs in over-all amino acid composition from $Gly(Gly_3,Ala_3)Tyr$ only by the presence of a valine residue in place of an alanine. It is possible that the less active peptide is not directly related to the actual combining site but functions as a cross-reacting substance which, owing to its bulky valine side chain, is bound less firmly by the antibody· combining sites.

An alternate explanation for the lower activity of the peptide that contains valine may be that it reacts only with certain sites on the antibody which are directed against its structure but that $Gly(Gly_3,Ala_3)Tyr$ can react with these same sites and with other antibody-combining sites as well.

2. The octapeptide $Gly(Gly_3,Ala_3)Tyr$ is a considerably more effective inhibitor in all five systems than the tetrapeptide $Gly(Gly,Ala)Tyr$. In the case of serum 202 the initial slope for octapeptide inhibition is about double that for tetrapeptide inhibition. At the other extreme, with serum 4386, the tetrapeptide is only about one-tenth as effective as the octapeptide. Since the tetrapeptide has the same qualitative amino acid composition as the octapeptide the results suggest a specific combining region on the antigen larger than four amino acids in length.

A few results comparing the activity of $Gly(Gly,Val)Tyr$ with $Gly(Gly,Ala)$ Tyr seem to indicate that both tetrapeptides are about of equal inhibitory activity in systems 4386, 202 and 201.

3. In systems 201 and 202 the increase in effectiveness of the dodecapeptide fraction compared with the octapeptides is greater than the difference in effectiveness between octapeptides and tetrapeptides. The initial slopes of plots of dodecapeptide inhibition are about three and four times that of the octapeptide plots for systems 201 and 202 respectively. In system 4386 only about a doubling in initial slope was observed. It should be noted that, compared with $Gly(Gly_3, Ala_3)Tyr$, the dodecapeptide contains not only an additional segment of glycyl, alanyl and valyl chain but also an additional tyrosine residue situated internally rather than terminally.

4. In Figure 2 the inhibitory effect obtained in systems 201 and 202 by adding equimolar amounts of $Gly(Gly_3,Ala_3)Tyr$ and $Gly(Gly,Ala)Tyr$ to the same reaction mixture is shown by the circled crosses; these are located along the scale of inhibitor concentration at positions corresponding to the concentration of a single one of the peptides in the reaction mixtures and therefore are directly comparable with dodecapeptides, in which the octapeptide and tetrapeptide con-

TABLE 2

*Comparison of Inhibitory Activity of Various Tyrosine-containing
and Tyrosine-devoid Peptides*

Inhibitor	202		199	
	μm/ml	% inhibition	μm/ml	% inhibition
Gly-L-Ala	26	−4.5	26	−1.5
	52	0	46.8	0
		0		0
Gly-L-Tyr	26	5.2	26	5.0
		6.7		
	48	10.6	43	0
		12.2		−4.0
Gly(Gly$_3$, Ala$_3$)Tyr	21	43	15	33.4
Gly(Gly$_3$, Ala$_3$)	21	23.4	15	11.5
				19.6
Gly(Gly$_3$, Ala$_2$, Val)Tyr	19.5	31	8.5	23.5
				23.9
				20
Gly(Gly$_3$, Ala$_2$, Val)	19.5	15.6	8.5	12.0
		16.2		7.5
				8.0

stituents are joined by a peptide bond. The mixture of the two peptides caused
less inhibition than produced by the same amount of these components joined
in a dodecapeptide, and the mixture was also found to be equal to or greater
in effectiveness than the sum of its components tested separately.

5. The single quantitative result for the major acidic peptide of soluble
hydrolysate shows it to have negligible activity in the system 4386 (Fig. 3).

These results will be subjected to theoretical, quantitative treatment in the
discussion section.

Contributions Made by Tyrosine to the Binding of Inhibitors to Antibody.—
Having shown that peptides containing a (glycyl,alanyl) chain and a carboxyl
terminal tyrosine are effective in inhibiting the fibroin-antifibroin reaction, we
investigated the relative importance of the component parts of active peptides
in their interaction with antibody.

The peptide Gly(Gly$_3$,Ala$_3$)Tyr was taken to represent at least part of the
antigenic combining site and it was assumed that the dipeptides Gly-L-Ala and
Gly-L-Tyr represented units within this peptide. When these synthetic dipeptides were tested for inhibitory activity at concentrations up to 52 μm/ml,
Gly-L-Ala was found to be completely inactive in systems 199, 201 and 202.
The dipeptide Gly-L-Tyr was found to be similarly inactive at concentrations
up to 48 μm/ml in systems 201 and 199. Table 2 shows some of these results.
The data in this table also shows that Gly-L-Tyr was slightly active in system
202, causing about 6% inhibition at 26 μm/ml and 11.5% inhibition at 48
μm/ml.

Thus, except for the interaction of Gly-L-Tyr with serum 202, neither of the dipeptides appeared to have sufficient specific structure to bind with antibody at the concentrations tested. These results are in accord with the lower activity of Gly(Gly,Ala)Tyr compared with Gly(Gly$_3$,Ala$_3$)Tyr, which suggested a specific region of binding larger than the length of the former peptide. The small amount of inhibition produced by Gly-L-Tyr in system 202 suggested the possibility that tyrosine was an important component of the antigenic combining site. This possibility was investigated by specific removal of carboxyl-terminal tyrosine from active octapeptides by the use of carboxypeptidase.

The rate of removal of carboxyl-terminal tyrosine from peptides by carboxypeptidase hydrolysis proceeds much faster than subsequent removal of alanine or glycine. Therefore, conditions could be found which allowed removal of tyrosine from nearly all of the substrate octapeptides without any appreciable amount of further degradation. The reaction mixtures were then resolved on Sephadex G-25 (Fig. 4). The presence of tyrosine in a peptide acted to retard its passage through Sephadex G-25 columns as compared to peptides of similar size that did not contain tyrosine. Thus, nonhydrolyzed peptide could be separated from peptide which had undergone loss of its tyrosine. Since the amino acids glycine, alanine, and valine are retarded less than free tyrosine but more

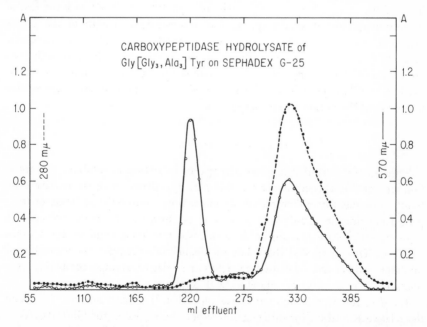

FIGURE 4

First peak (solid line) represents tyrosine-free heptapeptide. Small amount of unhydrolyzed octapeptide emerges between 220 and 275 ml and free amino acids other than tyrosine emerge at about 275 ml. Second large peak (solid line and dotted line) represents free tyrosine.

than the peptides, they appear as an intermediate fraction which may be taken as a measure of further degradation of peptide beyond tyrosine removal.

After treatment with carboxypeptidase and separation of the reaction product on Sephadex, the peptides derived from $Gly(Gly_3,Ala_3)Tyr$ and $Gly(Gly_3, Ala_2Val)Tyr$ were taken to be $Gly(Gly_3,Ala_3)$ and $Gly(Gly_3,Ala_2,Val)$, respectively. Although these products are heterogeneous to some extent, they appear to consist predominately of the heptapeptides designated above.

The inhibitory activities of these tyrosine-lacking heptapeptides were compared on an equal molar basis with the same preparations of octapeptides from which they were derived, and the results of these inhibition tests are shown in Table 2. The comparisons of two different octapeptide-heptapeptide pairs in two different serum systems show that the inhibition produced by the tyrosine-lacking peptides is only about 50% as great as that given by the octapeptides containing carboxyl-terminal tyrosine. In other words, the increase in binding associated with the presence of a tyrosine residue is of the same order of magnitude as the increase in binding of an octapeptide over a tetrapeptide in system 202 or of a dodecapeptide over an octapeptide in system 199.

If we are to generalize from the results obtained with Gly-L-Ala and Gly-L-Tyr and the change in inhibitory activity of a peptide associated with the loss of a tyrosine residue, it would appear that a considerable length of the glycyl, alanyl chain is required for detectable specific combination. The tyrosine residue accounts for a disproportionate amount of the interaction of binding with antibody compared with any other single residue present in the inhibitors but its presence in Gly-L-Tyr is not sufficient to enable this peptide to cause appreciable inhibition of the fibroin-antifibroin system.

DISCUSSION

Since, in the general case, plots of per cent inhibition *vs* inhibitor concentration are not linear, their slopes cannot be used to deduce accurate relative combining constants for inhibitor-antibody interaction. To explain deviation of these plots from linearity, Pauling *et al.* [1944] assumed that antibody molecules in a given serum were heterogeneous with respect to their affinities for a given inhibitor. They suggested that plots of amount of precipitate *vs* logarithm of inhibitor concentration be used to determine relative average combining constants (K_0) of a series of inhibitors with antibody.

The data for peptidic inhibition was plotted in the above manner. To obtain the relative K_0 values for different inhibitors, the K_0 value for $Gly(Gly_3,Ala_3)Tyr$ was taken as unity in all systems. Plots of measured inhibition *vs* logarithm of inhibitor concentration were extrapolated to 50% inhibition where experimental data for this region was lacking. The distance along the abscissa (concentration axis) between any two curves is a measure of the logarithm of the ratio of combining constants for two inhibitors, providing that a given serum shows the same degree of heterogeneity towards each of them. Effects due to varying values of σ were minimized by measuring distances between experimental curves along a line parallel with the log (I) axis at 50% inhibition. However, most of the experimental curves were roughly parallel so differences in σ for the various inhibitors seemed to be small for any given serum system. It is pertinent to note here that Nisonoff and Pressman [1958] found in equilibrium dialysis experiments that antibodies in a given population showed nearly equal degrees of heterogeneity for combination with a series of related haptens, all of which appeared to combine with the same antibody sites.

By comparing plots of experimental data with a family of theoretical curves plotted from a theoretical equation derived by Pauling et al. [1944], the indices of heterogeneity, σ, were found to be in the ranges 1.5–2.0, 2.0–3.0 and 2.0–3.0 respectively, for sera 202, 201, and 4386 for the peptide inhibitors. The σ for the interaction of serum 4260 with $Gly(Gly_3,Ala_3)Tyr$ was near zero whereas the corresponding σ for $Gly(Gly_3,Ala_2,Val)Tyr$ was near 3.0.

The relative K_0 values for binding of one tetrapeptide, two octapeptides and the dodecapeptides with antibodies in four different sera are tabulated in Table 3. The Δ ($\Delta F°$) values represent the difference in change in standard free energy for the combination of two different peptides with antibody. These values were calculated as described by Kabat [1956].

For systems 201 and 202, the increment in the $\Delta F°$ of combination with antibody between octapeptides and tetrapeptides is of the same order of magnitude as between dodecapeptides and octapeptides. The latter value is somewhat larger than the former but this difference may be ascribable to the presence of an additional tyrosine residue per molecule of dodecapeptide as compared with the octapeptide. Thus, an increment of about -700 calories in the $\Delta F°$ of binding with antibody appears to be associated with each additional four residues present in the inhibitor. In contrast, for systems 4386 and 199 the difference in $\Delta F°$ of combination with antibody between tetrapeptide and octapeptide is about three to four times greater than that for octapeptide and dodecapeptide.

One possible interpretation of the results obtained with antisera 4386 and 199

TABLE 3

Relative Average Combining Constants, K_0, of the Peptide Inhibitors

	201		202		199		4386	
Inhibitor	$K*_0$	$\Delta\Delta F°$ cal.	K_0	$\Delta(\Delta F°)$ cal.	K_0	$\Delta(\Delta F°)$ cal.	K_0	$\Delta(\Delta F°)$ cal.
Dodecapeptides	4.0		5.0		2.3		1.8	
		780		910		470		330
$Gly(Gly_3, Ala_3)Tyr$	1.0		1.0		1.0		1.0	
		670		670		>1300		>1300
$Gly(Gly, Ala)Tyr$	0.3		0.3		<0.1		<0.1	
$Gly(Gly_3, Ala_2, Val)Tyr$	0.6		0.5		0.65		0.2	

* $K_0 = K_0(rel)$.

is that the antigenic site specifically bound is larger in size than a tetrapeptide. Since an increase in chain length beyond eight amino acids results in a relatively small $\Delta F°$ increment compared with that between tetra- and octapeptide, perhaps the size of the optimum combining site for the antibodies in these sera is being approximated by a dodecapeptide. On the other hand, in systems 201 and 202 the value of $\Delta(\Delta F°)$ is relatively greater between dodecapeptide and octapeptide than the corresponding value between octa- and tetrapeptide, so a specific antigenic site larger than a dodecapeptide is probably indicated.

That $\Delta(\Delta F°)$ values for the peptide inhibitors actually constitute a measure of relative *specific* binding with antibody is supported by comparison of the two octapeptide inhibitors. If both of these had equal affinities on an immunologic basis for antibody but the over-all binding was in considerable part nonspecific, then $Gly(Gly_3,Ala_2,Val)Tyr$, presumably more hydrophobic and less water soluble than $Gly(Gly_3,Ala_3)Tyr$, might be expected to have the largest K_0 and $\Delta F°$. Instead, in all cases $Gly(Gly_3,Ala_3)Tyr$ is the superior inhibitor and the difference in $-\Delta F°$ of combination compared with the valine-containing octapeptide is about 280, 390, 240 and 910 calories for systems 201, 202, 199 and 4386, respectively. These data suggest that $Gly(Gly_3,Ala_3)Tyr$ is more firmly bound by antibody largely because it has in fact the appropriate structure. It seems reasonable to assume that the $\Delta(\Delta F°)$ for other pairs of peptides probably primarily reflects difference in their *specific* binding to antibody.

Another property of the peptide inhibitors which would affect the use of $\Delta(\Delta F°)$ in inferring the size of a specific antigenic combining site is secondary structure. In systems 4386 and 199 one might suppose the relatively large $\Delta(\Delta F°)$ between tetra- and octapeptides reflects the transition of inhibitor from random structure to helical configuration. Indeed it would be informative to make physicochemical measurements on the series of peptide inhibitors. However, the amount of helical form displayed by any of the peptides in the size range studied is probably extremely small in aqueous solution. The fact that systems 201 and 202 do not show the largest $\Delta(\Delta F°)$ between tetra- and octapeptides also seems to indicate that secondary structure of the antigen fragment is not of major importance for specific binding.

Concerning the size of specific combining sites of antigens there is not much data available. Kabat has studied the inhibitory effects of homologues of the isomaltose series on the dextran-human antidextran system. The results led Kabat to assume that the size of the optimum combining site of antigen or antibody is approximated by a hexasaccharide. The calculated size of such a site is 32 × 12 × 7 Å. Kabat has suggested that the combining sites of dextran are the chain ends of the branched molecule.

In the silk fibroin system, the specific combining sites of the antigen appear to consist of at least 8 to 12 amino acids. Fully stretched octapeptides and dodecapeptides are about 29 and 44 Å in length respectively, a size range encompassing Kabat's value of 32 Å. In the event that octapeptides and dodecapeptides existed as helices their lengths would be about 11.8 and 17.6 Å, respectively. If one bears in mind the low number of combining sites occupied on fibroin at equivalence (2.6–3.2 sites for 60,000 molecular weight for four of the five systems studied), it seems possible that the chain ends of soluble fibroin could act as combining sites.

Of considerable interest is the change in activity of the peptide inhibitors of the fibroin system that is associated with the loss of a tyrosine residue. The importance of tyrosine residues in the determinant groupings of protein antigens has often been suggested. The low antigenicity of tyrosine-poor gelatins which can be improved by the addition of tyrosine derivatives to the protein and the loss in reactivity with antisera which other proteins undergo upon alteration of their tyrosine residues have served as indirect bases for the suggested role of tyrosine in protein-antibody combination. The results obtained with the silk fibroin inhibitor provide direct evidence for the involvement of tyrosine in protein antigen-antibody interaction.

The evidence given in this report indicates that the combining sites of silk fibroin with which most, if not all, of the specific antibodies react either are closely approximated by or actually are chains of glycine and alanine containing a few tyrosine residues. Specific combination appears to involve particularly the aromatic tyrosine residues but also a sizeable portion of the essentially nonpolar glycyl, alanyl chain containing at least 8–12 residues. The amino acid residues involved are among the most common in fibroin and the actual sequences of the inhibitory fragments occur several times in a single molecule. There is no evidence to implicate the rarer amino acids of silk, such as the acidic and basic ones, as participating in specific combination. Thus, the amino acids not occurring as glycine, alanine, serine, and tyrosine certainly do not form "unique patches" of polar amino acids which, according to Marrack's suggestion, function as determinant groups. . . .

An animal infected by a virus is sometimes rendered resistant to infection by a different virus. The two viruses need not be closely related, and cross-immunity seems not to be involved. Tissue cultures infected by one virus may be protected against subsequent infection by another virus. Even a dead, viz., heat-inactivated, noninfectious virus, may confer a high degree of protection against infection by another virus.

This phenomenon is called *viral interference.* Its role in nature is unclear, but it is thought to be considerably important in the protection of man and the higher animals against virus infection.

A substance called *interferon* is apparently responsible for most, if not all, of the effects involved in viral interference; it has been obtained from chick embryos or tissue cultures infected with certain myxoviruses. Interferon appears to be a protein and is probably a metabolic product of the disordered protein-synthesizing mechanism of the infected cell. Introduced into tissue cultures, interferon confers upon them a high degree of protection against infection by a wide range of viruses.

When introduced into the cells of a susceptible host, viruses affect the protein-synthesizing and nucleic-acid-synthesizing machinery of the cell. Synthesis of RNA and proteins normal to the uninfected host cell is gradually diverted into synthesis of *one* abnormal nucleic acid (either RNA or DNA, apparently never both) that is characteristic of the virus rather than the host, and of one or more proteins that are unlike any found in the uninfected host cell. Apparently the viral nucleic acid is formed in one part of the infected cell, the viral protein in another. For a while these two abnormal products accumulate separately; then they come together to form the complete virus, which consists of a nucleic acid core surrounded by a protein coat, the capsid (see article by Horne and Wildy, pages 78 to 105 in this volume). In addition to "complete," i.e., infective, virions, "incomplete" virus particles consisting only of virus protein are sometimes formed. These, naturally, are noninfectious.

Interferon appears to be an abnormal protein formed by the protein-synthesizing machinery of the infected cell. In the instances in which interferon has been carefully studied, it has been found to be serologically distinct from virus protein. It appears to be a different substance altogether, and its source and the mechanism of its formation remain fascinating puzzles for future investigators.

Equally challenging is the question of interferon's potential role in combating virus infection. Will influenza, the common cold, hepatitis, mononucleosis, and the virus diseases generally be controllable some day by judicious administration of interferon? This is a hotly debated problem, and the answer is not yet in sight.

Drs. Isaacs and Burke are eminent in research on interferon. Their work has been done mainly at the National Institute for Medical Research, Mill Hill, London.

From *Brit. Med. Bull.*,
15:185–188, 1959.

VIRAL INTERFERENCE AND INTERFERON

BY A. ISAACS AND D. C. BURKE

Interference describes the action of a virus, either live or inactivated, on cells, as a result of which the cells are rendered unable to support fully the growth of immunologically related or unrelated viruses.

The phenomenon of viral interference has been studied for over twenty years by workers who hoped it would uncover fresh information on the processes of virus growth. First mention of interference among animal viruses is often credited to Magrassi (1935) who described interference by a non-encephalitogenic strain with the growth of an encephalitogenic strain of herpes virus in rabbits, and to Hoskins (1935) who described protection by a neurotropic strain against infection with the viscerotropic strain of yellow fever virus. However, in both these cases protection might have been due, wholly or in part, to immunological factors, so that the findings of Findlay & MacCallum (1937) that Rift Valley fever virus protected monkeys from infection with the immunologically unrelated yellow fever virus gave the first clear example of virus interference.

In order to study this phenomenon further, the experimental system was simplified by using the allantoic cavity of fertile hen-eggs or tissue cultures. Experiments in eggs or tissue cultures can be conducted in various ways. The first method used (Andrewes, 1942) was to see whether the interfering virus reduced the yield of the challenge virus; Andrewes showed that the WS strain of influenza virus inhibited the growth of the neurotropic variant of this strain in tissue culture, as tested by intracerebral inoculation of culture fluids into mice (where only the neurotropic variant would multiply). A second experimental method measures whether the interfering virus reduces the number of cells which can support the growth of challenge virus, and Baluda (1957) looked for a reduction in the number of cell "yielders" in this way. However, reduction in the number of cell yielders is a rigorous test of interference since, if each cell produced only a fraction of its normal yield of virus, considerable inhibition of virus growth might occur in the absence of any reduction in the number of cell yielders. Thirdly, Le Bouvier (1954) showed that the MEF_1 strain of poliomyelitis virus, which produced only a very weak cytopathogenic action in monkey-kidney cells, protected the cells from the destructive effect of other strains of poliomyelitis virus and a strain of Coxsackie virus. This technique depends on the fact that in the majority of cases the cytopathogenic action of a virus is a function of virus growth. But this may not always be so and, in preparations of adenovirus, an early cytopathic effect is caused by a protein serologically related to the virus but separable from it by centrifugation (Pereira, 1958; Everett & Ginsberg, 1958). Of these three methods, reduction of the yield of challenge virus gives a simple and direct measurement of interference, and most studies on virus interference have been carried out in this way.

1. INTERFERENCE BY INACTIVATED VIRUS

One of the most important aspects of the phenomenon is that the interfering virus need not be used live but can induce interference when it has been inactivated, e.g., by heat, irradiation with ultra-violet light or treatment with formaldehyde or nitrogen mustard. Henle & Henle (1943) and Ziegler & Horsfall (1944) showed that inactivated influenza virus interfered with the growth of influenza viruses in the allantoic cavity of the chick-embryo, and this finding was the starting-point for many investigations on interference, particularly by Henle and co-workers. The system has two obvious advantages over the interference produced by live virus. Firstly, inactivated viruses induce less metabolic activity in cells than live virus, thus simplifying the search for the point where the interference with virus growth occurs. Secondly, inactivated viruses can induce interference at doses of virus which do not produce obvious cytopathic effects, so that cellular disorganization can be excluded as a cause of interference by inactive virus. Henle (1950) has reviewed very thoroughly the subject of virus interference, with special reference to studies with inactivated influenza viruses in the allantoic cavity, and among the points established by this and some later studies are these:

i. Interference is a function of the inactivated virus particle itself, as shown by studies of its physico-chemical properties and by the fact that the interfering activity is neutralized by specific antiserum to the virus particle.

ii. The interfering activity of the virus is distinguishable from other known properties of the virus by its different resistance to inactivation with ultra-violet light (Henle & Henle, 1947).

iii. About ten particles of influenza virus inactivated by ultra-violet light are sufficient to induce interference in a cell. With virus inactivated by heat or by larger doses of irradiation, larger doses of virus are required to induce interference.

iv. Interference is localized to the cells in direct contact with the inactivated virus. Thus, when interference was induced in the amniotic cavity of fertile eggs, the allantoic cavity was unaffected—and vice versa (Henle, Henle & Kirber, 1947).

v. Inactivated influenza viruses are able to interfere with the growth of other myxoviruses and of completely unrelated viruses such as those of western equine encephalitis (WEE) and vaccinia (Henle & Henle, 1945; Depoux & Isaacs, 1954).

vi. Interference is not established at once but takes some hours to become established (Fazekas de St Groth, Isaacs & Edney, 1952; Henle & Paucker, 1958).

These findings apply to one experimental system which was studied extensively, and it would be a great advantage to know how widely applicable they are. Unfortunately, little work has been carried out in eggs or tissue cultures with inactivated viruses other than myxoviruses. Ledinko & Melnick (1954) found that inactivated poliomyelitis virus did not prevent the cytopathogenic action of live virus subsequently inoculated into cultures of monkey testis; it would be interesting to look for a possible reduction in virus yield in this experimental system.

Lockart & Groman (1958) found that WEE virus whose infectivity was reduced 10^7-fold to 10^8-fold by prolonged incubation at $37°C$. inhibited the multiplication of homologous virus grown in monolayers of L-cells. As in the case of interference by inactivated myxoviruses, 12–14 hours' incubation of cells with inactive WEE virus were necessary to establish maximal interference. The partially inactivated WEE virus also reduced the number and size of plaques produced by homologous virus in chick-embryo monolayers.

Cooper (1958) has shown that partially inactivated vesicular stomatitis (VS) virus produces interference which seems to be quite unlike other forms of interference among animal viruses. VS virus inactivated by freezing at $-20°C$., and by irradiation with ultra-violet light to the point at which 10^{-4}–10^{-5} of the original infectivity remained, had the interesting property of completely inhibiting growth of VS virus of a different serological type in 60–80% of the cell population, although treated cells gave a full yield when infected by homotypic virus. The interference was rapidly established and addition of the second inoculum only 12 minutes after the first still gave significant interference. It would be interesting to know whether interference of this kind would occur with virus inactivated to the point at which no residual infectivity could be detected. Cooper, in the paper cited above, also refers briefly to the fact that stocks obtained by passaging virus in the undiluted state contain a non-infective component capable of causing marked homotypic interference.

2. SITE OF INTERFERENCE

In studies of interference by influenza viruses a frequently recurring theme is that interference is due to the interfering virus preventing the challenge virus from being adsorbed to the cell surface. The viruses of the influenza group have an enzyme (neuraminidase) which is able to destroy cellular receptors for other viruses of the same group and, when a large dose of enzymically active virus is used, it can induce interference by receptor destruction. Baluda (1959) finds that this is the mechanism by which large doses of inactivated Newcastle disease virus interfered with the growth of the same virus in tissue culture (Baluda, 1957). However, on inactivation by ultra-violet light, the interfering activity of influenza virus is lost before the enzymic activity of the virus is significantly affected (Henle & Henle, 1947), and conversely, interference can be induced by virus in which the enzymic activity has been destroyed (Isaacs & Edney, 1950). Also, interference is effective against viruses which do not share cell receptors with viruses of the influenza group (Schlesinger, 1951). Exclusion of challenge virus from the cell surface cannot therefore account for the interference described in many of the published reports, particularly where the use of excessively large doses of interfering virus is avoided.

Theoretically another possible mechanism of interference could be prevention of virus liberation from cells, an effect which occurs to a small extent after influenza-infected cells are treated with α-amino-p-methoxyphenylmethanesulphonic acid (Ackermann & Maassab, 1954). However, in allantoic cells in which interference had been induced, no evidence of accumulation of influenza virus or soluble antigen was found (Isaacs & Fulton, 1953). The absence of accumulation of soluble antigen is interesting, since recent work tends to confirm the important role which Hoyle (1953) attributed to it in the virus growth cycle. In particular, Breitenfeld & Schäfer (1957) have shown that the soluble antigen of fowl-plague virus (serologically an influenza A virus) is formed in the nucleus of infected cells; whereas the virus haemagglutinin is formed in the cytoplasm, the two being assembled together near the cell surface. It would seem then that interference affects an early stage in virus growth, but it is not known whether the block affects the production of soluble antigen itself or occurs before that stage. It is also not known whether interference occurs in the cell nucleus or the cytoplasm.

In interference induced by inactivated influenza virus with the growth of unrelated viruses, some hours are required for maximal interference to be established. However, Henle (1949) found that interference with the production of a single cycle of infective influenza A virus could still be induced by inoculating homotypic irradiated virus after the live virus. Heterotypic virus (influenza B) did not have the same effect. Significant inhibition of the virus cycle occurred even after an interval of three hours, by which time some soluble antigen production can normally be demonstrated. But it is not known whether the homotypic irradiated virus interrupts further production of the type-specific soluble antigen at this time or operates at a later stage in the virus growth cycle.

In summary, interference by live virus is likely to result from many different causes. Interference by inactivated viruses seems to include at least four distinct mechanisms.

i. Exclusion of challenge virus from the cell surface by a large dose of enzymically active virus.

ii. The effect of homotypic irradiated influenza virus inoculated after the challenge virus.

iii. Heterotypic interference produced by VS virus.

iv. The effect of inactivated myxovirus given some hours before challenge with a variety of unrelated viruses; this has been called "heterologous interference." There is some evidence that heterologous interference may be mediated through the production of a substance called "interferon."

3. CHARACTERISTICS OF INTERFERENCE PRODUCED BY INTERFERON

During studies of interference produced by heat-inactivated influenza virus in fragments of chick chorio-allantoic membrane, it was observed that, when the inactive virus and tissue were incubated together, a virus-interfering substance was produced with physico-chemical properties different from those of the inactive virus (Isaacs & Lindenmann, 1957). The substance was called "interferon" because it was found that interferon was formed under experimental conditions in which virus interference was established. In what follows, some of the characters of viral interference produced by interferon are described.

i. Interferon inhibits the growth of a wide variety of viruses, including strains of influenza A and B, Newcastle disease of fowls, Sendai (para-influenza 1), vaccinia and cowpox. The interference can be demonstrated in vitro and in fertile hen-eggs, and the degree of interference is independent of the dose of challenge virus over quite a wide range of dosage.

ii. Interference by interferon is not established at once, but takes some hours of incubation at 37°C. When adsorption of interferon was allowed to occur at 37°C., and the tissues were then washed, further incubation overnight at 37°C. before challenge resulted in greater interference than with overnight incubation at 2°C.

iii. Interferon had no effect on viruses in vitro; nor did it prevent the adsorption of fowl-plague virus or vaccinia virus to cells, as shown by our colleague Dr. A. C. Allison with isotope-labelled viruses. We have also found that interferon prevented the development of the soluble antigen of influenza virus when interference was established.

iv. The action of interferon has been demonstrated in different types of culture, e.g., in chick-embryo fibroblasts, calf-kidney cells and human cell lines. One especially interesting finding has emerged. Tyrrell (personal communication) found that interferon prepared in calf-kidney cells gave better interference when tested in calf cells than when tested with the same virus in chick chorio-allantoic membranes. Conversely, interferon prepared in chick chorio-allantoic membranes was more active when tested in chick cells than in calf cells. At the moment the reason for this apparent specificity of action of interferon is not known, nor is it known how general this effect is.

v. The assumption that interference by inactive virus is mediated through interferon is therefore based on the resemblance between the two forms of interference and the fact (described further in section 4) that establishment of . interference has been found to be closely correlated with production of interferon. There is one further resemblance between interference induced by heated influenza virus and by interferon. In each case, challenge by live virus is accompanied by the production of more interferon (Isaacs & Burke, 1958). This result could be interpreted as an explanation of heterologous virus interference by postulating that inactive virus induces cells to produce interferon, which may resemble an intermediate product of normal virus synthesis. This would so alter cells that, when they are then infected with live virus, they are induced to synthesize more interferon in place of the normal virus intermediate, i.e., interference represents a redirection of virus synthesis towards the production of interferon. This is a very speculative suggestion which may nevertheless be of value in stimulating alternative hypotheses and further experimentation.

4. PRODUCTION OF INTERFERON

Interferon has been produced from several kinds of cells treated with different strains of myxovirus which were inactivated by various methods. Variations in procedure have given products whose properties are superficially alike but, since there is no specific test for interferon, it is not yet known whether a single substance or a group of similar substances exists.

Various strains of influenza, fowl-plague virus and Newcastle disease virus all produced interferon that was found to be no more active against homologous virus than against heterologous strains. Inactivating influenza A virus by heating at 56°C. for one hour gave a product in which no residual infectivity could be demonstrated and this produced moderate yields of interferon. Inactivation at 60°C. for one hour abolished both the interfering activity and the ability to produce interferon. Inactivation by irradiation with ultra-violet light had been known to give a better interfering agent than heating at 56°C., and it also produced higher yields of interferon. Progressive irradiation of the virus led to a progressive loss of interfering activity and of the ability to produce interferon. Interferon was also produced by influenza virus inactivated by prolonged incubation at 37°C., and by incomplete virus prepared by the method of von Magnus (1951), but not by virus inactivated with 0.02% formaldehyde. In all these cases a correspondence was noted between the ability of virus to induce interference and to produce interferon. Another example of this correspondence is provided by experiments of Lindenmann (personal communication). It is known that interference by heated influenza virus is not established at once but requires some hours' incubation at about 37°C. Lindenmann found that production of interferon by heated influenza virus could be prevented by inoculating live virus along with the heated virus, i.e., interferon was not produced when interference was not yet established. This also suggests that in interference the cell was deflected from the synthesis of virus towards the synthesis of interferon, implying that two alternative metabolic pathways exist. Thus cells stimulated to produce live virus cannot at the same time be stimulated by heat-inactivated virus to make interferon, only one pathway being possible at a time.

Interferon is not a self-replicating molecule, and all attempts to show production of interferon by cells treated with interferon alone have proved negative. Production by live virus is a more complex problem. In early experiments live influenza virus was grown for 24 hours on the chick chorion, and its behaviour was compared with that of both ultra-violet-inactivated and incomplete viruses. Under these conditions the live virus did not produce interferon (Burke & Isaacs, 1958). Later Tyrrell (1959) found that when Sendai virus was grown in calf-kidney cultures interferon was produced after the first 24 hours' growth, at a time when virus production had passed its peak. Tyrrell's findings were confirmed with whole chick chorio-allantoic membranes infected with live influenza virus at high multiplicity. During the first 24 hours' incubation, virus production was at its peak and no interferon was produced. Later, as virus production was declining, interferon was produced (Burke & Isaacs, 1958). This action could conceivably result from the effect of virus spontaneously inactivated during the first 24 hours' incubation at 37°C. but, whatever the explanation, it seems that interferon is not produced while the cells are fully engaged in virus production.

Henle, Deinhardt, Bergs & Henle (1958) have studied cultures of human cell lines which were persistently infected with Newcastle disease and other viruses. The infected cells showed no spontaneous cell degeneration and they were resistant to the cytopathogenic action of viruses like VS virus. Resistance could also be induced by treating cells with Newcastle disease virus irradiated with ultra-violet light (Bergs, Henle, Deinhardt & Henle, 1958), and these effects seem to be manifestations of virus interference. Recently W. Henle (personal communication) and co-workers have found that the resistance induced by ultra-violet-inactivated myxoviruses in these cells could be accounted for by the production of a substance which closely resembled interferon in being inactivated by trypsin but unaffected by absorption with red cells, addition of viral immune serum or centrifugation at 25,000 g. Furthermore, Henle and co-workers have recently found that persistently infected cultures produce small amounts of interferon and it seems quite likely therefore that interferon is involved in the resistance shown by persistently infected cultures.

Ho & Enders (1959) have found that during the growth of an avirulent chick-embryo-adapted Type 2 poliomyelitis virus in human kidney cells a factor appeared in the medium which inhibited the infection of human amnion and renal cells by homotypic and heterotypic poliomyelitis viruses and by unrelated viruses. The inhibitory factor did not act on the challenge virus directly, nor did it prevent the uptake of challenge virus by cells. It was not neutralized by viral antiserum, it was non-dialysable, nor was it sedimented under conditions which would sediment poliomyelitis virus. This substance has similar properties to those described for interferon, and Ho and Enders suggest that it may play a role in the mechanism of resistance to viral infections.

5. PROPERTIES OF INTERFERON

Interferon differs in a number of ways from the inactivated virus from which it is prepared. It is serologically distinct from the virus, for its activity was not affected by a ferret antiserum of high potency for the strain of virus used. In contrast to the virus, interferon is not significantly absorbed by chick red cells. Interferon can also be distinguished from inactivated virus by physico-chemical tests; it was not sedimented by centrifugation at 100,000 g for four hours, whereas influenza virus is sedimented by 25,000 g in 30 minutes. Filtration through a series of gradocol membranes gave an end-point for interferon below 0.048 μ, but influenza virus is held back by a 0.18 μ membrane. However, interferon is non-dialysable, and so it is in the size range of many other bio-logically active macromolecules. It is stable in the cold for some weeks but activity is completely destroyed by heating at 60°C. for one hour, or at 100°C. for five minutes. Interferon is stable over the pH range 2–11, and its stability at pH 2 is useful for distinguishing its interfering activity from that of inac-tivated virus. Even when it is mixed with oily adjuvants, interferon appears to be non-antigenic.

Because interferon has not yet been isolated in pure form, its chemical nature has been studied so far only by observing the effect of specific enzymes and other reagents on its activity. The activity is not affected by ribonuclease, deoxyribo-nuclease or by the receptor-destroying enzyme of *Vibrio cholerae*. It resisted treatment with 0.001 M-sodium periodate (a reagent which reacts with many carbohydrates), but it was destroyed by shaking with ether. Several properties suggest that interferon is a protein. The proteolytic enzyme pepsin rapidly destroyed its activity, while treatment with trypsin led to partial inactivation. It was also destroyed by shaking with amyl alcohol–chloroform. It was only slowly inactivated by ultra-violet light with a maximal intensity at 2,537 Å and it was precipitated by saturation with ammonium sulfate. The slight residual activity after trypsin digestion was not affected by ribonuclease but, despite this, the possibility that there may be, for example, nucleic acid masked inside the protein cannot be excluded, and pure material must be obtained before its chemical constitution can be settled unequivocally.

The methods which are being used for the purification of interferon are those which have been worked out for the enzymes, the purification being followed by determination of the protein content of active solutions. The original solution contains too little protein for ammonium sulfate fractionation to be effective, but precipitation with ammonium sulfate is a convenient method of concentration. Pressure dialysis can also be used for concentration. Treatment overnight at pH 2 removes a considerable amount of non-protein material from solution and also serves as a convenient sterilizing step. However, although the biological activity is not affected by treatment at pH 2, the behaviour during chromatography on columns of modified cellulose (Peterson & Sober, 1956) is affected, probably because of some change in the charge of the active molecule. Chromatography on columns of the modified cellulose ion-exchange resins or on columns of calcium phosphate (Tiselius, Hjerten & Levin, 1956) gives some purification, and it is hoped that, by suitable combination of these methods, interferon substantially free from contaminants will be obtained. . . .

The medical microbiologist is constantly striving to understand the causation of disease. The mere presence of microorganisms in the body does not explain the occurrence of the fever, headache, inflammation, and malaise that ensue in infections by pathogenic bacteria. The problem of how and why bacteria cause illness has been greatly clarified by the study of *toxins,* chemical substances released by pathogenic bacteria.

Gram-positive bacteria release *exotoxins* into the culture medium and into the blood stream and tissue fluids; these are complex proteins that are often highly toxic. The characteristic symptoms of the diseases caused by gram-positive pathogens are consequences of the action of these exotoxins (see article by Halbert and Keatinge, pages 197 to 209 in this volume). Gram-negative bacteria do not secrete exotoxins; but on death and breakdown of the cells, toxins of a quite different kind, known as *endotoxins,* are set free. As will be shown in the article reproduced below, endotoxins may have striking biological effects.

In the present state of our knowledge, the term *endotoxin* designates a rather poorly defined group of lipopolysaccharide-protein complexes obtained from the cell wall of any of the gram-negative bacteria. Preparations of endotoxin are far from uniform in composition or in biological effects: they differ according to the species, and even the strain, of bacterium and according to the method of extraction employed.

Endotoxins are highly antigenic; they are, in fact, identical with the somatic or "O" antigens of the gram-negative bacteria. They are extremely potent fever producers (pyrogens): the minute traces of endotoxin that remain adsorbed on a glass vessel after thorough washing may be sufficient to produce fever in patients who receive intravenous injections of water or "physiological saline" from the contaminated vessel. A couple of decades ago, hospitals found it difficult to provide pyrogen-free water for intravenous use, and the supplying of such water was usually taken over by commercial concerns with the special facilities and know-how needed for the purpose.

Endotoxin may reduce the organism's resistance to infection by injuring or destroying the phagocytic cells of the blood stream (macrophages) and the "fixed" phagocytic cells that abound in the tissues (histiocytes) ; under certain circumstances, however, endotoxin stimulates the phagocytic cells to greater activity. There has been investigation of the possibility of enhancing the organism's nonspecific resistance to a wide variety of infections by administration of endotoxin, or similar substances, to stimulate the phagocytic capacity of the reticuloendothelial system, but so far without practical result. Endotoxin has many other effects on various organs and tissues. These are well summarized in the article that follows.

Dr. Wesley W. Spink is Professor of Medicine at the University of Minnesota Medical School, Minneapolis.

From *Yale J. Biol. Med.,*
30:355–367, 1958.

FROM ENDOTOXIN TO SNAKE VENOM

BY WESLEY W. SPINK

The host-parasite relationship in many infectious diseases of animals and of man continues to challenge the knowledge and imagination, not only of microbiologists and those in other basic disciplines, but that of clinicians as well. There remain many unexplained features of this relationship bearing on the problem as to why invading microorganisms cause illness. One aspect of this relationship which has attracted considerable attention in recent years involves Gram-negative bacteria. The metabolic and morphological alterations induced in the host by bacterial somatic preparations known as endotoxins have been studied intensively in many laboratories and clinics. The purpose of this report is not to review the extensive literature on the subject but rather to summarize the results of investigations which have been carried out by my associates and myself. I shall refer largely to various communications from our group in the Department of Medicine and from those of Dr. Maurice Visscher and his associates in the Department of Physiology, which in turn document the related work of others.

WHY INVESTIGATE THE ACTION OF ENDOTOXINS?

My interest in endotoxin was aroused almost 25 years ago while working on the problem of gonococcal arthritis with Dr. Chester S. Keefer. During the course of those investigations it was observed that gonococci, in common with many other species of Gram-negative bacteria, were killed by human blood without the intervention of phagocytes. In other words, fresh serum lysed the organisms. Further studies revealed that a suspension of lysed gonococci was extremely toxic when injected into the tissues of animals. In a discussion on the pathogenesis of gonococcal infections at the time, it was postulated that the inflammatory reaction induced by gonococci was due, in part at least, to the autolyzed organisms.

With the advent of the sulfonamides and antibiotics the problem of gonococcal disease offered less of a clinical challenge, and interest in endotoxin subsided until attention was attracted to the possible role of endotoxin in the pathogenesis of illness caused by brucellae. While investigating the therapy of brucellosis in Mexico City with my associate, Dr. A. I. Braude, and with Dr. M. Ruiz-Castaneda, an interesting sequence of clinical events aroused a further interest in endotoxin. Patients having severe and prolonged illness due to *Brucella melitensis* were given chlortetracycline. Shortly after the initial dose of the drug, the condition of several of the patients became worse. They exhibited a rise in temperature, tachycardia, and an alarming decline in blood pressure. Subsequently, they showed marked improvement. These manifestations suggested that the antibiotic shared in the destruction of large numbers of brucellae in the host with the liberation of endotoxin from the lysed organisms. It was postulated that the condition of the patients became worse not only because of the inherent toxicity of the endotoxin, but because they had acquired hypersensitivity to brucella antigen. This concept was to occupy our thoughts for several years.

Further general interest in endotoxin was stimulated by clinical observations in patients having systemic infections due to several species of Gram-negative bacteria commonly associated with urinary tract infections. These microbes are not highly pathogenic but they do threaten life when they invade the blood stream, probably largely due to the endotoxin of the organisms. The endotoxin frequently participates in the syndrome of shock. These clinical observations stimulated an extensive study on the hemodynamic changes induced by endotoxin in cooperation with the Department of Physiology.

INTRODUCTORY STUDIES WITH BRUCELLA ENDOTOXIN

Endotoxin has been described as a lipoprotein-carbohydrate complex localized on or near the surface of Gram-negative bacterial cells. Endotoxins have been prepared according to a variety of procedures. Elaborate techniques have been detailed for making "purified" material. Some have concluded that the toxic component in endotoxin is a macromolecular polysaccharide fraction. We believe that this concept of endotoxin is too narrow, although the carbohydrate moiety is an important toxic factor. It is not unlikely that the disintegration of bacterial cells in the host results in the liberation of several undefined, but active substances. The sum total effect of these somatic components on the host also remains undefined. At the present time, when purified somatic bacterial material is presented to the host, a reproducible train of events ensues, but this does not necessarily reflect the course of changes under natural conditions, in which the host is challenged with many unknown bacterial factors.

Nevertheless, in order to reduce the number of variables to a minimum, we have also tried to employ a standardized and partially purified preparation of endotoxin. With but few exceptions we have used a Boivin-type of endotoxin, which involves extraction of the bacterial cells with trichloracetic acid. The method for making the endotoxin has been given in detail elsewhere.

Many of our investigations with endotoxin have been carried out in mice. Again, this selection was carried out in an attempt to lend uniform conditions to the many experiments. Mice are quite suitable for comparative studies because a genetically homogeneous population was available, and, also, because relatively small amounts of endotoxin were necessary for experimental purposes. Our initial studies on brucella endotoxin in a population of male ABC mice compared the toxicity of endotoxin prepared from strains of brucellae having varying degrees of virulence. The toxicity of endotoxin had no relationship to the virulence of the living culture. Endotoxin prepared from a culture of Strain 19 of *Br. abortus,* having attenuated virulence, was just as lethal for mice as endotoxin made from a highly invasive strain of *Br. melitensis.* Death of the mice uniformly occurred between 12 and 24 hours. More recent studies have shown that endotoxins prepared from *Escherichia coli* and *Salmonella typhosus* were weight for weight more toxic for mice than brucella endotoxin.

STUDIES IN THE RELATIONSHIP BETWEEN ADRENOCORTICAL ACTIVITY AND ENDOTOXIN

Having established that endotoxin from brucellae, as well as endotoxin prepared from other species of Gram-negative bacilli, was lethal for mice, a series of studies was made on the role of the adrenal cortex in the defense mechanism of the mouse against brucella endotoxin as well as against viable brucellae. Interest in this aspect of the endotoxin studies was stimulated by the report of others stating that the generalized Shwartzman reaction induced by endotoxin in rabbits was greatly accelerated by administering cortisone. It was anticipated that cortisone would abet the lethal action of endotoxin in mice. On the contrary, it was demonstrated repeatedly that administering cortisone protected mice against lethal doses of endotoxin.

The influence of endotoxin on the normal temperature rhythm of the mouse was also studied in relation to adrenal activity. First, the 24-hour rhythm of temperature in the normal mouse was determined. The rectal temperatures varied between 36° and 39.5°C., with the lowest temperatures occurring during midday and the highest readings in the early morning hours. The peak of the temperature corresponded with the nocturnal activities of mice. This activity, in turn, can be directly correlated with adrenal function. It was observed that endotoxin caused a rise in temperature within seven to nine hours after endotoxin was administered, and then a profound drop in temperature to 30°C. occurred shortly before death. Very small quantities of endotoxin altered the physiological rhythm of the temperature without causing death. Adrenalectomized mice were particularly susceptible to the action of endotoxin, both with respect to lethality and to alterations in temperature. However, administered corticosteroid stabilized the temperature in intact and adrenalectomized mice given endotoxin, as well as protecting them against a lethal outcome.

Though not directly related to the problem of endotoxin activity, observations were made in mice which were *simultaneously* infected with brucellae and given cortisone. Under these circumstances a relatively benign disease was converted into a fulminating infection with a marked proliferation of the brucellae in the tissues. Adrenocorticosteroid administration had little adverse effect on more chronically infected mice. These observations in mice could not be correlated with subsequent investigations in human patients. The differences observed between acute brucellosis in mice and in humans, and the response to steroids, could be ascribed to the fact that brucellae and steroids were given to the mice at the same time, whereas in man, invasion of the tissues by brucellae had occurred before the steroid was given. This permitted stimulation of the defense mechanism in the human host and the establishment of an immune response before exposure to exogenous steroid. Another possible explanation for the difference is the relatively large dose of steroid used in mice. Patients seriously ill with acute brucellosis were dramatically improved within a short period of time when given steroid. These studies have resulted in the recommendation that steroid therapy over a brief period of time should be employed along with the antibiotics in the management of the more severely ill patients.

A series of studies has been directed by Melby and Egdahl on the effect of endotoxin on activity of the adrenal gland in the dog. By direct cannulation of the adrenal vein the secretion of hydrocortisone was measured under different circumstances. Brucella or *E. coli* endotoxin administered intravenously to dogs resulted in a prompt rise in the output of hydrocortisone. This effect was mediated through the pituitary gland, since administered endotoxin was without effect in hypophysectomized animals, although a rise in the level of hydrocortisone could be provoked in these animals with ACTH. This pointed out quite clearly that in the dog the effect of endotoxin on adrenal activity was mediated through the pituitary. Similar observations have been recorded by others for the rat. Following the initial response of the adrenal to endotoxin in intact animals, a further response could be elicited by ACTH but not as marked as that obtained prior to the administration of endotoxin. It was concluded that although endotoxin caused an increased secretion of cortical hormone, the functional capacity of the cortex was temporarily diminished by the endotoxin.

These studies were extended to human patients having shock due to bacterial infections. It was observed that the blood levels of hydrocortisone were considerably higher in the patients with shock than in normal controls. Of further interest was the finding that administered hydrocortisone disappeared more rapidly from the blood of the patients with shock than from the blood of normal persons. But this rapid metabolism of exogenous hydrocortisone uniformly took place only in the patients who recovered. In the patients dying of shock the half-life of administered hydrocortisone was more prolonged than in normal individuals and considerably more so than in patients with shock who recovered.

STUDIES ON THE HEMODYNAMIC CHANGES INDUCED BY ENDOTOXIN

In an attempt to acquire more precise information concerning the nature of shock induced by endotoxin a group of experimental studies was designed in cooperation with members of the Department of Physiology. When large doses of endotoxin prepared from either *E. coli* or *Br. melitensis* were injected intravenously into dogs, a two-stage decline in arterial blood pressure was observed. Within 30 seconds following the administration of endotoxin there was a precipitous drop in the systemic arterial pressure, and a simultaneous rise in the pressure of the portal vein. As the portal vein pressure returned to the preinjection level, a rise in the femoral arterial pressure took place. This was then followed by a gradual decline in the systemic pressure over a period of several hours ending in death of the animals. It was demonstrated quantitatively that the *immediate* drop in arterial pressure was due to the pooling of the blood in the liver and intestine, and a reduction in venous return to the heart. This immediate effect on pressure could be abolished by eviscerating the animal. However, this did not prevent the secondary decline in blood pressure. A progressive fall in blood pressure occurred in the eviscerated dog when cardiac filling was maintained at a constant level, which indicated a decline in total peripheral resistance. It is unlikely that in the dog the shock induced by endotoxin is mediated through the central nervous system. It was concluded that the critical problem in the dog with endotoxin shock was the initial pooling of blood in venous beds. This results in a failure of venous blood to return to the heart, causing in turn a diminution in cardiac output. However, it should be emphasized that a species difference has been observed in the response to endotoxin by Dr. L. Hinshaw and his group working in Dr. Visscher's laboratory. Immediate engorgement of the liver was not noted in the cat, rabbit and monkey, possibly because constriction of the hepatic vein does not occur in these species as in the dog. But a progressive fall in systemic blood pressure was seen similar to that in the eviscerated dog. Thus, there is no evidence in the cat, rabbit and monkey for pooling of blood in the splanchnic bed, but a gradual decline in peripheral resistance does occur.

The foregoing observations in the dog implied that if the arterial pressure was to be stabilized in endotoxin shock, the cardiac output must be increased. This could possibly be accomplished by decreasing the pooling of blood peripherally. Vasopressor agents were evaluated experimentally, and it was observed that metaraminol (Aramine) did diminish the venous pooling in the dog and increase the return of venous blood to the heart. These observations were further extended to human patients in the treatment of shock.

The rapidity with which endotoxin altered the hemodynamics in the experimental animal and the apparent primary vascular effect of endotoxin prompted further quantitative studies employing different techniques. Using the method of MacLean *et al.* for weighing the liver, direct observations on the dog's kidney were made in a similar way in the eviscerated dog. As quickly as 15 seconds after the injection of *E. coli* endotoxin into the femoral vein there was a marked decrease in the weight of the kidney. In fact, the size of the kidney diminished under direct observation. The arterial pressure fell *after* the change in kidney weight, indicating that the vasoconstriction occurring in the kidney was not initially due to the decline in blood pressure. The effect of *E. coli* endotoxin on renal function was studied on the isolated and perfused kidney of the dog. When the kidney was perfused with heparinized blood at a constant pressure from a heart-lung preparation, impairment of renal tubular function occurred. There was a prompt and progressive deterioration in the rate of para-amino hippurate clearance, and the specific gravity of the urine decreased markedly. Recent unpublished data by Hinshaw and others have shown that the changes in renal function are probably related to the effect of endotoxin on the renal blood flow. The [renal clearance of para-amino hippurate] is not appreciably altered after endotoxin. When the influence of *E. coli* endotoxin on the pulmonary circulation was studied in the isolated heart-lung preparation of the dog and cat, the outstanding feature was an increase in small vein resistance with a gain in the weight of the lung.

ACQUIRED RESISTANCE TO ENDOTOXIN

Endotoxin rapidly effects changes in the tonicity of the vascular system, which in turn contributes to further physiological and morphological alterations in the host. Many of these resultant abnormal factors can, and have been measured. A phenomenon of endotoxin activity that has been well confirmed in many laboratories is the development of tolerance or resistance of animals to endotoxin following the injection of repeated doses of the material. But, here again, the problem is complicated. Tolerance to the fever-promoting property of endotoxin is not synonymous with the development of tolerance against the lethal action of endotoxin. Recently, dogs have been made tolerant to endotoxin by Drs. Egdahl and Melby so that no fever was induced by endotoxin, but the same animals continued to manifest increased adrenocortical activity.

That aspect of the problem of resistance that has engaged our group more prominently has been related to the lethal activity of endotoxin. This interest was an outgrowth of the observation that ACTH and the adrenocorticosteroids protected animals against lethal doses of endotoxin. It was also observed that totally unrelated substances such as chlorpromazine, and the polymer, polyvinylpyrrolidone (PVP), protected mice against the lethal action of brucella endotoxin. Protection has also been afforded by antihistaminics (Benadryl), yeast extracts, barbiturates (Nembutal), and an environment of lowered temperature.

One of the perplexing problems of endotoxin resistance that has been explored is the duration of resistance against a lethal dose of endotoxin following the injection of sublethal amounts. In mice it was found that a single sublethal dose of brucella endotoxin offered homologous protection for as long as four months, and after three weekly injections of sublethal amounts, protection was extended as long as ten months. Heterologous protection against other endotoxin was of shorter duration. The precise nature of this form of immune response is not clearly understood. It was of further interest to demonstrate that mice challenged with a lethal dose of endotoxin but simultaneously given either adrenocorticosteroid or chlorpromazine were protected against subsequent lethal doses of endotoxin. Brucella endotoxin administered to mice also resulted in increased resistance to living brucella organisms.

ACQUIRED SENSITIVITY TO ENDOTOXIN

The preceding discussion has been concerned with the acquisition of increased resistance of mice to endotoxin. It was possible to alter the response of this species so that they became more susceptible to the lethal action of endotoxin. It has been generally confirmed that mice are relatively resistant to histamine, but an increased susceptibility, in some strains of mice at least, develops following injection with *Hemophilus pertussis* vaccine. Since the administration of endotoxin to the dog is followed by the liberation of histamine into the blood stream, it was of interest to see if pertussis vaccine increased the susceptibility of mice not only to histamine, but also to brucella endotoxin. A series of experiments in this direction has revealed further the complicated nature of the problem. It was observed that pertussis vaccine increased the susceptibility of Swiss-Webster, but not ABC mice, to histamine. The injection of brucella endotoxin was not followed by increased susceptibility to histamine in either strain of mice. Both Swiss-Webster mice and ABC mice became more susceptible to brucella and to typhoid endotoxin after the administration of *H. pertussis* vaccine. And finally, the protective action of chlorpromazine and Benadryl against endotoxin was abolished after pertussis vaccination, but the protection offered by adrenocorticosteroids remained unaltered.

An increase in the susceptibility of mice to endotoxin was demonstrated in another way. Mice were infected with a small inoculum of *Br. melitensis*. Approximately seven days to four weeks later a dose of brucella endotoxin that was not lethal for uninfected mice was injected intraperitoneally into the infected animals, and death ensued within 24 hours. Repeated minimal injections of the endotoxin in the infected animals was associated with a marked inflammatory reaction in the visceral peritoneum. This was at first interpreted as a manifestation of specific brucella hypersensitivity. However, subsequent experiments showed that mice infected with brucella were also more susceptible to the endotoxin of *E. coli* than normal controls. This sensitizing effect of an infection to endotoxin has been noted by others, who have concluded that an explosive multiplication of bacteria induced by the endotoxin was responsible for the accelerated lethal effect. Perhaps this affords an explanation for our own results, since we have been able to protect mice infected with brucellae against endotoxin by the simultaneous administration of chlortetracycline.

AND NOW—TO SNAKE VENOM

It became known to us that the train of events induced in animals by endotoxin could be produced by many other agents. Furthermore, the action of endotoxin simulates the manifestations associated with anaphylactic shock, although the latter involves a specific immunological mechanism. The term "anaphylactoid shock" has been employed in the past for the nonspecific reactions caused not only by endotoxin but by many colloidal preparations.

Peptone is one of many substances that have been studied intensively in an attempt to elucidate the mechanism of anaphylactoid shock. We observed that a population of ABC mice were resistant to an injection of peptone, but peptone proved to be lethal to mice six days after the administration of *H. pertussis* vaccine. In addition, mice sensitized to pertussis vaccine could be protected against the lethal action of peptone with cortisone, chlorpromazine, and an antihistaminic agent.

In comparing other substances with endotoxin we became particularly interested in snake venom because of the observations reported by Essex and his associates. They stated that the administration of rattlesnake venom to the dog was followed by a prompt drop in systemic blood pressure, similar to that which we had observed following the injection of endotoxin. But instead of noting a rise in the weight of the liver, Essex and his group recorded a drop in the weight of this and other organs. Dr. Essex kindly supplied us with the rattlesnake venoms, *Crotalus terrificus and Crotalus atrox*. Studies in mice have been made with these and also with moccasin venom, *Agkistrodon piscivorus piscivorus*. Some preliminary studies have also been made with a tropical rattlesnake venom, *Crotalus terrificus terrificus* and also with a venom from *Bothrops jararaca,* supplied to us by the Butatan Institute in Brazil. We have observed in the dog that rattlesnake venom caused a prompt drop in blood pressure, but the pressure eventually became restored at normal levels. The gradual secondary decline in pressure seen with endotoxin did not take place. It has become quite apparent to us from observations made on mice that rattlesnake venom obtained from different snakes of the same species will produce varying results. This is attributable to the fact that snake venom is such a complicated biologic material. In this respect the complexity of endotoxin simulates snake venom. It should also be appreciated by the investigator that venom obtained from the same snake at different periods of time will vary in biologic activity.

Direct observations on the vascular effects of snake venom have been made by Fulton *et al.,* employing the everted cheek pouch of the golden hamster.

Moccasin venom injected beneath the epithelium results shortly thereafter in a marked arteriolar constriction, stasis of the blood, and then the appearance of petechiae, with a diapedesis of erythrocytes through the vessel walls at venous junctions.

Possible immunological relationships between snake venom and endotoxin have been explored just enough to invite further investigations. It has been observed in studies on the Shwartzman reaction that the administration of moccasin venom made animals refractory to endotoxin. In the experiments cited rattlesnake venom was not effective. Others noted some cross protection in animals between moccasin venom and the endotoxin of *Salmonella typhimurium*. We have found that populations of ABC mice can be protected against lethal doses of rattlesnake venom (*Crotalus terrificus*) following three weekly injections of brucella endotoxin. This resistance has endured for as long as 6 weeks after the last injection of endotoxin. Protection against such venom has also been demonstrated after the administration of *E. coli* and *S. typhi* endotoxins. The three endotoxins also gave good protection to mice against moccasin venom and the venom of *Bothrops jararaca*.

Further investigations are under way with the precipitin test, which has included the gel-diffusion technique, in an attempt to elucidate further the immunological relationship between endotoxin and snake venom. To date, with this technique it has not been possible to demonstrate cross precipitins in the sera of mice immunized with endotoxin or snake venom. Several well-defined precipitin bands could be demonstrated when antivenom horse serum and venoms were employed in the gel-diffusion method.

THE CRUX OF THE ENDOTOXIN PROBLEM

In attempting to formulate a basic concept concerning the mode of action of endotoxin we have looked upon endotoxin as promptly "triggering" alterations in vascular activity. Vasoconstriction, vasodilatation, and increased permeability of the vessels are rapidly followed by profound metabolic and morphological changes in the tissues of the host. Various substances such as norepinephrine, serotonin, histamine, heparin, and proteolytic enzymes are very likely liberated into the blood stream, and these in turn alter the physiological and metabolic equilibrium of the host. Endotoxin sets in motion a chain reaction within the tissues and body fluids of the host that may result in death.

The most outstanding feature of endotoxin activity is the rapidity with which endotoxin acts when introduced into either the circulation of the intact host or into the perfusate of isolated organs. Changes in vascular activity can be measured within 10 to 15 seconds after the administration of endotoxin. This would indicate that either endotoxin acts directly upon the endothelial wall or that it causes an alteration in the blood, which in turn affects the function of the vessel. If the primary action of endotoxin occurs in the blood, the changes may involve enzymatic activity because of the almost immediate response induced by relatively small amounts of material.

There is some suggestive evidence that the primary action of endotoxin operates through some factor or factors in the blood, and then secondarily upon the tissues of the host, including the vascular endothelium. Rosenfeld found that endotoxin prepared from *Pseudomonas aeruginosa, E. coli,* or *Serratia marcescens* inhibited the *in vitro* adrenocortical activity of the calf adrenal only when the perfusate consisted of homologous whole blood. No effect of endotoxin was elicited when artificial physiological perfusates were employed. Likewise, Hinshaw and his associates working with the isolated and perfused lung of the dog, observed a pulmonary vascular response when heparinized blood was used as a perfusate, but not when dextran was employed. Also, there was little effect from endotoxin when defibrinated blood was used in the heart-lung-kidney preparation in place of heparinized blood.

The accumulating evidence emphasizes that the action of endotoxin is complex. Effects of endotoxin action must not be mistakenly offered as basic causes for the alterations induced in the host. Endotoxin "triggers off" a chain reaction of vascular and metabolic changes. The crux of the endotoxin problem in the host-parasite relationship resides largely in the few seconds that elapse after endotoxin appears in the blood stream of the host.

MICROBIAL ECOLOGY

According to contemporary biological thinking, life must have originated in ponds or oceans very early in the earth's history. The microbial flora and fauna of the oceans are believed to contain groups of ancient as well as recent origin. The ancient forms appear to be extensive and diversified.

The surface of the sea is in contact with the atmosphere, and the atmospheric gases, particularly oxygen and carbon dioxide, diffuse across the air-water interface and dissolve in the ocean. Solution of these atmospheric gases is promoted by wave action; advancing wave crests tend to trap air, and the turbulence of water in the upper layers also facilitates the mixing of air-rich surface water with the more nearly air-free water beneath. It has been estimated that the air above one acre of sea (or land) contains 18 to 20 tons of carbon dioxide and that the total carbon content of the atmosphere is of the order of 600 billion tons. In the ocean, the amount of carbon dioxide, in solution or in the form of bicarbonates, is probably at least 100 times greater.

The upper layers of the ocean are well lighted. Light intensity falls off with increasing depth, becoming negligible at about 600 feet. The green, red, and brown algae and some of the pigmented bacteria actively carry on photosynthesis in the illuminated zone, converting the dissolved carbon dioxide into sugars and polysaccharides; these in turn form the basis of the synthesis of the proteins, fats, and other substances that constitute the food of the myriads of organisms present in the seas. In view of the large extent of the oceans, the amount of solids formed by photosynthesis in the sea is probably many times greater than that synthesized by land plants.

Wherever photosynthesis is possible, oxygen is released during daylight hours, greatly supplementing the oxygen that enters by diffusion across the air-water interface. Aerobic bacteria can flourish under these conditions.

The oxygen of sea water is consumed by metabolic processes in living organisms and in the decomposition of the bodies of dead organisms. The exhaustion of the oxygen held in solution gives rise to anaerobic conditions in which only anaerobic organisms can flourish. Some of these can derive energy by coupling the partial oxidation of carbon compounds with the reduction of sulfate to H_2S or to other highly reduced sulfur compounds. Reducing conditions often exist, and hydro-gen-sulfide-producing anaerobes often prevail, in coastal muds. Occa-sionally the smell of escaping hydrogen sulfide may serve as an indication of anaerobic conditions.

The anaerobe *Desulfovibrio* is one of the many bacteria that produce hydrogen sulfide. This organism also possesses an enzyme, hydrogenase, which enables it to oxidize molecular hydrogen.

The following article is an excellent summary of recent studies on marine microbiology. Dr. E. G. Ferguson Wood wrote this review while at the Division of Fisheries and Oceanography, Cronulla, Aus-tralia. He is presently at the Marine Laboratory of the University of Miami, in Florida.

From *Bacteriol. Rev.,*
22:1–19, 1958.

THE SIGNIFICANCE OF MARINE MICROBIOLOGY

BY E. J. FERGUSON WOOD

I. INTRODUCTION

Oparin [1938] considers that bacteria were the first organisms to become differentiated from the primordial slime; this has been tacitly assumed by many people because of the primitive nature of these organisms. Ycas [1955] suggests that a series of mutually interacting catalysts were the forerunners of life. He states: "In this stage, however, there are no discrete organisms and there exists only one living thing, the metabolizing ocean. The further evolution of this system presumably led to the production of catalysts of high molecular weight and peptide nature. These may have agglomerated and eventually the system would have become delineated into small, discrete masses, the living organisms." If this concept is true, and it seems logical, marine microorganisms were the first discrete, living organisms. These organisms would begin to react upon their environment and modify it in many ways. From this time on, marine microorganisms have been acting as geobiological agents, and while many of their earlier activities must remain the subject of interesting if unprofitable speculation, others of these activities have impressed themselves on the geological record.

The relationship between microorganisms and geological processes has been the subject of some wishful thinking, in that geologists have tended to assign to biological agents many things which they could not readily explain, and microbiologists have not been as helpful as they might have been in suggesting how microorganisms influence the environment. The latter question is important as the organisms are ephemeral and can only be known from the past by their effect on the milieu in which they once lived.

There has been considerable study of microorganisms in the soil and, to some extent, in fresh water, but those in the sea have received far too little attention when we consider the vast potentiality of the sea both as an adjunct to man's survival and as the place of deposition of the major part of the world's sedimentary rocks and the minerals and ores contained therein.

As the most recent conspectus of marine microbiology is that of ZoBell [1946], it seems timely to give a brief account of the more recent studies on the activity of marine microorganisms, their ecology, and their possible economic and geobiological roles. This review will include photosynthetic as well as non-photosynthetic microorganisms.

II. CHEMICAL TRANSFORMATIONS

A. Sulfur.—The bacteria of the sulfur cycle are of major importance in inorganic transformations, not only because they largely control the availability of sulfur to animals and plants but also because of the effects they have on other elements. Sulfur has a large series of compounds at the several states of oxidation and reduction from sulfate to sulfide and these compounds vary considerably in solubility. The biological importance of sulfur and its compounds is shown by the fact that the sulfur microorganisms have a wider pH-Eh range for their environment than any other group, except perhaps the photosynthetic organisms, and it would appear that some of the algae (*e.g.,* the blue-greens) concern themselves with the oxidation of sulfur under anaerobic or very acid conditions. Further, reduced sulfur compounds assist in the deposition of silica in diatom tests and serve to facilitate diatom multiplication.

In the sea, only a small part of the potential environment of the sulfur bacteria is met with; this part, however, allows the maximum interplay between these organisms and the many other microorganisms which coexist with them, an interplay which has been called "metabiosis." In this metabiosis, each organism conditions the environment for the others. It is more than a simple cycle or succession, because, in nature, each component remains in the system, becoming dominant, declining, and resuming its activity as soon as the environment becomes favorable again.

The sulfur cycle can best be observed in the estuarine environment where the rapid decay of algal blooms or other rotting matter produces conditions suitable for the sulfate-reducing bacteria which attack the sulfates contained in sea water. These are reduced to hydrogen sulfide chiefly by *Desulfovibrio desulfuricans,* but, as there is usually an excess of iron in the water and in the muds, black ferrous sulfhydryl or hydrotroilite is formed. *Desulfovibrio* is widely dispersed through marine environments though it is usually regarded as a member of the benthic community. However, Kimata *et al.* [1955] have found this organism in sea water up to 2000 m offshore near Miyajima (Japan), and I have isolated it from estuarine water in Lake Macquarie and from aseptically collected net phytoplankton samples 10 miles east of Cronulla (Australia). In the last-mentioned case, the organism could have been autochthonous or could have been derived from the bottom 100 m below.

In the muds, *Desulfovibrio* may be regarded as a normal member of the community from the shoreline to the greatest depth. In some estuaries, the strains of *Desulfovibrio* lack hydrogenase, but in others and in marine muds this enzyme is present.

Baas Becking and Wood [1955] have recorded wide ranges of pH, temperature, and salinity for the growth of *Desulfovibrio*. Below pH 5.8 iron sulfide was not produced. In the alkaline range, natural muds and pure and mixed cultures of *Desulfovibrio* grew at pH values up to 9.4, at which pH HCO_3^- ion is the limiting factor in sea water owing to the presence of calcium ion. The hydrogen gradient required by *Desulfovibrio* may be demonstrated by growing hydrogenase-positive strains in a hydrogen-oxygen gradient in tubes, where the growth will be found to occur about 2 cm below the hydrogen and 6 to 8 cm from the external air. The Eh has an upper limit of about +110 mv at pH 7 and a lower limit below −300 mv.

The effect of cations on sulfate reduction in marine environments has been discussed by Baas Becking and Wood [1955]. Marine strains were selected to grow in salt concentrations of as high as 21 per cent but the time required for the commencement of reduction was almost a linear function of the salt concentration; in the absence of sodium chloride, sulfate reduction was retarded. Much of the iron in sea water and mud is bound as ferric phosphate, which occurs in the fecal pellets of marine animals, and in particulate matter in the sea. The ferric phosphate, though relatively insoluble, is less so than hydrotroilite, so the latter is precipitated, allowing phosphoric acid to go into solution. In this way, as Baas Becking and MacKay [1956] have shown, sulfate reduction releases phosphates in the sea, and the reduction of sulfates, accompanied as it is by decrease in oxygen in the water, is also accompanied by a high phosphate content.

The oxidation of sulfides on the sea bottom is brought about either abiologically or by sulfur-oxidizing and other bacteria. Abiological oxidation takes the sulfides to sulfur, and bacterial action is necessary for oxidation to sulfate. Many of the sulfur-oxidizing bacteria oxidize sulfides and thiosulfates as well as sulfur. The thiobacilli are important in the estuarine environment and are strictly autotrophic. They are probably equally important in the deeps to complete the sulfur cycle, though their presence has yet to be demonstrated. Marine thiobacilli appear to belong to the thioparus group and true *Thiobacillus thiooxidans* was not isolated from sea water or mud. The thioparus was shown to oxidize sulfur and thiosulfate anaerobically. The anaerobic *T. denitrificans* is common in the estuarine muds, and we have found it also in estuarine waters. The pH-Eh relationships of thiobacilli are very wide, from about −200 mv at pH 7 to +700 mv in the acid range. Their occurrence is possible at any Eh to be found in the estuarine or marine environment. In shallow water, and in places where organic matter is abundant, the peculiar forms *Thiovulum*, *Thiothrix*, and *Beggiatoa* occur. These forms seem to require organic matter, and Scotten [1953] grew beggiatoae on organic media without sulfur. The photosynthetic green and purple sulfur bacteria occur at definite hydrogen sulfide tensions and they are possibly endemic in marine environments where photosynthesis is possible. Although one rarely sees recognizable patches of purple or green sulfur bacteria in marine environments, I have isolated them from phytoplankton tows 10 miles offshore, from cultures of *Enteromorpha intestinalis* taken from just below low-tide mark, and from mussels collected from a depth of 20 feet in a coastal lagoon. Kriss and Rukina [1953] record purple bacteria from muds in the Black Sea well below the photic zone. The occurrence of photosynthetic bacteria in phytoplankton swarms is of interest as, if these bacteria are autochthonous, they could be active in the regeneration of sulfate from reduced sulfur compounds of the phytoplankton. Further, as photoreduction using H_2S as a hydrogen source is about 8 times as efficient thermodynamically as photosynthesis using H_2O, these organisms, as well as the photoreducing algae, would have a greater compensation depth. Postgate [1954] has demonstrated that the sulfur deposits of certain Cyrenaican lakes are due to sulfate reduction followed by purple bacteria. Baas Becking and Kaplan [1956] believe that the sulfur-gypsum concretions of Lake Eyre (Central Australia) are due to bacterial reduction of the sulfate of the gypsum followed by oxidation to sulfur by thiobacilli.

ZoBell [1952] has found numerous bacterial species including the sulfate reducers in the ocean deeps, down to 10,000 m. L. H. N. Cooper (*verbal communication*) has observed that, in the deep oceans, there is a decrease in phosphorus in the bottom 20 m, with a concentration in the muds. This could be explained by the utilization of phosphorus by microorganisms close to and on the bottom, the adsorption of these microorganisms on the mud particles, and the subsequent release of the phosphate by the sulfate reducers in accordance with the scheme discussed above.

In addition to the inorganic sulfur compounds that are made and broken down by bacteria, organic sulfur compounds such as methionine, taurine, cysteine, and cystine are formed by bacteria and plants from sulfates. Bywood and Challenger [1953] have shown that *Enteromorpha* and other algae produce reducing substances such as mercaptans and dimethyl sulfide from methionine. Wood [1953] has suggested the formation of similar compounds by the sea-grasses and Starkey *et al.* [1953] have found that methionine is broken down by bacteria to mercaptan and dimethyl sulfide whereas cystine, taurine, etc., are decomposed to give sulfur, sulfites, sulfates, and polythionates. Postgate [1954] recently discussed the importance of bacterial sulfur in the world's economy, stressing its importance to man. Here we are concerned with its importance to life in the sea, for it is to the sea that the increasing population of the world must increasingly turn for the additional food and clothing that will be required in the future.

B. Phosphorus.—Marine biologists have long been interested in the phosphorus cycle in the sea, and it has been shown that the plants, including the phytoplankton, utilize inorganic phosphate, converting it to an organic form, whence it is available to the animals that live in the sea. The cycle is completed by the bacteria which decompose organic matter, finally releasing the phosphate. However, a large part of the organic phosphate is converted to calcium phosphate in bone, or to ferric phosphate in fecal pellets of marine animals, and it was long thought that this represented a steady drain on the system. Cviic [1956] has recently shown that phosphates are liberated from natural muds more rapidly under anaerobic than aerobic conditions and it seems possible that much of this liberation is due to the reduction of sulfate as described above. In addition, phosphate can be "solubilized" by hydroxy acids, and such acids are frequent in the decomposition of carbohydrates, including the hemicelluloses and uronic acids of marine plants. Mackereth [1953] has pointed out that the fresh water diatom *Asterionella formosa* can concentrate phosphorus from water with only 1 μg per L; further, 0.06 μg of this element is sufficient for a million cells. This agrees with the Goldberg *et al.* [1951] figure of 0.05 μg per million cells for *A. japonica.* Despite the low solubility of ferric phosphate, bacteria can grow on media with this as the sole source of phosphorus, and calcium phosphate is used as readily as more soluble forms. From this it appears that both bacteria and phytoplankton can exist in relatively large numbers on very small amounts of phosphate, amounts that are too small to measure by conventional chemical analyses. A fruitful avenue for investigation would be a method and a suitable marine organism for the bioassay of phosphorus in hydrology.

C. *Nitrogen.*—Waksman and his co-workers [1933] studied the nitrogen cycle in the sea and showed that it is essentially the same as on land. They reported nitrogen fixation by both aerobic and anaerobic bacteria, nitrification occurring chiefly in the muds and being insignificant in the ocean waters, and denitrification occurring especially in tropical waters. Jensen [1954] has recently pointed out that we still do not know the actual importance of nitrogen fixation in the soil. In the sea, our knowledge is still more vague. Waksman *et al.* [1933] reported the presence of *Azotobacter* in the sea but I have found only rare instances of its occurrence in Australian estuaries, and even then it is doubtful whether the strains isolated were autochthonous (Wood, *unpublished data*). Waksman and his co-workers also recorded *Clostridium pasteurianum* and the presence of nitrogen-fixing clostridia is probable. In the absence of oxygen, the purple sulfur bacteria, sulfate reducers, and many clostridia can fix nitrogen, but this can be important only in estuaries, in plankton swarms, and on the ocean bottom where the redox potential is sufficiently low. Species of some genera of blue-green algae, *e.g., Nostoc* and *Anabaena,* can and do fix nitrogen aerobically, and these forms are found in the sea, notably on coral reefs.

Denitrification can be carried out by a large number of bacteria; Drew [1914] believed that bacterial denitrification was responsible for much of the calcium deposition on coral reefs. This hypothesis is no longer maintained in its entirety, for, despite the great potential among marine bacteria for denitrification, it is generally conceded that though this is performed by bacteria in culture, it is not as extensive in the ocean as Drew suggested. The answer to the questions of nitrogen balance in the sea and of the nitrogen budget in terms of space and time is dependent on quantitative estimates of nitrogen fixation and denitrification, and we have very little information to offer. We do not know whether there is at the present time a net gain or loss of nitrogen in the sea.

The matter of nitrification, *i.e.*, the oxidation of ammonia to nitrite or nitrate, is important in determining whether the growth of phytoplankton organisms will consist of those using ammonia or nitrate as a nitrogen source. Nitrification is accomplished not only by the autotrophs, *Nitrobacter* and *Nitrosomonas,* but also by a number of heterotrophs. Fisher *et al.* [1952] record nitrification in soils by pleomorphic gram negative rods and as similar forms are very common in the sea, it seems desirable that studies of marine nitrification should include these forms. Castell and Mapplebeck [1956] record the production of nitrite from hydroxylamine by species of *Pseudomonas, Microbacterium,* and *Proteus* obtained from marine fish. Some of these bacteria also reduced nitrite. Once again, our knowledge of the quantitative importance of nitrifying bacteria is slight but it appears that they are abundant in muds. Hutchinson [1944] has shown that certain diatoms (*Fragillaria*) form blooms when nitrates are abundant and the ammonia-utilizing blue-green *Anabaena* blooms when the nitrates have been used up. Ryther [1954] has demonstrated a similar selection of ammonia-using *Chlorophyceae* over nitrate-using diatoms in Moriches Bay. Unfortunately for the investigator, all the inorganic nitrogen compounds concerned in nutrition in the seas are soluble and the reactions between them are easily reversible.

D. *Decomposition of Organic Matter.*—The breakdown of organic matter in the sea by bacteria has been extensively studied by earlier workers but in more recent years studies on marine cellulose, agar, and chitin digestion, on the marine occurrence of lipolytic anaerobes, and on marine bacteria producing phenols have been mainly taxonomic. Organic nitrogen compounds, even such refractory substances as chitin, are decomposed to carbon dioxide or methane and ammonia. The sulfur compounds are broken down to mercaptans, thioethers, etc., and then to their inorganic components. Pectin, agar, alginates, cellulose, and starches are all attacked by marine bacteria. Marine heterotrophic bacteria are often very catholic in their tastes, and can utilize a number of substrates. Digestion of cellulose is not confined to any particular genus or group, but is carried out by certain cytophagas, corynebacteria, and others. Agar and chitin digestion occur as a rule only if more available nutrients are lacking. Proteolytic ability also is possessed by a number of bacterial genera. Many members of the phytoplankton also can live by heterotrophic nutrition but the importance of these organisms in the decomposition of organic matter in the sea has not been assessed.

Cellulose is decomposed by microorganisms under anaerobic conditions as far as methane and hydrogen and this methane serves as a basis for the occurrence of methane bacteria, as has been discussed by Hutton and ZoBell [1949, 1953]. These organisms oxidize ammonia to nitrite in addition to the oxidation of methane. The hydrogen, whether produced from the decomposition of organic matter or from magmatic sources, is available to a large number of organisms, *i.e.*, all those which possess a hydrogenase. This includes sulfate-reducing bacteria, and many anaerobes and facultative anaerobes.

It appears to have been tacitly assumed until recently that bacteria are responsible for the degeneration of organic matter in the sea. Now it is becoming increasingly recognized that some phytoplankton elements may play a part and that fungi may also play an important role as saprophytes, being especially important in lignin digestion.

Earlier studies did not suggest that fungi were important in the sea; in fact, Sparrow [1934] concluded that most fungi found in the sea originated on land. Barghoorn and Linder [1944] and, more recently, Meyers [1953] and Cribb and Cribb [1955] have isolated from estuaries a number of wood-destroying fungi which are characteristically adapted to a marine environment. Höhnk [1953] has shown that fungi are numerous in marine habitats and that certain forms are adapted to life in those habitats. He isolated both proteolytic and carbohydrate-utilizing forms from sea water and muds between Bremen and Helgoland. Sea water samples yielded 83 per cent positive cultures; mud and water samples, about 70 per cent positives. In sea water, the higher fungi predominated, whereas in muds and brackish water there was an increasing percentage of lower fungi. Ingold [1954] points out that no basidiomycetes have been recorded from either fresh or salt water. Yeasts have been recorded from marine environments.

E. Quantitative and Qualitative Aspects.—Quantitative aspects of marine bacteriology have not so far been satisfactory, owing in part to the small number of samples which have been recorded and in part to the difficulties of methodology. Speaking generally, the numbers of bacteria recorded in sea water do not seem sufficiently high for the performance of the reactions which are believed to be of bacterial origin. Recent work in different parts of the world show quantitative results comparable with those recorded by ZoBell [1946]. Direct counts of bacteria in sea water were attempted by Wood [1953] without success and viable counts have well known limitations. It would seem from the work of Velankar [1950, 1955], Venkataraman and Sreenivasan [1954] in India, of Cviic [1955] in the Adriatic, ZoBell [1946] in California, and of Wood [1953] in Australia that in coastal waters in various parts of the world, viable bacterial counts of heterotrophs are of the same order. Differential counts have been made for certain bacteria by Velankar, Venkataraman and Sreenivasan, and Cviic, Wood, and ZoBell . . . found that the maximum bacterial population in sea water occurs in depths between 25 and 50 m and this agrees with findings of several earlier workers. Wood showed a maximum bacterial population in sea water in June-July on the Pacific coast of Australia; ZoBell, a maximum in

September with a lower peak in February off Southern California; but Velankar found a rather irregular pattern in the Gulf of Mannar, with the probability of summer and winter maxima. Cviic also records two peaks, one in late summer and one in late winter. Morita and ZoBell [1955] have found bacteria ranging in numbers from hundreds to thousands per g of wet mud in cores to a depth of 8 m, representing at the lowest part a geological age of more than 1,000,000 years.

Taxonomic studies on marine bacteria have recently been made by Cviic [1955], Velankar [1950, 1955], Venkataraman and Sreenivasan [1954] and Wood [1953]. The sea water floras found by Cviic and by Wood are very similar if considered as cocci and gram positive and negative rods, whereas that recorded by Venkataraman and Sreenivasan tends to resemble the flora recorded for soil by Taylor and Lochhead in Canada [1938].

III. PHOTOSYNTHESIS

The only way in which the earth can gain biological energy is by utilizing the sun's energy in photosynthesis, *i.e.,* the transformation of carbon dioxide by an endothermic reaction into sugars, fats, starch, and their derivatives, which can be regarded as storehouses of chemical energy. In the sea, this is performed chiefly by microorganisms of the phytoplankton, some of which are only 1 μ long. The large seaweeds occur only around the fringe of the land masses, and mainly in the colder regions of the world, so their total contribution is relatively insignificant. Braarud [1955] estimates the area occupied by the seaweed flora as 2 per cent of the area covered by the oceans. The phytoplankton community is formed from several thousand species of microorganisms, belonging to several groups. These include the diatoms, the blue-green algae, dinoflagellates, coccolithophores, silicoflagellates, chrysomonads, cryptomonads, and chlamydomonads. The smaller forms of the phytoplankton are called microplankton or nannoplankton. This includes such forms as the coccolithophores, chrysomonads, and cryptomonads. The quantitative contribution of the phytoplankton as food for the inhabitants of the sea is often known as primary production.

Unfortunately, the word "production" (and also "productivity") are used with several different meanings. I would apply "productivity" to "ability or capacity to produce," and "production" to "quantity produced." "Total productivity" would be the total light energy converted by photosynthesis into organic matter and "net productivity" to the photosynthate remaining after respiration. Productivity may be compared with the capacity of a field to support stock.

One may talk of plant production and animal production, the former representing the amount of plant material available, the latter the animal population depending on it. In the measurement of production there are two concepts: annual (or daily production), which introduces a time factor, and standing crop, which is a measure of a state. If standing crop is measured, the rate of change must be known to give a measure of production.

There are several methods used for such a measurement. The earliest means were the consumption of inorganic phosphorus and nitrogen and these chemical measures were followed by studies of the balance between photosynthesis and respiration. Gran [1932] took samples of phytoplankton in sea water and placed them in clear and dark bottles in the sea. After a time, he estimated the increase in oxygen in the illuminated bottles, and determined the rate of respiration from the reduction of oxygen in the dark bottles. This enabled him to measure the net photosynthesis of the sample. More recently Steemann Nielsen [1952] has devised a method of estimating the intake of carbon dioxide by the phytoplankton contained in a given water sample. In this method, a quantity of bicarbonate containing C^{14} is added to the sample, which is then exposed to light for a certain time and filtered, after which the uptake of radioactive carbon is measured, certain corrections are applied, and the rate of assimilation is regarded as a measure of the production of the sample. Ryther [1956] contends that this method measures net and not gross production. Various improvements in the original Steemann Nielsen method are necessary. For example, in sampling, plastic tube-samplers of uniform bore and with large end-pieces are sometimes used to avoid bubbling effects which seriously affect the results of C^{14} analyses.

The chlorophyll method of estimating standing crop devised by Harvey [1934], and since modified in several ways, consists of the extraction of the chlorophyll from the water sample with acetone and the determination of the chlorophyll present. The method assumes that the amount of the sun's energy utilized by the phytoplankton is proportional to the amount of chlorophyll.

Richards and Thompson [1952] estimated chlorophylls a, b, and c, but Ryther [1956] contends that there is a linear relationship between chlorophyll a and photosynthesis and does not include chlorophylls b and c. He believes that chlorophyll measurements give data from which it is ultimately possible to establish an equation for total production, *i.e.*, to proceed from standing crop measurements to a dynamic estimate of production.

These methods represent the best that we can do at the moment to assess the plant production of the sea but unfortunately many assumptions have still to be made. The question is particularly fluid at the moment and a great deal of investigation is in progress, though not yet at the publication stage. Diatoms and dinoflagellates have been found to depths of 1000 m, and coccolithophores to 4000 m. In addition, diatoms have recently been observed apparently living at over 7000 m. It is obvious that photosynthesis is impossible at such depths, as there is no light. It is usually considered that photosynthesis does not occur below 300 to 400 m in the tropics or below 100 m in Arctic and Antarctic waters, whereas the compensation points (*i.e.*, the points at which photosynthesis and respiration are equal) have been estimated at depths between 10 m in Oslo Fjord and more than 100 m in the Mediterranean. Blinks [1954] considers that under certain circumstances it is possible that some of the accessory pigments can become important in photosynthesis and Duysens [1952] has shown their activity as exciters of chlorophyll a. This means that accessory pigments may convert light of various wave lengths into a form of energy suitable for use by chlorophyll a.

Let us look at the picture from another angle for a moment. Apart from the oceanographers, who are interested in the ocean as an entity, the primary interest in the question of production is practical, *i.e.,* in the fish we can get out of the sea. Fishery biologists, using such criteria as market statistics and population studies, have computed the possible world fish catch at 50,000,000 metric tons a year. Because there is usually more than one link in the food chain, with a loss of energy at each link, this yield has been estimated to represent $\frac{1}{1000}$ to $\frac{1}{10,000}$ of the energy supplied by the phytoplankton, which, to maintain an equilibrium, must yield at least 50,000,000,000 metric tons a year to feed the estimated marine fish.

If the sea were an independent system, the cycle of life could obviously continue independent of photosynthesis, except for the losses of energy and materials such as nitrogen gas and carbon dioxide to the air above. Thus, photosynthetic energy would act like a boy's hand bowling a hoop. The hoop has kinetic energy of its own but requires added energy to overcome that lost by friction. However, the sea is not independent but derives nutrients and organic matter, including microorganisms, from the land, while man and birds remove life from the sea and carry it back ashore. The balance here is in favor of the sea but would probably not replace the total energy lost from the sea to the air above. From productivity figures derived from the work of such researchers as Steemann Nielsen [1952] and Riley [1941], there would not be enough photosynthetic energy supplied by the phytoplankton to allow the removal of the calculated 50 to 80 million tons of fish a year, allowing for wastage. This suggests either that our methods of estimating productivity and production are inadequate, and that we are measuring only the residue of the standing crop after grazing by marine animals, or that we are living on a reserve of photosynthetic activity derived from past ages.

As most of the biological activity of the sea occurs near the surface and transformations here are usually rapid, any reserve in this region would soon be dissipated. Below 1000 m and possibly below even 100 m, biological activity is slight and slow, and the gradient of phosphate, silica, and other substances becomes negligible down to the vicinity of the bottom, where there is an increase of activity. Thus, the sea bottom would have to be the store-house of past activity, if such a store-house exists, and the key would be held by the microorganisms living there. Emery *et al.* [1955] conclude that "the brevity of these renewal times (of phosphorus, nitrogen, and silica) and the character of the

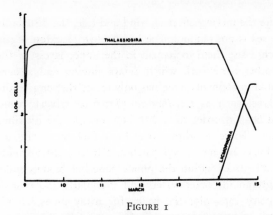

FIGURE 1

Growth rates of 2 diatoms in sea-water, showing the logarithmic, stationary, and death phases of *Thalassiosira* and the logarithmic growth phase of *Licmophora*. Note that there is a succession here similar to that often seen in the sea.

geological record, suggesting that the total life in the ocean has been more or less constant over long periods, indicate that steady state conditions exist." If the estimates of standing crops of phytoplankton by the C^{14} or chlorophyll methods are reliable, discrepancies must come from our ideas of the rate of reproduction of phytoplankton, of the rate of grazing by marine animals, or from the diversion of photosynthate into excreted metabolites such as polypeptides and carbohydrates, which may account for as much as 50 per cent of the total nitrogen assimilated, according to Fogg [1957]. This author suggests that the excretion of carbon in such metabolites could cause a serious underestimate of production by the Steemann Nielsen technique. In phytoplankton swarms at latitude 34°S, I have found the generation time of *Chaetoceros curvisetum* and *Asterionella japonica* is of the order of 4 hr, and that of the nannoplankton about 50 min during the logarithmic growth phase. In sea water samples brought into the laboratory, but without added nutrients, the generation time of *Thalassiosira aestivalis* ranged from $1/2$ to $2\frac{1}{2}$ hr and *Licmophora flabellata* from 3 to 4 hr (figure 1). These reproduction rates are far higher than those noted by Harvey *et al.* [1935] for the English Channel and by Gran [1932] for the Gulf of Maine. It is possible that the difference is due to the higher temperature of Australian waters. In Port Hacking, from which the *Thalassiosira* samples were taken, the population did not increase during the time of the experiment (9 days). This suggests that the grazing rate was keeping pace with the rate of multiplication of the diatom and is in line with the conclusion of Riley [1941] that there is no great difference between annual production in tropical and temperate waters.

The biggest difficulty in productivity studies, and in marine microbiology as a whole, is that of sampling. Barnes and Marshall [1951] and others have shown that despite the mixing effect of wind and tide, the distribution of micro-organisms in the sea is not random. The larger phytoplankton organisms possess appendages which assist them to remain in the upper layers of the sea and to form rafts, or rather a network which delays sinking and also enmeshes the smaller phytoplankton elements. One has only to see the long reddish windrows of blue-green algae, such as *Oscillatoria* (*Trichodesmium*), which gives the name to the Red Sea, in order to realize how uneven the distribution of such forms can become. These windrows may be a foot to a mile in width and, sooner or later, break up into small patches. Further, phytoplankton occurs at low intensity in all places within the photic zone but blooms suddenly, chiefly in spring and autumn in cooler waters and irregularly and more often in the tropics. Such blooms can color the water for many miles, forming the well known "red tides" of certain regions. Such "red tides" may consume all available oxygen and kill off the animal life in the locality, dying and disappearing as suddenly as they appear. The study of marine phenomena must be based on observations made from ships, which are expensive to run and can cover only a small area at a time, so observations of phytoplankton and hydrology are sparse and widely scattered, except in the North Sea and adjacent waters. For this reason alone, it would seem that quantitative estimations of productivity are at best informed guesses and must be accepted as such. They represent a valiant attempt rather than a solution.

One more difficulty in assessing true productivity is the ability of a number of phytoplankton organisms to live heterotrophically, that is, using organic carbon compounds instead of, or as well as, carbonic acid for nutrition. Some of the flagellates including many dinoflagellates (*Heterodinium, Amphisolenia, Triposolenia,* and some of the *Ceratia*) are normally phagotrophic or hetero-trophic, and others are facultatively so. Some, at least, of the diatoms can also live heterotrophically. The importance of heterotrophy among phytoplankton is difficult to assess. Hutner and Provasoli [1955] found no organic substrate which would stimulate the growth of their dinoflagellates and they failed to grow them in the dark.

IV. INTERRELATIONSHIPS OF MICROORGANISMS IN THE SEA

It will be realized that life in the sea is a vast symbiosis or metabiosis and that no organisms can exist independently of others. Moreover, the sea is never actually without organisms even in a particular region. There are always enough nearby to start another bloom if conditions are favorable.

An easy way of demonstrating this is to place some beach sand in a bottle with a piece of kelp or a handful of sea-grass on top, fill the bottle with sea-water, replace the lid, and then place the bottle in the dark or in subdued light. In a week or so, as the weed is decomposed by heterotrophs, the sand will turn black owing to the formation of hydrotriolite by sulfate-reducing bacteria, chiefly

Desulfovibrio. If the bottle is illuminated by a lamp or by light from a window, the sand will regain its color as the sulfur becomes oxidized, the oxygen being supplied by photosynthetic organisms. Patches of brown (diatoms) and dark green (blue-green algae) will appear and, lower down, where the oxygen tension is low, the purple and green of the purple and green sulfur bacteria. Later, after 6 months or so, the surface of the water will be covered with green and blue-green algae and diatoms. If the bottle is replaced in the dark, all the colors will disappear and the sand will turn black. The cycle can be repeated indefinitely merely by changing the position of the bottle, *i.e.,* varying the illumination, which in turn alters the redox potential and, within narrow limits, the pH.

This experiment served as a starting point for the investigation into the cycle of microbial life in estuaries that has been recorded by Baas Becking and co-workers, and others. An effort has been made to dissect out the activity of each component and to find its relationship to the other members of the community. From this study has emerged the story of the sulfur cycle and its relation to the release of phosphorus, which has already been told. It has been found that blue-green algae can exist at very low oxidation-reduction potentials, *i.e.,* anaerobically, equal to the lowest at which the purple sulfur bacteria remain active. Moreover, some blue-greens and other phytoplankton organisms can tolerate a high hydrogen sulfide tension. Diatoms have been found viable at a pH of 1.2, in the pH-Eh range dominated and controlled by *Thiobacillus thiooxidans,* and at low oxygen tensions. Both in pure culture and, given favorable opportunity, in mixed culture, many of the marine organisms can tolerate a very wide range of conditions, far wider than they will find in the marine environment. Yet, under actual conditions, these organisms will appear, bloom, and disappear rapidly, without obvious changes in the environment, because the marine environment gives the requisite conditions for the maximum of microbial activity, as may be seen from figure 2.

There is evidence that many marine microorganisms can produce extracellular organic substances, including antibiotic substances that inhibit competitors, though often not all competitors. It is probably these substances which bring about plankton blooms of single species or of single genera but there are species which usually coexist in blooms, such as *Rhizosolenia robusta* and *Coscinodiscus grani,* which are almost always found together in the estuarine plankton blooms of eastern Australia.

Although the presence of bacteriophage in the sea was recorded previously, its possible importance has only been emphasized recently by Kriss and Rukina [1947], who detected bacteriophages from the water and silts of the Black Sea down to 2000 m and who believe that, though widely distributed, they are not the sole cause of the bactericidal property of sea water.

Cviic [1953] has re-examined the relations between bacteria and phytoplankton. He found that the maximum bacterial population occurs normally below the maximum phytoplankton zone but within the photic zone. Free phos-

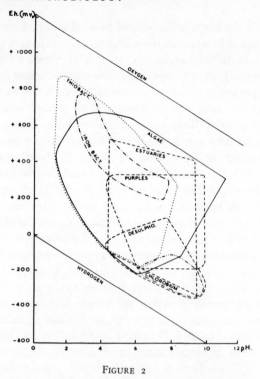

FIGURE 2

Eh-pH relations of microorganisms (modified from Baas Becking and Wood [1955]). The estuarine environment lies in the region where several autotrophs can coexist, and a change in Eh alone will determine the active microorganisms.

phate correlates with the vertical distribution of bacteria and inversely with phytoplankton, confirming the results of Waksman and Carey [1935]. Cviic records a daily vertical fluctuation of phytoplankton and bacteria, both sinking at night and rising in daylight. He did not find any direct correlation of phytoplankton-bacteria populations with salinity or temperature but did find correlation with oxygen and free phosphate.

The effect of hydrostatic pressure on marine microorganisms is important because of the great depths which occur in the oceans, pressure increasing by 1 atm per 10 m so that at the greatest depths, ca. 10,000 m, the pressure is 1000 atm. ZoBell [1952] and his co-workers were the first to show that marine bacteria can and do exist at these maximum pressures and depths, though viable bacteria had been found down to 5000 m by earlier workers. ZoBell and his school have also investigated the biological effects of pressure on marine microorganisms.

Wood [1956], working with ZoBell and subsequently, brought evidence to suggest that diatoms may live heterotrophically at great depths. Many of the species he found were epontic, *i.e.,* attached to various living and nonliving substrates. Others were estuarine or coastal, and only the very rare *Ethmodiscus rex* could be considered oceanic.

On considering the results of the Danish *Galathea* expedition as a whole, it seems logical to assume that the ocean deeps form a biosphere of their own. In this biosphere are a rich flora and fauna consisting of few species, which are unable to adapt readily to normal pressures (barophilic species) and are separated by a barren zone containing few organisms from the still richer photic and subphotic zones near the surface. As the water becomes shallower near the continents, the barren zone disappears, the bottom forms become more diverse and less barophilic, and there is increased mixing with the flora of the photic zone. In estuaries, the photic zone reaches the muds in many places and the biological picture becomes increasingly complex. It seems highly improbable that the barren zone in the oceans is at any time completely sterile.

V. MICROORGANISMS AS FOOD FOR MARINE ANIMALS

If production is to be maximal, all available plant material must be converted for use by the marine animals. However, we know that there is wastage and that this is considerable. We know very little about the actual rate of consumption of phytoplankton in the sea or about the selective feeding of the larger organisms. There is evidence that the copepod *Calanus finmarchicus* (a filter feeder) continues to filter far more plankton food than it can digest but that it tends to avoid the diatoms *Chaetoceros* and *Rhizosolenia* when these are present in blooms. However, it probably feeds on the organisms living on the decomposing blooms of these diatoms, *e.g.,* bacteria and photosynthetic and colorless flagellates, thus introducing another link in the food chain, with a corresponding loss of energy. The employment of laboratory cultures of organisms in feeding experiments requires great care in the interpretation of results, as organisms may change their feeding habits and ingest and digest material that would normally be foreign to their diet.

Diatoms.—The role of planktonic diatoms in the food chain has been studied by a number of authors, most recently by Marshall and Orr [1955]. These authors, using *Skeletonema costatum,* showed that *Calanus* digested 60 to 75 per cent of the diatoms ingested under the conditions of the experiment. On the other hand, Manteufel [1941] gave evidence that the larger rhizosolenias were not acceptable to *Calanus* which tends to avoid large blooms of this genus. Studies made in estuaries by the author show that phytophagous fish (*e.g., Mugil cephalus*) consume large quantities of epontic diatoms (*Licmophora, Melosira,* and *Synedra*) and that these are completely disintegrated in the mullet stomach-mill. Pilchard stomachs were also found to contain large quantities of planktonic diatoms.

Flagellates.—Dinoflagellates are frequently found in the gut of salps, mullet, and other phytophagous fish but are probably not nearly as important as the smaller flagellates. *Crypotomonas, Syracosphaera,* and *Chlamydomonas* are readily digested by *Calanus.* British workers have shown that oyster larvae feed on several microflagellates, while Imai *et al.* [1951] found that *Crassostrea gigas* depends on a colorless flagellate (*Monas*) for the development of its larvae in Mangoku inlet. This flagellate appears to feed on bacteria, which in turn are in the water.

Ciliates.—Tintinnids can frequently be seen in the digestive tract of salps but many marine animals appear to reject ciliates, which may thus be regarded as to a large extent short-circuiting the food chain.

Rhizopods.—These too do not appear to be important in the food chain in the sea.

Bacteria.—Bacteria serve as food for a number of phagotrophic micro-organisms, *e.g., Monas,* as has been mentioned. . . . Baas Becking and Wood [1955] found ciliates (*Euplotes*) in cultures of *Desulfovibrio* growing in a purely inorganic medium at very low redox potentials (*ca.* −200 mv). Ketchum *et al.* [1952] have considered the predation of protozoa on bacteria in connection with the diminution of sewage pollution in estuaries. ZoBell and Feltham have shown that bacteria can serve as food for mussels and oysters and it seems probable that they are also used by higher animals. The fact that nonfeeding fish have a sterile gut suggests that the bacteria ingested with the food are also digested.

Blue-Green Algae.—That these may be important sources of food for fish is emphasized by Schuster [1949], who shows that they are of great value in the tambak culture (brackish water fish pond) of *Chanos chanos,* a fish which is also marine. Mullet and other phytophagous fish also eat blue-greens. The large "red tides" of *Oscillatoria* in the tropics do not, however, appear to serve as food for marine animals and there are records of toxicity in the blue-greens which has been blamed for the death of fish and herbivorous animals grazing near ponds.

VI. GEOLOGICAL CONSIDERATIONS

The microorganisms of the sulfur cycle act in the formation of sulfide ores associated with sediments. The microbial formation of iron sulfides under alkaline conditions tends to give pyrites rather than the more easily decomposed hydrotroilite and, if copper, zinc, and lead are present, the sulfides of these will be precipitated in accordance with their solubilities. This type of reaction can be assumed to account for the concentration of sulfide ores of the heavy metals in the vicinity of coral reefs with adjacent volcanism. The availability of manganese, copper, and other elements required in small traces by animals and plants is also controlled to an extent by the sulfur cycle in the sea.

The iron cycle in marine sediments is largely influenced by microorganisms.

Particulate iron in the sea exists largely as ferric phosphate and is reduced in the muds as a result of bacterial sulfate reduction. Ferrous iron is precipitated in the pectinous tubes of the iron bacteria (*Sphaerotilus*), whereas iron is oxidized by such organisms as *Thiobacillus ferrooxidans*. In addition, many photosynthonts and miscellaneous heterotrophic bacteria can affect the oxidation and reduction, or the solution and precipitation of iron by varying the pH or Eh of their environment or by their effect on other substances, *e.g.*, carbonate.

There have been suggestions from time to time that sulfate reduction is a factor in the formation of petroleum, hydrocarbons being formed by reduction of carbon dioxide within the bacterial cell. Brongersma-Sanders [1948] considers that petroleum formation is brought about by so-called "red tides"—accumulations of dinoflagellates, diatoms, or blue-green algae—which often cause a mass mortality of fish and other marine animals. In shallow waters, these organisms sink to the bottom and supply the necessary organic matter for large-scale reducing conditions, including sulfate reduction with the formation of hydrocarbons. We know that petroleum is associated with marine sedimentary deposits but, as it has never been found at the site of formation, it is extremely difficult to demonstrate its mode of origin. It seems safe to conclude that bacteria play a part.

A considerable advance has been made in the study of bacterial methane and hydrogen production and utilization and the possible effects of these processes in hydrocarbon formation. The work of Baas Becking and Kaplan [1956] on Lake Eyre suggests the biological process which could have produced the Louisiana sulfur domes. Thode *et al.* [1953] have shown that the ratios of S^{32}/S^{34} are different depending on whether the sulfur has been produced by microbial or magmatic agency, and Jones and his associates [1956] have also carried out some work on this. There is reason to believe that the fractionation is more complex than the foregoing authors envisaged, various members of the microbial sulfur cycle each having definite characteristics.

The activity of bacteria and blue-green algae in the precipitation of calcium carbonate has also been mentioned. Lalou [1954] has shown that precipitation of calcium carbonate occurs with the addition of glucose to the mud. The utilization of glucose by marine bacteria causes a drop in the redox potential and this drop permits the anaerobic growth of sulfate-reducing bacteria. The autotrophic growth of the sulfur bacteria would, by removing carbon dioxide, cause the precipitation of calcium carbonate according to the law of mass action: $Ca(HCO_3)_2 \rightarrow CO_2(utilized) + CaCO_3$ at the pH values of marine muds and sea water. This mechanism would apply to marine muds with a low redox potential. In addition, the foraminifera and coccolithophores produce calcareous skeletons and the diatoms and the radiolaria produce siliceous ones; these form vast beds, sometimes thousands of feet thick. Geologists describe radiolarian jaspers and cherts and foraminiferal limestones in sedimentary rocks of various ages.

VII. PATHOGENIC MICROORGANISMS IN THE SEA

The story of microorganisms in the sea would not be complete if we left out those which are pathogenic to marine plants and animals. The most important parasites in the sea are the protozoa, of which a large number of species belonging to a number of orders have been recorded from marine animals. Some of these protozoa bring about mass mortalities such as those which cause tens of thousands of small fish to be cast up at times on Australian beaches. A protozoan infection of snoek (*Thyrsites*) causes heavy losses to the fish trade in South Africa and Australia by digesting the flesh after death. The effect of this parasite on the living fish is difficult to estimate. In fact, little progress has been made in the study of diseases in marine fish because it is so hard to watch fish populations in the sea. It is to be expected that diseased fish will lag behind the schools and so evade capture or be swiftly removed by predators.

A number of bacterial diseases of fish have been recorded, the most important being furunculosis (caused by *Aeromonas salmonicida*), ulcer (*Hemophilus piscium*), and a number of infections caused by pseudomonads. Furunculosis has been the subject of considerable study, the most recent description of the causative agent being that of Griffin *et al.* [1952]. The bacterial infections have recently been discussed by Griffin [1953]; and a disease due to the myxobacterium *Chondrococcus columnaris,* by Rucker *et al.* [1953]. A micrococcal infection of lobsters has been described by Snieszko and Taylor [1947].

A myxomycete (*Labyrinthula*) wiped out beds of the sea-grass *Zostera marina* in northern Europe and eastern America some years ago and this caused heavy losses to the oyster industries of several countries, because oysters depend for their food on microorganisms which live in association with *Zostera.* There have been suggestions that a parasite attacking the eggs of the pilchard may be a factor in the virtual disappearance of the fish off the Californian coast.

A fungal parasite (*Dermocystidium marinum*) of the oyster has been recorded. Fungal parasites (chytrids) have frequently been recovered from diatoms, chiefly in fresh water lakes, but their effect on the bloom does not seem to be great.

Little is known about the effect of parasites on the phytoplankton of the oceans but a bacterial parasite has been observed in the giant kelp, *Macrocystis pyrifera,* in Californian waters.

Virus diseases are considered by Watson [1953] to be more numerous than is at present generally realized. Lymphocystis and a number of non-neoplastic diseases of fish have been shown to be caused by infective, filterable agents, probably viruses.

VIII. ECONOMIC CONSIDERATIONS

The effects of marine environments on hygiene are important to us from two aspects. It has been shown by several bacteriologists that fish, when taken from the sea, are contaminated with bacteria in the slime, gills, and often in the gut. These organisms can multiply after the death of the fish and are the main cause of fish spoilage. However, fish bacteria are rarely pathogenic to humans and they do not produce toxic substances in the flesh. An exception is the red bacterium isolated recently by Bein [1954] at Miami, which is stated to cause toxicity in shellfish. This toxicity affects the humans who eat these shellfish. Normally, shellfish poisons are believed to be due to dinoflagellates belonging to two genera, *Gonyaulax* and *Gymnodinium,* though all members of these genera do not appear to be toxic.

Recent studies on teleost fish spoilage include those of Shewan [1944] and of Venkataraman and Sreenivasan [1954], together with work on preservation by antibiotics and bacteriostatic substances largely carried out at the laboratories of the Canadian Fishery Research Board.

Elasmobranch fish spoilage has a somewhat different flora from that of teleost fish, no doubt associated with the high urea content of the sharks and rays. Three authors have found a large number of gram positive bacteria including species of *Corynebacterium, Micrococcus,* and *Flavobacterium* associated with these fish, both on the surface and in spoilage, but Velankar and Kamasastri [1955] found chiefly gram negative rods.

A detailed microbiological investigation of whale meat has recently been made. The flora has greater affiliations with that of land mammals than of fish and the finding of *Escherichia coli* in the intestines of a wild sea lion is interesting in this-connection. From whales, *Clostridium perfringens, C. tertium, C. novyi, C. sporogenes,* and *C. histolyticum* were isolated, as well as protei, streptococci, and other mesophilic organisms. One must deduce that the warm-blooded flora is passed on from parents to offspring, as these organisms have not been recovered from the open sea or from the food of these animals.

The second hygienic aspect is the effect of sea water on bacteria from the land, chiefly the intestinal bacteria of human origin. ZoBell [1946] believes that the effect is largely due to antibiotics, which Rosenfeld and ZoBell [1947] have shown are produced by some marine bacteria, and the work of Ketchum [1953] tends to confirm this. Be that as it may, sea water is fatal to many land forms and this is important in that the sewage of coastal cities and towns is almost invariably discharged into the sea where it would cause a serious hazard to health if it were not for the purifying effect of sea water. Examples are Sydney, Australia, and Los Angeles and San Diego, California, where the sewer outfalls are in close proximity to popular bathing beaches, but there is little or no evidence of human disease caused by pathogens of human origin from these outfalls. An exception is an infection of fishermen and others by the fungus *Erysipelothrix* in Mission Bay near San Diego; there is some evidence that this infection is derived from local pollution. The distribution of pollutants in estuaries has been computed.

Sewage pollution in juxtaposition with shellfish beds as at Conway in Wales may, however, cause a serious health hazard. A solution to the problem of polluted shellfish was offered by Dodgson and has been successfully applied on a commercial scale, with modifications of the original system. Dodgson's system was essentially to place the washed shellfish in a false-bottomed tank, cover with sterile water for a period, and allow the shellfish to pump the water through, thus cleansing themselves internally. The feces and pseudofeces settled below the false bottom of the tank. The water was drained off, the shells washed, and the tanks refilled to allow a further period of purification. After another draining and washing, the shellfish were covered with a strong chlorine solution in sea water. This was to sterilize the surface of the shell, and was effective because the molluscs immediately closed in the unfavorable environment and were not affected by the chlorine. The principal modification of the original method is the re-use of the water after filtration and chlorination, the chlorine being neutralized by thiosulphate. Studies on the effectiveness of this purification have been published.

An important economic aspect of marine microbiology is the microbial fouling and corrosion of ships and other structures. Bacteria were found to be the cause of primary fouling films in California but diatoms and algae were more important in Australian waters. All authors are agreed that sedentary animals attach more readily if a microbial film is present. Many marine bacteria are resistant to high concentrations of copper and mercury.

Several workers have made studies on microbial corrosion of steel in fresh water environments. The process was found to be largely due to the activity of *Desulfovibrio*. This organism is equally active in sea water.

IX. THE PLACE OF MARINE MICROBIOLOGY IN OCEANOGRAPHY

Marine microbiology has a great contribution to make to oceanography but has largely been neglected in oceanographic institutions. Major studies have been made in a number of laboratories on the taxonomy and relative abundance of larger phytoplankton organisms and there are a few studies of the bacterial populations of the sea and marine muds, both quantitative and descriptive. Latterly, there have been a few investigations on the distribution of bacteria and phytoplankton in estuaries and in the oceans and on the factors governing that distribution, but a great deal still remains to be done. Work on microorganisms as food for marine animals still requires a great deal more attention. The microbiologists have also a large contribution to make on the nutrition of phytoplankton and on the interrelationships of phytoplankton and bacteria. Diatoms and dinoflagellates have been studied as food organisms particularly in the North Sea, on the east coast of America, and in California, but it has only recently been realized that the organisms which pass through the finest plankton net may be from 10 to 3000 times as abundant as the larger forms which are retained by the net. Bacteriology of the oceans has been greatly neglected despite the work of Lloyd [1930] in the Clyde Sea, of Waksman and his co-workers in the Gulf of Maine, and of ZoBell and his school in Southern California. It is unfortunate also that microbiology has been used so often as a synonym of bacteriology, as this tends to delay the recognition of the interplay of forces between bacteria and the other microorganisms.

Especially in the sea is this interplay all-important, since equilibrium conditions therein are essentially dynamic and microbial populations rapidly become adjusted to the slightest change of conditions. This sensitivity to environment is such that many chemical methods used in oceanography are not sensitive enough to measure the cause of the changes in microbial populations such as phytoplankton blooms. Increased sensitivity in analysis may well be obtained with bio-assays as suggested by Hamilton *et al.* [1952].

On the sea floor, processes of sedimentation are important to the microbiologist and it is here that he can give assistance to the sediment petrographer and to the mineralogist. Recent contributions on microbial processes in sedimentation include papers by ZoBell [1946, 1952], Emery *et al.* [1955], Baas Becking and co-workers [1955–1957], and Siebert and Schwartz [1956].

Probably the most significant fact that can be gleaned from marine microbiological studies to date is that the microbes have micro requirements for nutrients and growth factors. A microgram of phosphorus, for instance, may support a million cells. One is afforded the conception of a very great dilution of nutrients spread over 70 per cent of the earth's surface, causing a very large aggregate of biological activity.

A mantle of bacteria surrounds plant roots and the microscopic root hairs near the elongating tips of rootlets. Bacteria live within the outer cells of the root, in the root-hair cells, and in the soil immediately adjacent to roots; their numbers diminish with increasing distance from the root surface. Fungi as well as bacteria are present in, on, and around roots; in fact, many trees and shrubs are able to thrive only when certain types of fungi, known as *mycorrhizae,* are present in and around their outer cell layers.

The biological relationship between roots and the bacteria and fungi associated with them is complex. Exudates from roots undoubtedly constitute the culture medium which nourishes these microorganisms, and at least some of the soil bacteria will not grow unless supplied with specific amino acids, and perhaps vitamins, which in nature could come only from roots. The bacteria, in turn, undoubtedly furnish nutrients to the plant. Some, such as *Azotobacter* and *Rhizobium,* transform atmospheric nitrogen into organic nitrogen compounds ultimately useful to the plant. Others decompose the dead roots and organic substances remaining in the soil from previous years' growth. Still others, by their organic secretions, help to solubilize the soil minerals that are essential for plant nutrition. In one way or another, most of the root bacteria contribute to the nutrition of the plants with which they are associated.

The bacteria and fungi associated with plant roots constitute a rich pasture for innumerable protozoa, nematodes, rotifers, and other lower invertebrates that are present in the soil. The rhizosphere is actually a biological community comprising plant roots (often of many species), bacteria, fungi, insect larvae, and protozoa (and other microorganisms) that prey on bacteria, fungi, rootlets, and on one another. The rhizosphere is a microcosm, a community of small beings usually kept fairly stable by mutual interaction, as long as environmental temperature is favorable and adequacy of water supply permits the group to thrive.

A detailed glimpse of this intriguing world of the very small is provided in the review paper that follows. The author, Dr. Robert L. Starkey, is Professor of Agricultural Microbiology at Rutgers University. He is eminent for his studies of soil microbiology and related topics and has carefully reviewed 147 research papers dealing with the interrelations between microorganisms and plant roots.

From *Bacteriol. Rev.,*
22:154–172, 1958.

INTERRELATIONS BETWEEN MICROORGANISMS AND PLANT ROOTS IN THE RHIZOSPHERE

BY ROBERT L. STARKEY

I. INTRODUCTION

Plants affect microorganisms in soil in many ways. They remove water and mineral salts from the soil and, on death, leave their roots in the soil and the aerial parts on the soil surface. There is a decrease in the amounts of soluble mineral substances and a desiccating effect on the soil. During periods of growth, the roots permeate the soil, affecting its structure and the movement of gases and water. The roots attract various organisms, some of which feed on them directly. Roots absorb oxygen and release carbon dioxide, thus increasing the amounts of carbonates. The root area is a critical one for terrestrial plants and the site of intense chemical and biological activity in soil.

This region of contact between root and soil where the soil is affected by roots was designated the "rhizosphere" by Hiltner in 1904. He recognized that there were many microorganisms in this region, and it was his opinion that the rhizosphere microorganisms play important roles in plant development. Where reference is made to soil in comparison to rhizosphere in the following discussion, reference is made to that portion of the soil that is not the rhizosphere. The rhizosphere has indefinite dimensions, depending on the soil and plant. The greatest effects of the plant appear on the root surface and in the soil in contact with the root, but effects may extend for several millimeters beyond the root where fungus mycelium penetrates the soil from the rhizosphere which is the food base. . . .

Most rhizosphere microorganisms are saprophytes, but not all of their relations to plants are incidental. Some microorganisms live on the root surface, whereas others penetrate the roots. Some are restricted to the cortical cells, but others go deeper, passing between the cells and invading them. Some are innocuous and others are destructive or have favorable effects on development of the host.

II. THE EFFECTS OF PLANTS ON MICROORGANISMS IN THE SOIL

A. Abundance of Microorganisms in the Rhizosphere.—In a generally over-looked report on interrelations between plants and microorganisms, Hoffmann reported in 1914 that bacteria were generally more numerous adjacent to plant roots than in soil a foot or more distant from the plants. Numbers were greater adjacent to the roots in 27 of 32 tests, but the differences were smaller than those noted in more recent experiments. Many subsequent studies concerned with populations clearly established that microbial cells were much more abundant in the rhizosphere than in the soil. According to the plate method, the increase in numbers of aerobic bacteria was much higher than that of actinomycetes and filamentous fungi. Certain bacterial types were more affected by rhizosphere conditions than others. For example, *Agrobacterium radiobacter* was affected proportionally more than the general bacterial population. However, cells of this bacterium represented but a small portion of the total bacterial population.

The fact that the microbial population is dense on plant roots and that this occurs at all stages of plant growth and not only after the plants have died has been verified repeatedly. The importance of the phenomenon is twofold: the plant roots affect microbial development, and the plant in turn is affected by the increased activity of the microorganisms in the rhizosphere. Details of the causes and effects are still obscure. The information is suggestive but, save for exceptions, is inadequate to indicate the extent to which plant development is affected by the rhizosphere microorganisms, and whether plant growth is enhanced or impaired.

Evidence that there is a more abundant population of microorganisms in the rhizosphere than in soil rests not only on plate counts but on visual evidence. By means of the Cholodny buried slide technique it has been shown that not only large roots but small roots and root hairs have large numbers of bacteria on the surface and inside of the cells as well. In some cases the bacteria occur as a mantle of cells about the root hairs. Filaments of actinomycetes and filamentous fungi were occasionally detected also. With death of the root parts a mixture of cells of diverse microorganisms appears.

This effect was demonstrated by Linford [1942] by other procedures. In one case roots were stained after their removal from soil. He also noted development of large colonies about newly formed roots of corn, lettuce, cowpea, and pineapple plants. In another case, seedlings were grown in small soil boxes with windows consisting of cover glasses. The roots that grew against the glass windows could be examined in place microscopically. Essentially the same results were obtained by both procedures; large colonies of bacteria developed about the young growing roots. Another staining method was used by Rovira [1956] who determined the degree of bacterial development on roots of seedlings grown in a mineral solution on quartz sand. The results were like those of Linford in that the bacteria were abundant during the earliest period of root growth.

From determinations of numbers of bacteria on the seeds and roots of seedlings of tomato and oats, Rovira observed that bacteria were present on the dry seeds, and that they developed rapidly on the roots as the seeds germinated. The first oat roots had many bacterial cells, whereas on tomato roots the bacteria developed more slowly. He reported that root tips were free from bacteria, whereas other results suggest that this may not be the case invariably. Filamentous fungi were found occasionally on oat roots but were absent from tomato roots. Rovira clearly indicated that there was extensive bacterial development on seeds of oats and tomatoes almost from the start of germination.

Metz [1955] noted that, when seeds germinated in soil under nonsterile conditions, bacteria produced mantles of growth about the roots and root hairs, more with roots of Cruciferae than Gramineae.

The nonsporulating, gram-negative rods are the most prominent group of bacteria in the rhizosphere, as determined both by direct staining and by tests of the bacteria recovered from agar plates. This has been verified repeatedly.

Gyllenberg [1957] reported that the composition of the rhizosphere bacterial population of oats was similar from seedling stage to maturity, whereas the soil population differed from the rhizosphere population throughout most of the period but became similar to it late in the season. This was ascribed to migration of the bacteria from the rhizosphere into the soil. It was observed also that the rhizosphere population of grasses was more abundant than that of trees.

Agnihothrudu [1955] noted that fungi occurred predominantly as spores in soil (70 to 90 per cent) whereas they occurred mostly as vegetative material in the rhizosphere (>70 per cent). According to Garrett [1956], root-inhabiting phytopathogenic fungi typically produce a spreading epiphytic growth over the surface of the root preceding and following root invasion. This occurs also with ectotrophic mycorrhizal fungi.

It has been reported that roots of varieties of some plants susceptible to wilt disease support larger bacterial populations than nonsusceptible varieties of the same plants. This was observed for black root rot of tobacco and for flax wilt by Lochhead et al. [1940], Timonin [1941], and West and Lochhead [1940], and for Panama disease of bananas by Harper [1950]. Observations of Rombouts [1953] failed to support the conclusions of Harper.

Buxton [1957] found that exudates from roots of three varieties of peas had different effects on spore germination of three strains of Fusarium oxysporum f. pisi, a fungus causing pea wilt. The exudates had a greater depressing effect on the strains to which the plants were resistant than on those to which they were susceptible. Similar results were obtained with extracts of the rhizospheres of the three pea varieties.

Numerous rhizosphere studies indicate that the abundance of microbial cells is affected by the kind of plant and its stage of development and vigor. The greatest effect occurs during periods of active plant development and the effect disappears promptly on death of the plant. Therefore, it is an effect associated with normal growth.

In addition to bacteria, other groups of microorganisms are also more abundant in the rhizosphere than in soil. There is more development of both actinomycetes and fungi but generally the increase is proportionally less than that of the bacteria. Nevertheless, where mycorrhizae are formed, root and soil conditions are such that the fungi are the dominant root microorganisms and they have important favorable effects on development of various plants, coniferous trees in particular [1948]. According to Thornton [1957], there were more fungi in the rhizosphere of wheat and clover than in soil, and the kinds of fungi recovered from the roots varied at different stages of plant growth. According to Tolle and Rippel-Baldes [1958] the ratio of numbers of fungi in rhizospheres of cereals to numbers in soil varied from 1.4:1 to 3.0:1. Similar kinds of fungi were isolated from thoroughly washed roots of oats, wheat, rye, and barley.

Both protozoa and nematodes are frequently more numerous in the rhizosphere. The destructive effects of the latter are being increasingly recognized. Algae are little affected and may even be less numerous in the rhizosphere than in the soil.

B. *Physiological and Nutritional Groups of Bacteria in the Rhizosphere.*— The results already mentioned indicate that the microbial population of the rhizosphere is quantitatively different from that of soil. Other results show that the population differs qualitatively. Katznelson [1946] and Katznelson *et al.* [1956] noted that the aerobic cellulose-decomposing bacteria, anaerobic gas-producing bacteria, and anaerobic bacteria in general, as well as ammonifying and denitrifying bacteria, were more abundant in the rhizospheres of wheat and mangels, whereas the nitrifying and anaerobic cellulose-decomposing bacteria were less numerous and *Azotobacter* showed no rhizosphere effect.

The abundance of the various groups of microorganisms does not necessarily reflect a proportional activity in the transformations implied by their designations, nor does it exclude this. For example, there is no evidence that denitrification is rapid in the rhizosphere, although it may be more rapid than in soil owing to the greater microbial activity which might provide local areas of anaerobiosis. Recent results of Skerman and MacRae [1957] show that there is no denitrification where there is a determinable quantity of oxygen in solution.

In order to characterize the bacterial population of soil, Lochhead and associates determined the ability of the isolated cultures to grow in media varying in complexity, that is, a simple medium and media containing accessory growth substances. Thus they estimated the relative abundance of soil bacteria of each nutritional group. These studies have provided a wealth of information on the soil population and the effects of various soil factors on the proportional abundance of bacteria of the different groups. Many of the studies have been concerned with microorganisms of the rhizosphere. In brief, the following procedure was used. The soil material was plated on a soil-extract-agar medium and all of the bacterial colonies (frequently about 100) on a certain area of a plate were isolated. The ability of each to grow on the following media was determined: (a) basal medium containing glucose, nitrate, and mineral salts; (b) medium like (a) but supplemented with several amino acids; (c) medium like (b) but containing several vitamins also; (d) medium like (a) but supplemented with yeast extract; and (e) medium like (d) but containing soil extract also. On occasions, additional media were used. Ability to grow on the basal medium or requirement for growth factors served to characterize the bacterial population into a few groups that could indicate qualitative changes with soil treatment.

One of the most consistent results was the presence of a higher percentage of amino-acid-requiring bacteria in the group isolated from the rhizosphere than in the group obtained from the soil. It was reported also that in the rhizosphere there was a higher percentage of bacteria that grew on the basal medium and a lower percentage of those with requirements for undetermined growth factors contained in soil extract. Young but not older plants had fewer bacteria requiring yeast extract. Among the preformed organic materials frequently required was the sulfur-containing amino acid methionine.

In referring to the predominance of amino-acid-requiring bacteria in the rhizosphere, Gibson [1957] stated that this suggests leakage of amino acids but not of growth factors from the roots, whereas the work on mycorrhizal fungi indicates that growth factors, coming from the roots, are responsible to a considerable degree for the mantle of filaments of mycorrhizal fungi on the roots. Possibly this is an indication of differences in the materials exuded from roots of different plants.

It was found by Lochhead and Burton [1957] that of 499 soil bacteria tested, a high proportion (27 per cent) required one or more vitamins preformed. The same authors reported that the percentage of bacteria isolated from the rhizosphere that required vitamin B_{12} was somewhat smaller than that of bacteria obtained from soil. Nevertheless, the actual number of these bacteria was greater in the rhizosphere. It is presumed that both the vitamins and the amino acids required preformed were obtained either from the plant residues, from plant root excretions, or from excretions of associated microorganisms. Since vitamins and amino acids are susceptible to decomposition they are likely to be more available in those regions of the soil where there is extensive microbial development which would provide a continuing supply of the compounds.

Various bacteria recovered both from soil and rhizosphere produced extracellular amino acids and vitamins when cultivated on a simple medium with nitrogen supplied as nitrate and it was presumed that, in associations of microorganisms in the rhizosphere, the fastidious bacteria would derive the required preformed organic compounds, at least in part, from the products of bacteria that excreted the materials. The percentage of the rhizosphere bacteria that excreted certain vitamins into the medium was not always greater than the percentage of the bacteria isolated from soil that did this, but the actual number was much greater. In one test of 30 cultures with simple nutritional requirements, 22 cultures liberated amino acids into the medium. Ten different amino acids were detected, but no more than 4 were produced by any one culture. It was concluded that excretion of amino acids is a fairly general property of soil bacteria that have simple nutritional requirements.

Rouatt and Katznelson [1957] verified recently the fact that bacteria determined by the plate method were much more abundant in the rhizosphere than in the soil, that, of the bacteria isolated from plates, the percentage requiring amino acids was higher in the rhizosphere isolates than in the soil isolates, and that conditions were reversed for those bacteria that required yeast extract or both yeast extract and soil extract. Although the relative abundance of the bacteria of the various nutritional groups differed in the soil and rhizosphere, the cells of all groups were much more numerous in the rhizosphere. Possibly emphasis on the percentage increase in each group obscures the great increase in numbers of all of the nutritional groups. It is of interest that, of the isolates from both the rhizosphere and soil, the bacteria that grew on the simple basal medium were much fewer than those having requirements for preformed organic substances.

Characterization of the bacterial flora of soil and rhizosphere by tests of cultures isolated from plates is affected by the procedure used, and different procedures yield different results. For example, by use of different methods from those of Lochhead, Taylor [1951] found that the incidence of nutritional groups of bacteria isolated from several soils differed from that reported by Lochhead *et al.* King and Wallace [1954, 1956] used different physiological tests to characterize the bacterial population and found little consistent difference in the physiological groups in the cultures isolated from soil and rhizosphere. In general, there was little difference in the incidence of the groups of bacteria from rhizosphere and soil that reduced nitrate, fermented glucose, or hydrolyzed gelatin or starch. . . .

There are various limitations inherent in any plating procedure for estimating numbers of microorganisms in soil or for isolating cultures for studies of physiological characteristics. By plating procedures one obtains colonies of only a small fraction of the soil bacterial population, probably less than 10 per cent. These organisms are the selected group that is able to grow on the medium used for their isolation. It is possible that important groups of bacteria are not recovered. Furthermore, whereas the ability of the bacteria to grow in various media characterizes the bacteria somewhat, little indication is obtained on what these bacteria do in the soil. As stated by Thornton [1956]: "When data have been derived from plate cultures, any generalizations based on these data, whether as regards the numbers or quality of the microflora, refer only to the species that will grow on the medium used."

C. *Physiological Activity of the Rhizosphere Bacteria.*—From tests made with cultures isolated from the soil and rhizosphere, it was noted that the bacteria of the rhizosphere are physiologically more active than the soil bacteria. The mere fact that bacterial cells are more abundant in the rhizosphere than in the soil is evidence that they were more active physiologically in their natural environment, irrespective of their inherent physiological characteristics or what they did in the soil. Rovira [1956] and Rouatt and Katznelson [1957] observed that the rhizosphere isolates generally grew more profusely than the soil isolates in various media. Katznelson and Rouatt [1957] also found that the rhizosphere bacteria were more active as reducers of methylene blue and resazurin in various media, in production of acid and gas from glucose, in liberation of ammonia from peptone, and in denitrification. The rate of oxygen uptake by the rhizosphere bacteria was more rapid with substrates of glucose, alanine, and acetate, and oxygen uptake by rhizosphere soil supplemented with casamino acids, mixtures of carbohydrates, or organic acids was more rapid than that of nonrhizosphere soil. Furthermore, oxygen uptake of unsupplemented rhizosphere soil was greater than that of control soil but this has doubtful significance because roots probably become incorporated with the rhizosphere soil in sampling.

Rovira [1956] reported that root exudate of seedlings of oats and peas increased the activity of the soil population. He noted the following when air-dried soil was moistened with a solution of root exudate: there was an increase in the number of gram-negative bacterial rods but not of fungi; there was no effect on release of ammonia from soil or added peptone; there was no effect on release of phosphate from soil or added nucleic acid; there was an increase in the oxidation of added glucose. From this he concluded that the rhizosphere bacteria exert little effect on the rate of decomposition of the soil organic matter. If this is so, it would indicate that readily decomposable organic matter does not appreciably accelerate decomposition of the soil organic matter. This supports the conclusions of Pinck and Allison [1951] but is contrary to those of [several other investigators].

The diverse tests of the rhizosphere populations provide additional evidence of a high level of microbial activity in the rhizosphere although most of the evidence has been obtained under conditions unlike those of the rhizosphere. Consequently, in interpreting the results one might consider the probability that what the microorganisms do in soil is different from what they do in the test media. There is no evidence that the rate with which a culture decomposes some simple compound such as a sugar or amino acid is correlated with the rate with which it decomposed the compounds which supported it in the rhizosphere. Some of the organic nutrients in the soil may have been relatively resistant substances.

There is conflicting evidence regarding development of *Azotobacter* in the rhizosphere, but critical tests have indicated that there is little or no development of these nitrogen-fixing bacteria about roots. Nevertheless, there are claims that inoculation of seeds with *Azotobacter* results in improved growth of various plants, including legumes. Clark [1948] found that where roots of tomato were inoculated with cultures of *Azotobacter* before being planted, the numbers decreased during subsequent plant growth. According to Jensen [1942], growth and nitrogen content of white clover and alfalfa were not increased by inoculation with *A. chroococcum* in agar or sand. Furthermore, root excretions failed to support appreciable growth of the bacterium, and the number of cells of *A. chroococcum* was little or no greater in planted sand or in rhizosphere material of the legumes than in unplanted sand. Recently, Parker [1957] reported that significant amounts of nitrogen became fixed by nonsymbiotic nitrogen-fixing bacteria developing in the rhizosphere of nonleguminous plants on organic matter coming from the roots. It was stated that more nitrogen was fixed under grass crops than from addition of 3000 pounds of sugar per acre. Based on these results he concluded that, "The soil data presented and the microbiological evidence cited, together make a strong case for a reappraisal of the role of the free-living microorganisms in the nitrogen economy of the finer textured soils."

It was observed by Metz [1955] that roots or root sap of various plants differed in their effects on *Azotobacter*. Some were strongly inhibitive, others weakly inhibitive, and still others were nontoxic. However, toxicity of the plant sap was not closely correlated with occurrence of *Azotobacter* about the roots under soil conditions.

More claims of practical significance of *Azotobacter* in soils may be expected because of the erroneous prevailing idea that bacteria of this genus are some of the most important microorganisms in the soil, and that, theoretically, conditions in the rhizosphere should be favorable for their development.

D. Organic Matter Excreted from Roots.—The dense population of microorganisms in the rhizosphere is evidence that roots supply considerable quantities of readily decomposable organic matter. Information is still fragmentary on the excretion of organic matter by roots, the amounts and kinds of compounds, and the conditions affecting excretion. Among the organic materials reported as coming from roots are the following: amino acids, vitamins, sugars, tannins, alkaloids, phosphatides, and unidentified substances that are toxic or stimulatory to other plants and various microorganisms.

It has long been known that roots of legumes excrete materials that increase the number of cells of *Rhizobium*; this was recently verified by Purchase and Nutman [1957]. Virtanen developed a theory of nitrogen fixation based largely on detection of certain amino acids in excretions from nodules of legumes.

Preston *et al.* [1954] recovered α-methoxyphenylacetate in the root exudate of plants after treating the tops with the substance. Similar results were obtained with 2,3,6-trichlorobenzoic acid and 2,3,5,6-tetrachlorobenzoic acid. The compounds placed on stems or leaves were absorbed, translocated to the roots, excreted, absorbed by roots of nearby plants, and translocated upward, inducing modification of the above-ground parts. Turner [1955] reported that the bentonite about roots of legumes and nonlegumes became colored, apparently from organic materials coming from the roots. It was postulated that these were compounds of indole or salicylic acid. Fries and Forsman [1951] found that cotyledons of pea seeds excreted various amino acids, purines, and pyrimidines during germination. Root sections exuded various constituents of nucleic acids, most of which were high molecular weight phosphorylated compounds.

Bhuvaneswari and Subba Rao [1957] identified tartaric acid, oxalic acid, D-xylose, and D-fructose in exudates of roots of sorghum and mustard. Malic acid, citric acid, D-glucose, and maltose were also detected in exudates of mustard roots.

Scopoletin (6-methoxy-7-oxycumarin) is excreted by roots of germinating oats, and more was released under conditions somewhat unfavorable for seedling growth. The fact that culture filtrates of certain microorganisms increased the amount of substance excreted is suggestive in that it indicates that development of microorganisms in the rhizosphere may affect the amount and kind of organic matter that is excreted.

When Metz [1955] added root fragments or root sap to agar plates and tested their effects on development of microorganisms, he observed that generally there was no inhibitive effect, but there was toxicity in some cases. The results were variable, but occasionally the root or root sap of a plant was nontoxic to bacteria isolated from roots of this plant and it was more toxic to bacteria from roots of another plant or to bacteria isolated from soil. More frequently, root bacteria, irrespective of origin, were less sensitive than soil bacteria. In one plant the sap obtained from the roots during the vegetative period of plant growth was less inhibitive than that obtained from the plant in the fruiting stage. Inhibition of bacteria was greatest from root sap of *Chelidonium majus, Crepis virens, Hieracium pilosella, Hypericum perforatum,* and *Viola tricolor.*

Rovira [1956] observed that considerable amounts of organic matter were excreted from roots of seedlings. Most of the organic matter obtained from the roots was excreted material and there were smaller amounts of cell debris. More organic matter was produced by the roots of the older seedlings but the amount was not proportional to the root size. In a test of the effects of the root exudate on development of various bacteria, Rovira found that cultures from both soil and rhizosphere were stimulated, irrespective of the complexity of the basal medium, but in general the cultures isolated from the rhizosphere grew more abundantly than those from soil. It was Rovira's opinion that most of the organic matter was excreted by the roots although some might have arisen by autolysis of sloughed-off cells.

Metz [1955] reported that soil from the rhizospheres of the plants *Hypericum perforatum* and *Chelidonium majus* inhibited growth of a gram-positive rod. A thermolabile substance having antimicrobial action is produced by potato buds.

The fact that spores of various fungi fail to germinate in soil even though they germinated in pure water led Dobbs and Hinson [1953] to conclude that soils contain inhibitive substances, the influence of which must be counteracted before the spores can germinate. The inhibitive effect may be overcome by glucose and by other required nutrients such as vitamins. As Garrett [1956] indicated, many substances stimulate germination of spores of some fungi whereas one or few compounds stimulate germination of other spores. Whatever is required by the spores of root-inhabiting parasites is provided by the roots of the host, and sometimes by roots of nonsusceptible plants. Spores of soil-inhabiting fungi are similarly affected. Jackson [1957] observed that spores of *Gliocladium roseum* and *Paecilomyces marquandii* failed to germinate in plant-free soil but did so in soil in close proximity to roots of seedling peas. Similar effects were obtained with seedlings of pea, wheat, and lettuce on spores of three cultures of *Fusarium*. The results of Tolle and Rippel-Baldes [1958] indicate that the effects of roots on spore germination are selective in that spores of fungi isolated from roots of cereal plants germinated in the rhizosphere of the cereals but not in rhizospheres of unrelated plants or in soil. Furthermore, roots of the cereals failed to promote germination of spores of all fungi.

According to Buxton [1957] the exudate of roots of certain varieties of peas and also the extracts of the rhizospheres of these plants lowered germination of races of *Fusarium oxysporum* to which the pea varieties were resistant but not those to which they were susceptible. The evidence suggests that root exudates of the pea varieties differed. Furthermore, with any one variety the exudate differed with age of the plant. "Results of the inoculation experiments described here show that soil can be made inhibitory to a particular race by previously cropping it with a pea cultivar which resists that race, but how long such inhibition persists, and whether or not similar methods might be of value for controlling certain races of the fungus, are problems which need further investigation."

Recently, considerable attention has been directed to the excretion of amino acids from roots. Kandler [1951] reported that the following amino acids were excreted from excised roots of corn grown in the absence of microorganisms: asparagine, alanine, serine, aspartic acid, valine, glutamic acid, leucine, and glutamine. There was a proportionality between the concentration within the roots and the amount excreted. Corn embryos excreted only a small amount of glutamine in one case. Fries and Forsman [1951] found that amino acids and various other nitrogenous compounds were excreted by roots of pea seedlings. Parkinson [1955] grew plants free of microorganisms in sand that was periodically perfused and detected several amino acids in the perfusate. Katznelson *et al.* [1954, 1955] found amino acids in leachings from the nonsterile sand substrate of various plants, but considerably larger amounts were obtained when the plants wilted owing to desiccation of the sand just before it was leached. Nine amino acids were identified, namely, glutamic acid, aspartic acid, proline, leucine, alanine, cysteine, glycine, lysine, and phenylalanine. Also there was reducing material, possibly glucose, a pentose, and another substance. Small amounts of ninhydrin-positive substances were detected in solutions in which wheat and peas were grown free from microorganisms. The various solutions stimulated growth of amino-acid-requiring bacteria.

Rovira [1956] grew seedlings of peas and oats in sterile sand and then extracted the sand with water to recover the soluble organic substances after the seedlings had grown for 10 and 21 days. Many amino acids were detected in the washings, a greater variety of amino acids and larger amounts from peas than from oats. Twenty-two amino compounds were detected from peas and 14 from oats. Both glucose and fructose were detected in the washings from both plants at 10 days but practically none at 21 days. Ultraviolet-absorbing and fluorescent materials were also present. Mucilaginous material was noted on roots of the oat seedlings. The sulfur compounds methionine, cystine, and taurine were either not detected in the root exudate or were present in very small amounts. In tests of the response of growth of bacteria in diverse media supplemented with the root exudates, there was evidence that in some cases the enhanced growth was due to amino acids, but the principal effect was ascribed to vitamins or other growth factors.

Andal *et al.* [1956] reported that the four amino acids, aspartic acid, glutamic acid, tryptophan, and lysine were excreted from roots of germinating rice, from varieties both susceptible and resistant to root-rot by *Fusarium moniliforme.* Four other amino acids (cystine, methionine, asparagine, and tyrosine) were present in the exudate of the resistant varieties but they were absent from exudate of the susceptible ones.

It has been mentioned previously that amino acid-requiring bacteria have been found to comprise a larger portion of the bacterial population of the rhizosphere than of soil. Frequently, they were more abundant than the bacteria of the other nutritional groups of Lochhead. It is not surprising, therefore, that the high incidence of the amino acid-requiring bacteria in the rhizosphere has been ascribed, in part, to the availability of amino acids in the root exudates.

E. *Factors Affecting Development of Microorganisms in the Rhizosphere.*— Norman [1955] refers to the rhizosphere effect as an enrichment phenomenon owing to the nutritional circumstances in the zone. Concerning the rhizosphere, Bawden [1957] wrote as follows: "The rich population here may in part reflect the action of the root exudates in stimulating dormant microbes to activity, but there are probably many other contributing factors. Some of the microbes may be living on sloughed-off root hairs or epidermal cells, and others on sugars and amino acids secreted by the thin-walled living cells; as the root grows and respires, it must alter the soil locally, both physically and chemically, and so present habitats in which microbes with special needs can multiply. It is important to remember that, even with a dense stand of plants, the soil is still far from filled by roots and, on microbial standards, much of the soil microflora remains remote from living tissues."

The growth of root-inhabiting parasitic fungi and mycorrhizal fungi on roots of the host is due to something provided by the host, otherwise the fungi would grow from the roots into the soil instead of being restricted to the root surface. The effect of the root need not be that of providing the major organic nutrients, because these are derived from invaded root tissue from which the spreading mycelium develops. In some cases this may be an effect of reaction because it was observed by Thom and Humfeld [1932] that the rhizosphere is more nearly neutral in reaction than the soil. The concentration of carbon dioxide in the rhizosphere is also one of the numerous factors affecting development of fungus parasites on roots and affecting root penetration by them.

In the rhizosphere the microbial population differs both quantitatively and qualitatively from that in the soil, and conditions are changing continuously because the rhizosphere population is determined to a large extent by the root metabolism, which is affected by both soil and atmospheric conditions and the stage of plant growth. Furthermore, the rhizosphere effects vary with different plants. Also, the soil conditions, as they are affected by moisture, temperature, aeration, reaction, and fertility, affect microorganisms through their influences on plant development. Plant vigor is also affected by illumination, air humidity and temperature, and disease. All of these effects will be reflected in the microbiological status of the rhizosphere. To some degree the rhizosphere population is also affected directly by soil conditions.

III. THE EFFECTS OF RHIZOSPHERE MICROORGANISMS ON PLANTS

The opinion has been expressed that each kind of plant has a typical rhizosphere population and that, therefore, inoculation with rhizosphere microorganisms will hasten plant growth and secure vigorous plant development. There is still very little information about the kinds of microorganisms in the rhizospheres of different plants and their significance in development of the plants. However, there is no convincing evidence that inoculation with rhizosphere microorganisms is of practical value, with the exception of legume bacteria and mycorrhizal fungi. Furthermore, the activities of some rhizosphere microorganisms, such as phytopathogens, are unfavorable to plant development. The majority of the rhizosphere microorganisms are saprophytes and convert both organic and inorganic material in the rhizosphere. The products of these transformations may be beneficial or injurious. Certain rhizosphere organisms have more direct effects on plants through symbiosis or parasitism.

Bawden [1957] stated: "Resistance to infection is the normal condition of plants, and susceptibility the exception." In our present ignorance of the mechanisms of resistance and pathogenicity this is more surprising than may be apparent, because there is a host of saprophytes that should be able to destroy the plant and, indeed, one another except for some unknown protective effect. Virtanen et al. [1957] found antifungal agents in all of several cereal and food plants tested and were of the opinion that the substances were important in providing resistance of the plants to fungus attack. Two of the antifungal agents were identified as 2(3)-benzoxazolinone and 6-methoxy-2(3)-benzoxazolinone.

The influence of environmental effects on susceptibility of the plant to microbial attack was recently illustrated by Harley and Waid [1955], who observed effects of light intensity on development of beech seedlings and the composition of the microbial population of the roots. High light intensity favored seedling vigor and development of mycorrhizal fungi, whereas low intensity resulted in poorer plant development and in appearance of pathogenic types of fungi on the roots. The degree of light intensity determined whether or not the root fungi had favorable or unfavorable effects on the plant, by affecting plant composition. Bjorkman [1949] found that high light intensity and low levels of nitrogen and phosphorus promoted the formation of mycorrhiza of forest trees apparently by increasing the amount of carbohydrate in the roots. The fact that mycorrhiza of certain pine species form after the first leaves appear and that with alfalfa, infection by the nodule bacteria occurs with appearance of the first leaf, is additional evidence that plant composition, as influenced by photosynthesis, affects the rhizosphere population.

The effects of microorganisms on plants in the rhizosphere may be diverse, in that microorganisms affect soil structure and availability of plant nutrients. Furthermore, soil microorganisms may favor or inhibit development of one another.

A. Occurrence of Microorganisms in Plants.—Whereas saprophytic microorganisms are prominent on root surfaces there is some evidence that they are not confined to the tissue surfaces. There may be invasion by microorganisms other than the pathogens and the symbiotic bacteria and fungi, but the significance of this penetration is obscure. Bacteria have been isolated from roots more frequently than from other plant parts but they have been isolated also from stems, leaves, and flowers of healthy plants. However, it is not known whether the microbial cells merely survive or make limited development in the tissues.

It was reported by Jodidi and Peklo [1929] that seeds of English rye grass and certain kinds of wheat and barley contain smut fungi located in the aleurone layer, that they affected seed composition, and that they were normal seed associates. Sathe and Subrahmanyan [1931] failed to find microorganisms in the seeds of diverse plants and concluded that there was no evidence of any symbiotic or mutual relation between seeds and microorganisms. Hennig and Villforth [1940] found bacteria in leaves, stems, twigs, and roots of 28 different apparently healthy plants in all stages of development. Whereas some fruits and seeds seemed to be sterile, others yielded bacteria, yeasts, and fungi in studies of Marcus [1942]. Sanford [1948] recovered bacteria from the interior tissues of mature potato tubers and from the stele of apparently healthy stems of potato and garden bean and from tap roots of alfalfa and sweet clover. Fungi were seldom found in sound potato tissue. Tervet and Hollis [1948] and Hollis [1951] also isolated bacteria from potato stems. Bacteria of five different genera other than *Rhizobium* were isolated from roots of red clover and subterranean clover by Philipson and Blair [1957].

In a doctor's thesis, "Bacteria in their relation to vegetable tissue," H. L. Russell reported in 1892 studies on the fate of bacteria injected into plant stems. Some of the saprophytic bacteria persisted for more than a month but they had no noticeable effect on the plant. Animal pathogens survived for only short periods. There was some upward movement of the bacteria but practically no downward movement. His findings, indicating that the environment of a healthy plant was not favorable for development of the bacteria, still apply to the great majority of microorganisms.

B. *Influence of Organic Materials on Plant Development.*—Organic materials in the rhizosphere may have various effects on plants. They may be absorbed and stimulate the plant, injure it, or affect the food value of the plant. The development of pathogens in the rhizosphere may also be influenced by the organic compounds in the rhizosphere.

Cholodny [1951] made the interesting observation that gaseous substances that were produced by microorganisms in soil were capable of inducing root growth, geotropic reactions of roots, and production of root hairs. Various volatile organic compounds are produced by microorganisms, including ethylene and other hydrocarbons, methyl thiol, and dimethyl disulfide. Information is lacking, however, on the kinds of volatile organic materials that are produced in soil and their effects on plants. Furthermore, it is not known whether the condition observed by Cholodny was exceptional or common.

Becker *et al.* [1950, 1951], Becker and Gyot [1951], Winter and Schönbeck [1954], and Schönbeck [1956] found that extracts of cereal stubble fields or of soil to which cereal straw had been added were toxic to wheat seedlings. Furthermore, extracts of cereal straw and of green and mature leaves of various plants were toxic to seedlings and to germination of seeds of many plants. Leaf extracts were also toxic to bacteria, those of dead leaves being more inhibitive than those of green leaves. The effects were interpreted as indicating that various plant residues have direct inhibitive effects on microorganisms in soil and on plant development.

It has been reported that on removal of old peach trees there is toxic material that interferes with development of newly planted young trees. The root bark contains the cyanoglucoside, amygdalin, from which the toxic factor was apparently liberated as a result of microbial action. Whether the toxicity was due to hydrocyanic acid, benzaldehyde, or some other products produced from amygdalin is unknown. Both hydrocyanic acid and benzaldehyde were toxic but they might not persist in the soil.

Residues of quack grass were reported to be toxic to alfalfa by Kommendahl *et al.* [1957] and both filtrate and residue of rhizomes of the plant had inhibitive effects. The substance was thermolabile. Toxicity, possibly caused by organic substances, has been reported also for several other plants.

In an investigation of the unfavorable effects of stubble mulching on crops, McCalla and Duley [1949] found evidence that the plant residues contained substances toxic to plants. In soil mulched with wheat straw that was kept wet, there was 44 per cent germination of corn, whereas in unmulched soil germination was 92 per cent. Seeds soaked in extracts of sweet clover or wheat germinated abnormally; the roots were short and in some cases grew upward. Various nitrogenous organic materials were incorporated in agar which was inoculated with soil. Seeds that were placed on the agar surface frequently germinated abnormally. The factor responsible for the effects was not stated, but the possibility that it was free ammonia or high alkalinity was not excluded. Inhibitive materials such as coumarin may have been contained in the plant residues or produced by microorganisms.

The likelihood that effects such as those observed by McCalla and Duley were due to organic substances of microbial origin is supported by results of Stille [1957] who found that culture solutions of various bacteria, actinomycetes, and fungi were toxic to roots and root hairs of young seedlings. Although toxins were produced by phytopathogenic fungi, they were produced also by many saprophytes. Culture filtrates of fungi isolated from roots of cereal plants were both stimulating and toxic to root growth; at certain concentrations they promoted root development and at higher concentrations they were inhibitive. In these studies the cultural conditions of the microorganisms were so different from those in the rhizosphere that the results suggest rather than prove that microorganisms affect roots through organic substances produced in the rhizosphere.

In certain yellow podzolic soils (granite origin) of New South Wales, difficulty was encountered in securing inoculation of subterranean clover. Hely *et al.* [1957] attempted to ascertain the reason for this. Seeds were germinated on agar slants of a mineral salts medium containing no nitrogen and inoculated with the legume bacteria and soil or soil dilutions, one or two weeks after adding the seeds. Nodulation was inhibited in tubes inoculated with material from the problem soil but not in those inoculated with soil from a field where there was normal nodulation. Furthermore, the inhibitive factor was transferable. It was concluded that, "in the soil under investigation, a microorganism (or -organisms) colonizes the rhizosphere of subterranean clover plants and prevents their normal multiplication and spread of nodule bacteria within."

The probability is great, however, that where legume seeds are inoculated with a culture of effective bacteria, there will be nodulation even though soil conditions are unfavorable for plant development and even for the bacteria. Some evidence for this was obtained by Hoffmann [1942] who planted soybean seeds in a very poor acid soil (pH 4.5). The plants were less than a foot high at maturity and had very few leaves, but they set pods. Even under the adverse soil conditions, the roots became inoculated and the inoculated plants made more growth than the uninoculated ones.

Roots of legumes excrete organic materials that increase the number of legume bacteria in the rhizosphere and affect nodulation. Nutman [1957] found that the excreted materials increased the rate of nodule formation and, at high concentrations, reduced the number of nodules.

Garrett [1956] cited examples of antagonism of phytopathogenic fungi by the rhizosphere population, that by *Trichoderma viride* in particular. The possibility that antibiotics produced in the rhizosphere are a factor in immunity to phytopathogens was discussed by Metz [1955] and he presented evidence that plants contain and excrete organic materials inhibitive to microorganisms. The fact that in the rhizosphere there is an abundance of microorganisms that are able to produce antibiotics stimulates interest in the subject. Nevertheless, the potential antibiotic-producing microorganisms are present not only in the rhizosphere but also in the soil. Agnihothrudu [1955] isolated actinomycetes from rhizospheres of varieties of pigeon pea resistant and susceptible to wilt caused by *Fusarium udum*, and found greater numbers of cultures strongly inhibitive to the fungus in the rhizospheres of the resistant varieties. It was suggested that root excretions of the resistant plants contained materials favoring development of antagonistic actinomycetes. Thornton [1957] reported that there were more streptomycin-resistant bacteria in the rhizosphere than in soil, particularly with older plants and those growing in "clover sick soil."

Antibiotic-producing cultures have been used with variable success to control plant pathogens. The significance of antibiotics in control of root parasites has been discussed recently in an interesting report by Brian [1957], where he stated: "While we can now say with some confidence that some microorganisms can produce antibiotics in soil in quantities sufficient to account for some observed biological antagonisms, we have yet to show that the two phenomena are connected. The evidence is mainly indirect, probably necessarily so."

It is probable that some of the organic materials produced by microorganisms in the rhizosphere are absorbed by the plant, but the kind and amounts are not known. From what has been reported on uptake of organic materials it is probable that plants can absorb many different kinds of compounds, including those of large molecular weight. There are numerous reports concerned with the uptake of sugars, amino acids, and other organic compounds by plants. The systemic action of bactericides, fungicides, and insecticides is based on the uptake of the organic compounds by the plant tissues and their persistence in the tissues. The antibiotics, streptomycin, chloramphenicol, and griseofulvin have been identified in shoots of plants whose roots developed in solutions containing the compounds. The molecular weight of streptomycin is 581. The fact that the chemical structure of a compound is as important for uptake as molecular size was shown by Pramer [1955, 1956] who found that the ionized basic antibiotic, streptomycin, was rapidly absorbed by active transport whereas a neutral substance, chloramphenicol, was absorbed more slowly and in smaller amounts by diffusion.

The uptake of pesticides and herbicides by plants causes serious problems because the plants that contain them may be unsatisfactory as human foods and animal feed. Absorption of auxin (indolyl acetic acid) becomes evident from its typical effects on the plant. The manifestations of kinetin and gibberellic acid on plant growth are evidence of their entry into plant tissues. Although gibberellic acid is a product of the fungus *Gibberella fujikuroi,* the possibility that it is produced commonly by microorganisms in soil seems unlikely because Curtis [1957] found that of approximately 1000 cultures of fungi and 500 of actinomycetes isolated from soil, none showed evidence of producing it when cultured in a corn steep, cerelose medium. Brian *et al.* [1954] found that gibberellic acid could be absorbed by plants not only from nutrient solutions but from soil, but it underwent slow decomposition in unsterilized soil. There was evidence of decrease in amount on the sixth day, and it had apparently all disappeared in 31 days.

There is some evidence that exceedingly large molecules or particles may be absorbed by plants. Some years ago Moritz and vom Berg [1931] and Moritz [1934] reported uptake and translocation of ovalbumin in plants. *Vicia* plants were watered with a solution containing ovalbumin, which was later detected in the aerial parts of the plants by an anaphylactic technique. The guinea pig used as the test animal was either sensitized with leaf material and then tested against pure ovalbumin, or the animal was sensitized against pure ovalbumin and then tested against the leaves.

The uptake and translocation of animal virus by plants was reported by Skarnes [1952]. The plant roots were kept in a mineral solution to which the mouse encephalomyelitis virus was added, and the solution was renewed periodically. The aerial portions of the plants were tested for the virus by hemagglutination, by mouse infection, and by virus-neutralization tests. In one series of 112 tests with various plants, including tomato, bean, lettuce, radish, and pea, 14 (12 per cent) were positive. Most of the positive results were obtained with tomatoes. In most cases the virus was recovered in 3 to 7 days after adding the virus to the mineral solution. The implications of these results are important. If particles the size of the virus (20 to 50 mμ) enter plants through the roots and are translocated, it is possible that many of the organic compounds produced by microorganisms in the rhizosphere also penetrate plant tissues.

C. *Effects of Microorganisms on Availability of Nutrients in the Rhizosphere.*—Associated with all microbial development are the two processes of assimilation and formation of inorganic products. In addition, there are secondary changes of other materials in the environment where the reactions occur. It is to be expected, therefore, that the availability of plant nutrients would be affected by microbial activity in the rhizosphere. Some interesting evidence of this has been obtained. Some years ago (1918–1919) Fred and Haas clearly demonstrated that the microorganisms on roots increased markedly the solvent effect of roots on calcium carbonate. This was apparently due to the carbon dioxide of microbial origin. Others, as Metzger [1928], found that the amount of bicarbonate was greater in the rhizosphere than in the soil.

Some of the most striking evidence of the solvent effects of microorganisms in the rhizosphere has been provided by Gerretsen [1948]. The plants were grown in sand moistened with mineral solution, and the phosphorus was supplied as the mono-, di-, and tri-calcium salts, bone meal, rock phosphate, and ferrophosphate. Where microorganisms were present, compared to sterile conditions, there was greater plant growth and more phosphate was absorbed from the various phosphorus compounds. The effects of the roots on solubility of phosphate was shown by use of sand cultures, where the plants were grown in such a way that they passed over the surface of a glass sheet on which there was an agar film in which the insoluble phosphate was dispersed. During plant growth numerous clear areas appeared at certain spots around the roots where the phosphate became dissolved, and this was ascribed to microbial activity. In some cases microbial development at the root surface had the opposite effect, that is, it increased the amount of insoluble material.

Plant growth affects the availability of nitrogen by its influence on growth of microorganisms in the rhizosphere. It was clearly shown by Goring and Clark [1948] that less nitrogen is available to the plant than would have been transformed to nitrate in the soil if the soil had not been planted. A significant amount of nitrogen becomes assimilated by the rhizosphere microorganisms and is immobilized temporarily. Therefore, the crops reduced the amount of nitrogen available for plant growth. The inhibitive effect began to become apparent in 9 weeks, following which it was strong. Quoting from Bartholomew and Clark [1950]: "Nitrogen immobilization in the soil, believed to be accomplished by the rhizosphere microflora and by nonrecoverable root sloughings, accounted for an appreciable portion of the added nitrogen (fertilizer nitrogen)." During 16 weeks after cropping, the mineralization of nitrogen exceeded that of uncropped soil and the excess was approximately the same as the deficit during the preceding period of plant growth.

These results have been verified by others, including Harmsen and van Schreven [1955]. The immobilization of nitrogen occurs about all living roots but becomes particularly prominent in permanent grassland.

Conditions leading to immobilization of nitrogen are generally those where the percentage of nitrogen in the organic matter is low. The results suggest, therefore, that most of the organic matter coming from roots, whether as root exudate, sloughed-off cells, or whole roots, is low in nitrogen or is nonnitrogenous. If this is the case one might expect that microorganisms which can decompose these substances would be a significant portion of the rhizosphere population. Search for them is complicated by lack of knowledge of the actual substrates upon which they develop. It has been mentioned previously that amino acids are important excretory products of roots. From the results of Goring and Clark and others, however, it seems probable that the amount of carbohydrates and other nonnitrogenous organic material that is provided micro-organisms by the roots greatly exceeds the quantity of amino acids.

Theron [1951] and Theron and Haylett [1953] suggested that the reduction in the amount of available nitrogen in the rhizosphere was due at least in part to toxicity to the nitrifying bacteria of organic matter coming from the plant roots, but the explanation mentioned previously seems to be more adequately supported by the facts. The significance of the phenomenon is thoroughly discussed by Harmsen and van Schreven [1955].

IV. CONCLUDING REMARKS

The information derived from numerous sources in many different ways bears evidence that the rhizosphere is the seat of active microbial development and, for a soil microbiologist, one of the most interesting regions of the soil. It is also an important region because it is here that the principal effects of the soil are expressed on the plant. It is here that the diverse activities of microorganisms have their greatest influence on plant development. The relations between micro-organisms and plants are most obvious in the intimate associations between plants and the legume bacteria, mycorrhizal fungi, and pathogens. The studies of microorganisms in the rhizosphere indicate that, in addition to these intimate associations of plants and microorganisms, there are other important relation-ships between microorganisms and plants even where the roots do not become invaded by the microorganisms. It is probable that for most plants these rhizo-sphere effects are more important than those where the plant tissue is invaded.

Whereas there is considerable information about microorganisms in the rhizo-sphere, what is known is more general than absolute. The rhizosphere effect is definitely established but its significance is obscure. The extent of the absorption of organic materials by plants, particularly the organic compounds of microbial origin, and their effects on plant growth, are practically unknown. There is even limited information on the factors affecting uptake. There are suggestive results on the beneficial and injurious effects of the rhizosphere microorganisms on plants, but the effects have yet to be evaluated. The same applies to the antago-nistic and stimulating effects of the rhizosphere microorganisms on one another. The possibilities of controlling the population have been almost completely unexplored.

INDEX